Break Away with Intel® Atom™ Processors

A Guide to Architecture Migration

Lori M. Matassa
Max Domeika

Intel
PRESS

Copyright © 2010 Intel Corporation. All rights reserved.

ISBN 978-1-934053-37-9

No part of this publication may be reproduced, stored in a retrieval system or transmitted in any form or by any means, electronic, mechanical, photocopying, recording, scanning or otherwise, except as permitted under Sections 107 or 108 of the 1976 United States Copyright Act, without either the prior written permission of the Publisher, or authorization through payment of the appropriate per-copy fee to the Copyright Clearance Center, 222 Rosewood Drive, Danvers, MA 01923, (978) 750-8400, fax (978) 750-4744. Requests to the Publisher for permission should be addressed to the Publisher, Intel Press, Intel Corporation, 2111 NE 25th Avenue, JF3-330, Hillsboro, OR 97124-5961. E Mail: intelpress@intel.com.

This publication is designed to provide accurate and authoritative information in regard to the subject matter covered. It is sold with the understanding that the publisher is not engaged in professional services. If professional advice or other expert assistance is required, the services of a competent professional person should be sought.

Intel Corporation may have patents or pending patent applications, trademarks, copyrights, or other intellectual property rights that relate to the presented subject matter. The furnishing of documents and other materials and information does not provide any license, express or implied, by estoppel or otherwise, to any such patents, trademarks, copyrights, or other intellectual property rights.

Intel may make changes to specifications, product descriptions, and plans at any time, without notice. Fictitious names of companies, products, people, characters, and/or data mentioned herein are not intended to represent any real individual, company, product, or event.

Intel products are not intended for use in medical, life saving, life sustaining, critical control or safety systems, or in nuclear facility applications.

Intel, the Intel logo, Intel Atom, Intel Core 2, Intel Core i3, Intel Core i5, Intel Core i7, Intel Pentium, Intel MMX, Intel386, Enhanced Intel Speedstep Technology, Intel Turbo Boost Technology, Intel Itanium, Intel Xeon 5500, and Intel VTune Performance Analyzer are trademarks or registered trademarks of Intel Corporation or its subsidiaries in the United States and other countries.

† Other names and brands may be claimed as the property of others.

This book is printed on acid-free paper. ∞

Publisher: Richard Bowles
Editor: David J. Clark
Content Architect: Darren M. Smith
Text Design: InfoPros
Graphic Art: InfoPros (illustrations), Ted Cyrek (cover)

Library of Congress Cataloging in Publication Data:

Printed in China

10 9 8 7 6 5 4 3 2 1

First printing, October 2010

Notices and Disclaimers

The Intel® Integrated Performance Primitives (Intel® IPP) library contains functions that are more highly optimized for Intel microprocessors than for other microprocessors. While the functions in the Intel® IPP library offer optimizations for both Intel and Intel-compatible microprocessors, depending on your code and other factors, you will likely get extra performance on Intel microprocessors.

While the paragraph above describes the basic optimization approach for the Intel® IPP library as a whole, the library may or may not be optimized to the same degree for non-Intel microprocessors for optimizations that are not unique to Intel microprocessors. These optimizations include Intel® Streaming SIMD Extensions 2 (Intel® SSE2), Intel® Streaming SIMD Extensions 3 (Intel® SSE3), and Supplemental Streaming SIMD Extensions 3 (Intel® SSSE3) instruction sets and other optimizations. Intel does not guarantee the availability, functionality, or effectiveness of any optimization on microprocessors not manufactured by Intel. Microprocessor-dependent optimizations in this product are intended for use with Intel microprocessors.

Intel recommends that you evaluate other library products to determine which best meets your requirements.

Intel® Hyper-Threading Technology (Intel® HT Technology) requires an Intel® HT Technology-enabled system, check with your PC manufacturer. Performance will vary depending on the specific hardware and software used. Not available on the Intel® Core™i5-750. For more information, including details on which processors support HT technology, visit www.intel.com/technology/platform-technology/hyper-threading/index.htm.

Intel® Virtualization Technology requires a computer system with an enabled Intel® processor, BIOS, virtual machine monitor (VMM). Functionality, performance or other benefits will vary depending on hardware and software configurations. Software applications may not be compatible with all operating systems. Consult your PC manufacturer. For more information, visit http://www.intel.com/go/virtualization.

Intel® 64 architecture requires a computer system with a processor, chipset, BIOS, operating system, device drivers and applications enabled for Intel® 64 architecture. Processors will not operate (including 32-bit operation) without an Intel® 64 architecture-enabled BIOS. Performance will vary depending on your hardware and software configurations. See www.intel.com/info/em64t for more information including details on which processors support Intel® 64 architecture or consult with your system vendor for more information.

Contents

Foreword

Throughout the decades, Intel has taken a variety of approaches with processors and microcontrollers to target the embedded market. I was fortunate enough to have begun my career shortly after the company's introduction of the 8051, utilizing the microcontroller for one of my first engineering projects. Of course, since then, Intel has gone through many generations of embedded processors including variations of the 8086, 80186, 80386, i960, XScale, and so on. While each of these processor families has witnessed significant fame and glory, none seem to compare to the attention that the Intel® Atom™ processor is getting from the embedded industry as well as the media.

So why all the excitement about the Intel Atom processor? Unlike prior Intel architectures, the Intel Atom processor has a new architecture specially created to reduce power use. This helped the original Intel Atom processors target mobile Internet devices and is driving subsequent devices into many other areas of embedded where lower power is a key factor, as this book describes in Chapter 2, allowing these applications to expand their capabilities and scale between designs. However, this low power focus doesn't come without controversy, as Intel is targeting market segments where other processor architectures have dominated. Regardless, it will be very interesting to observe how Intel Atom processors evolve as they permeate the embedded market.

In writing the foreword to this book, I am intentionally not expressing my opinion on the qualities of the Intel Atom processor—that is for the reader to decide. On the other hand, through my work with the Multicore

Expo and Multicore Association, I have personally known and worked with the authors for many years and can testify to their due diligence on this book's content. Furthermore, anyone undertaking an embedded design that will utilize an Intel Atom processor will benefit from reading this book, especially if you choose to go below the surface and take advantage of any of the Intel Atom processor's optimized features.

—Markus Levy
Senior Analyst with the *Multicore Insider*

Preface

Exploration is really the essence of the human spirit.

—Frank Borman

Twenty years ago a software developer might have asked "So what's the big deal?" Back then architecture conversion was a routine process of designing and implementing the next "latest and greatest" product update. In my early years as a software developer, I worked for a high tech company that sold IBM-compatible mainframe and midrange computer system controllers and peripherals (terminals and printers). We started with products designed for the Zilog Z80 processor, and every line of code was written in Z80 assembly language. In the next generation of these products the C language made its debut, and all of the code was implemented again with enhanced features designed for the 68008. In the late 1980s those peripherals were extended to the early PC platform using an expansion card to emulate the peripheral. The emulated versions of these products rode the quickly advancing wave of Intel processors, catching the wave of the 8088 on the PC itself. The software would later be easily ported to the 80286, the Intel386™, and then finally to the Intel486™ processor in the early 1990s. In those days we didn't balk at opportunities to design on new architectures. We just did it. We embraced the challenge like a breath of fresh air, realizing the prospect for innovation and extending the products' capabilities each time. The benefit extended not only to the evolution of the end product's offerings, but also to expanding our own engineering experience and knowledge. It was at this point of enthrallment with Intel architecture that I actually became an Intel employee.

Today, with product cycles much shorter than in the old days, it's imperative to design for a computer architecture that will scale easily as industry trends advance. As with the architecture migrations that I engineered so many years ago, it's important to understand the goals and software implications before the port begins. This book is an opportunity to guide developers through the journey of migrating their software to Intel® Atom™ processor-based platforms, enabling their products to be well positioned for the future.

—Lori M. Matassa
June 2010

Acknowledgments

Architecture migration involves broad subject material and relies on domain experts for contributions and accuracy. This book involved contributions in various forms from a number of talented industry experts who we are honored to work with and who deserve acknowledgment.

For significant contributions to this book, we would like to thank Padma Apparao for power optimization information, Peter Barry for interrupts and exceptions information in Chapter 4 and Intel® architecture memory map and Master Boot Record information in Chapter 5, Pat Brouillette for SVEN information, Rajshree Chabukswar for performance optimization information, Mark Charney for details on XED, Steve Daily for cache optimization details, Mylinh Gillen for Intel® Atom™ processor roadmap information, Sven Dummer of Wind River for operating system information, David R. Hillyard and Peter Brink for the byte swapping overhead information in Chapter 4, Praveen Jayakumar for Hardware-Accelerated Video Decode in Chapter 7, Drew Jensen for Intel Graphics driver information in Chapter 4, Sonia Leal of LynuxWorks for operating system information, Philippe Lecluse and Philippe David Verbeiren for the optimizing 3D applications for Intel® Atom™ platforms in Chapter 7, Eng Kean Lee for real-time interrupt latency information in Chapter 4, Alex Leidinger of FreeBSD for operating system information, David Levinthal for help with Intel® IPTU, Felix McNulty for the on-chip debugger tools overview in Chapter 4, Graham Morphew of Wind River for operating system information, David Randall of QNX for operating system information, Mudit Vats for the embedded pre-OS graphics information in Chapter 5, and Chris Weaver for architecture discussion and clarification.

We would especially like to thank these talented engineers for major chapter content and case studies contributions:

- Jenny M. Pelner and Jim A. Pelner – Chapter 5 topic Intel® Atom™ Processor System Boot Flow.

- Ishu Verma – Chapter 6 topic MeeGo.

- Paul A. Fischer – Chapter 7 topic Intel® Per-formance Primitives.

- Dave Kleidermacher – Chapter 9 case study: Methods and Applications of System Virtualization Using Intel® Virtualization Technology, and operating system information.

- Robert Mueller – Chapter 10 Embedded Software Debugging and Chapter 4 topic – Intel® Tools for Intel® Atom™ Processors.

- Addicam V. Sanjay – Chapter 11 Case Study: Migrating Software to the Intel® Atom™ Processor.

No Intel Press book is published without peer review. For their careful reviews, constructive comments, and contributions we would like to thank Peter Brink, Peter Carlston, Garrett T. Drysdale, Peter Horn, Joshua Hort, Rob Mueller, Jim Nucci, Jayesh Patel, Karen Santa Cruz, Dale Taylor, and Michael Vierheilig, and all of the Intel Embedded and Communications Market Segment teams.

Max thanks his management, Joe Wolf and Kevin J. Smith, for support in this endeavor. Max thanks the lead author, Lori Matassa, in initally pitching the idea and receiving approval to proceed. It has been a productive and constructive partnership during the eight months of book development. Above all, Max is thankful for the support of his wife, Michelle, who was patient with the many nights and weekends consumed by this effort.

Lori thanks Intel's Embedded and Communications Group management including Ton Steenman, Jonathan Luse, and Sam Lamagna for approving the project. A special admiration is extended to Max for his expertise and dedication, and for making this venture enjoyable and rewarding. Lori also thanks her family, especially her brothers Bob and Lance who influenced her technical curiosity and her cherished, faithful friends Sondra, Rosie, and others who provided enthusiasm and support along the way and have always been an inspiration.

Chapter 1

Introduction

You don't concentrate on risks. You concentrate on results. No risk is too great to prevent the necessary job from getting done.

—Chuck Yeager

Consumers have an increasing desire for compute-like capabilities and benefits on devices that are beyond the PC. The result is that these additional features require more performance from low power products and at an affordable price. Intel developed the Intel® Atom™ processor in order to bring a new level of intelligence to a range of consumer electronics, mobile internet devices (MIDs), and embedded and communications products, including smart TVs, Blu-ray† players, media phones, in-vehicle infotainment, media tablets, smart phones, and more. It places the power of a computer in a processor so small and energy efficient that it can fit into the devices that we have become accustomed to using today, but in doing so transforms them into something more. Together, these devices will enable the power of the networked world in more places, more hands, more often. With the Intel Atom processor, devices once thought of as simple will become smart, allowing us to connect, share, and consume in new ways and from anywhere network communications are available.

One way to keep costs reasonable is the ability to scale the program source code across product lines, as well as the ability to repurpose the code into new products that can deliver new capabilities. Standardizing designs on Intel architecture allows for portability of data and content across devices and PCs. This is quite attractive to companies who want to minimize their software development costs and time to market for new products, and are therefore choosing to migrate to Intel Atom processor-based platforms.

This chapter explains the general challenge of architecture migration and also describes what you can expect in the remainder of this book.

What Is Architecture Migration?

The term *architecture migration* is used in this book to describe the task of taking software designed to run on one computer hardware and processor architecture and executing it correctly on a different architecture, which could require updates to the code. Another term that you might have heard that defines this same task is *architecture conversion*. Both terms imply the porting of software.

Architecture migration involves both hardware and software. After all, the program source code, whether implemented in a high-level programming language or low-level assembly language, is written with the capabilities of the hardware platform in mind, and is transformed into a binary program that executes machine-specific instructions. One very important fact to realize is that the software development effort required for an architecture migration can be as simple as recompiling the source code or require additional effort depending on the portability of the original source code. Source code that implements layers of hardware abstraction will realize a more straightforward migration.

Whenever possible, software development should use standards-based software libraries and tools, which will not only contribute to software portability, but also benefit performance and time to market. As you read further into the chapters you will discover that there are two parts to architecture migration. The first part focuses on successful execution of the migrated code on one CPU core of the target processor. The second part focuses on adopting specific processor and platform technologies that extend the benefits of the underlying target hardware into the software application. In addition, several examples of standards-based libraries that extract the benefits of Intel Atom processors are discussed.

Motivation for This Book

More product designers are realizing the benefits of Intel Atom processors and the vast Intel architecture ecosystem, and are choosing Intel Atom processor-based platforms to introduce more potential for their low power devices. As these products are developed, software engineers need to understand how to enable their software to run on Intel architecture. This book highlights hardware differences and software implications that are commonly encountered when migrating from one processor architecture to another.

First, it's important to understand the Intel Atom processor architecture. There are several Intel Atom processors and platform variants, each designed for certain use cases, but all are designed on the same Intel architecture instruction set. This in of itself is the reason why code designed for Intel architecture can be written once and will scale across current and future Intel architecture product lines, requiring new code to be developed only for the new features that are added.

The purpose of the book is to present information that will help software engineers understand available Intel architecture software solutions, and how to choose solutions that best fit their software migration and low power product requirements running on Intel Atom platforms. The book will guide software engineers through the steps of migrating their software to Intel Atom processor based designs, as well as how to adopt the added benefits of Intel Atom product technologies, enabling the potential for new features and higher performance in their products. The information covers Intel Atom processor details and related software topics. There is already a wealth of Intel architecture design information available to help the developer, but sometimes the challenge has been just in knowing what was available and where to find it—until this book.

Who Is The Reader?

Most of the topics in this book are related to embedded software design and programming. Readers are expected to be comfortable with C and C++ programming languages.

A few topics require specialized software development knowledge, such as the section "Intel® Atom™ Processor System Boot Flow" in Chapter 5, which requires low level programming knowledge related to hardware system initialization, and "Intel Multi-core Technology Solutions" in Chapter 9, which requires parallel programming knowledge. These topics, however, provide insight into the required programming and techniques.

Reasons to Migrate to Intel® Atom™ Processors

Intel architecture has established itself as a proven leader in performance and innovation over its entire history, and continues to offer a strong roadmap with products that are optimized for performance, power, value, and extensibility for the future. More importantly, when implementing software based on Intel architecture processors, a common software code base can be maintained across all Intel architecture processor-based solutions. The code base will scale between current and future platforms, which minimizes the software development and maintenance costs and shortens the software development cycle between generations of product evolution.

The key decision for developers is whether they prefer to keep changing their code every time a new version of the processor architecture is released or whether to invest in their products' future by adopting a processor architecture family that provides code scalability and a strong and innovative product roadmap.

Intel's involvement in developing and driving standards-based platforms has dramatically altered the computer industry. Today most companies demand standards-based open architecture and compatibility with legacy applications. In addition, Intel's initiatives in driving a strong ecosystem of independent hardware vendors and standards to address various form factors, helps developers to focus on their unique solution and enhance their Intellectual property.

Platforms based on the Intel Atom processor provide best-in-class performance and long battery life for mobile form factors. Plus, Intel embedded products offer a seven year life cycle. They are compatible with a range of general purpose and real-time operating systems including Microsoft Windows†, Linux†, MeeGo†, and more.

The Intel Atom processor is based on the same Intel architecture that powers over a billion personal computers. Hence, the Intel Atom processor benefits from the same software ecosystem that enables original equipment manufacturers to rapidly develop and upgrade devices at minimal cost.

The key decision for developers is whether they prefer to keep changing their code every time a new version of the core processor architecture is released or whether to invest in their products' future by adopting a processor architecture family that provides code scalability and a strong and innovative product roadmap.

Intel® Embedded Design Center

Intel provides the Intel Embedded Design Center (EDC)[1] to help developers get started with designing on Intel architecture. The EDC provides embedded hardware and software design information, as well as step-by-step guidance to design information and decisions including hardware schematics, downloads, and white papers. The EDC software portal contains downloads for drivers and tools, as well as technical documents. Furthermore, you will find books and videos for hardware and software developers, and training solutions provided by the Intel ecosystem, all at the EDC online training portal. My advice is to bookmark the EDC for quick access to all of the latest embedded Intel architecture product development information.

Another good source for Intel product information where you can find and compare products including boards, processors, and chipsets is http://ark.Intel.com.

Intel® Software Network

Intel has a global network of software tools and resources that bring together the proven depth and breadth of Intel's engineering expertise, technology leadership, strategic insight, and global reach to developers around the world. The Intel Software Network[2] allows community developers and engineers within the network to come together with forums and blogs, and access software development products and software development knowledge bases.

Intel® Atom™ Development Platform

The Intel Embedded and Communications Group is enabling an ecosystem of developers, scholars, students, and hobbyists adding hardware and software support for a related series of low cost embedded Intel Atom boards. The board is available for purchase at the EDC development platform Web site[3]. This platform is the ideal solution for anyone who wants to get their idea up and

---

[1] Intel Embedded Design Center. Web Site. http://edc.intel.com

[2] Intel Software Network. Web site. 2010. http://software.intel.com

[3] Intel Embedded Design Center, Development Board. Web site. 2010. http://edc.intel.com/go/devboard

running fast, without extensive hardware engineering, or for anyone who is now using or considering other embedded architectures and needs to develop a proof of concept using ready built hardware. Visit the EDC Web site for up-to-date information about the latest available development platform.

What Are the Contents?

- Chapter 1: Introduction providing the background of architecture migration and what you will find in this book.

- Chapter 2: Overview of several low power embedded and communications market segments and applications to establish a general understanding of design requirements for these applications and trends that are shaping these market segments.

- Chapter 3: Provides an understanding of the Intel Atom processor, which is needed for software developers to effectively develop and optimize for its architecture, and provides comparisons to other Intel architecture processors.

- Chapter 4: Discusses processor architecture differences and the related software implications of migrating software to the Intel Atom processor including topics such as endian architecture, software development tools, interrupt and exceptions, real-time considerations, graphics, and a migration design guide.

- Chapter 5: Overview of the Intel architecture system initialization solutions including custom boot loaders and Basic Input/Output System (BIOS).

- Chapter 6: Details a process for operating system selection for embedded development projects, including criteria and choices.

- Chapter 7: Details the Intel® Integrated Performance Primitives library and its use for embedded applications, and summarizes common operations of categories of library functions. Also includes a survey of the broader library ecosystem, which is important to Intel Atom processor software development.

■ Chapter 8: Instruction about the power and performance optimization process for systems based on the Intel Atom processor, including an overview of the optimization process from single-core analysis and tuning to multi-core analysis and tuning.

■ Chapter 9: A reference to the Intel Atom processor technologies. Explains the difference between Intel® Hyper-Threading Technology and multi-core, and techniques for adopting multi-core and Intel® 64.

■ Chapter 10: Embedded software debugging for Intel Atom processors is presented. Topics discussed include identifying coding issues, debugging techniques for embedded systems, and techniques that aid in bringing varying components of the embedded software stack to maturity.

■ Chapter 11: A case study of an ARM† to Intel Atom processor–based architecture migration. The case study follows the migration design guide explained in Chapter 4, and explains the software considerations involved in the migration.

Note

> MeeGo is Intel and Nokia's† open source operating system optimized for the Intel Atom processor. References made to Moblin™ in this book can also be applied to MeeGo.
>
> Intel® Atom™ processor E6xx series is the product name for the processor formerly codenamed Tunnel Creek.

Chapter 2

Low Power Embedded Market Segments and Applications

The wonderful thing about the Intel® Atom™ processor is that you are really looking at the classic x86 PC architecture shrunken down into an embedded platform. With the Intel Atom processor we are now using only a small percentage of the CPU's capacity. This means we have room to grow. So future multimedia applications no longer represent a challenge; instead they will present opportunities.

—Paul Krzyzanowski, Chief Technology Officer, OpenPeak

The variety of device types and applications where the low-power Intel® Atom™ processor can be applied spans the more familiar consumer devices, such as netbooks, set-top boxes, and mobile Internet devices (MIDs), to a growing array of embedded and communications devices. Cost-effectiveness, energy efficiency, seven-year lifecycle support, and deterministic real-time performance are some of the product requirements that are important within embedded market segments. Intel has been providing embedded solutions for more than 30 years that meet the needs for performance, functionality, support and cost, and nowadays, some form of low power requirements can be found in almost every embedded market segment.

Across each of the low power embedded market segments, applications running on Intel Atom processors garner performance benefits from Intel product technologies, such as Intel® Hyper-Threading Technology and Intel® Streaming SIMD Extensions 3 (Intel® SSE3). In addition, a variety of software development tools are available to assist software developers with adopting these performance benefits into their applications. More information about the Intel Atom processor technologies, as well as software development tools and software optimizations that apply to these market segments, will be covered in other chapters of this book.

This chapter provides an overview of several low power embedded and communications market segments and applications, which will give the reader a general understanding of the unique hardware and software requirements for these applications. The chapter also discusses the trends that are shaping these market segments, where the Intel Atom processor family is ideal for the space-constrained fanless design requirements of low power, low cost form factors.

Connected Services Gateway

A new market segment, referred to as the Connected Services Gateway (CSG), provides various home and small business services. The CSG is more than just a low end residential gateway. It's a modular open platform with I/O, storage, network, media, and content processing, and can support separate or integrated modem/cable technology. As a hub for the home LAN device connectivity, the CSG terminates the broadband, providing services of a firewall and wireless router, and connecting all client devices in the home to the Internet. It is also an applications server for downloadable home services. For example; the CSG delivers services for home control and security surveillance, home automation, home medical monitoring, personal and family content such as documents and pictures, and entertainment services such as downloading and streaming music and videos.

The CSG is a single point for all device management, which can be accessed locally, as well as remotely. Any remote device, a cell phone or personal computer for instance, can be used to access the home client devices through the CSG. Service providers could also use the CSG to provide support, remotely upgrade, and manage value added services, as well as provide troubleshooting. In a nutshell, the CSG replaces the wireless router that provides additional home services, communicating to the home devices using Wi-Fi[†], ZigBee[†],

6LoWPAN[†], and MoCA[†], and connecting to the service provider over broadband, 3G and 4G. Figure 2.1 shows a CSG conceptual design based on the Intel® Atom™ processor E6xx series.

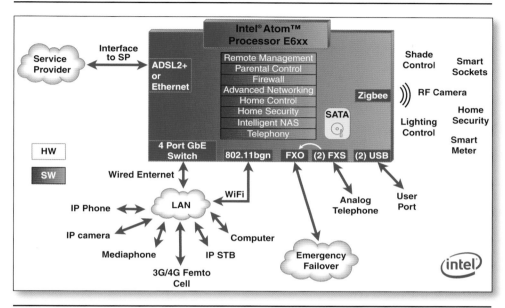

Figure 2.1 Connected Services Gateway Conceptual Design Based on the Intel® Atom™ Processor E6xx Series

Intel® Digital Security Surveillance

Intel® Digital Security Surveillance (Intel DSS) systems are composed of surveillance cameras, Internet Protocol (IP) video encoders, and digital video recorders/networked video recorders (DVR/NVR). Most traditional closed-circuit television (CCTV) video surveillance systems in use today are still dependent on personnel sitting in front of a large monitor with several smaller screens. The challenge is that one person cannot monitor more than a few screens and human error, fatigue, and distractions can result in missed security breaches. DSS application is an evolution to traditional CCTV video surveillance, incorporating new technologies including central management system, remote viewing, and Video Intelligence automated breech alerts without requiring security personnel to monitor the screens.

The advantages of DSS over the traditional surveillance systems that use recorded feeds include:

- *Archiving.* All data can be stored on hard drives or on a storage server, which requires only a few mouse-clicks to retrieve the digitally stored footage from a specific date and time.

- *Physical Storage Space.* While maintaining the video quality, large amounts of recorded data can be compressed into reduced files sizes using video compression technology. Today MPEG4 reduces file sizes by 25 percent over the older DVD MPEG2 video compression technology. The H.264 compression is even more advanced and reduces file sizes by 50 percent, as compared to MPEG2 compressed files.

- *Networking Capability.* DVR, NVR, and storage can easily be connected to an existing or dedicated network, which provides a centralized location for the monitoring system. Events are recorded from all of the system's remote locations and authorized users can log on to the system remotely from anywhere to access data or monitor video feeds.

- *Video Intelligence.* Software ecosystem partners introduced video content analytics (VCA) into digital surveillance security systems reducing the level of dependence for security personal. The applications can monitor restricted areas for intruders, detect suspicious unattended luggage, and send alarms through e-mails, instant messages, or text messages. The result is that monitoring capabilities are increased and human error is reduced.

DSS solutions based on Intel embedded platforms serve the full spectrum of security surveillance requirements in facilities like airports, railway terminals, government and corporate buildings, utility infrastructures, educational campuses, financial institutions, and retail locations. The Intel Atom processor is perfect for less computing-intensive DSS applications including mid-range 4-channel DVR/NVR, encoders, and IP cameras where low thermal design power (TDP) and small form factors are desirable. Mid-range installations, such as residential, small retail store, and small office/home office environments benefit from the small form factor because of its more practical and aesthetically pleasing.

A DVR designed with the 1.6-GHz Intel Atom processor N270 can connect up to four channels of analog cameras with a Peripheral Control Interconnect Express† (PCIe) or PCI-based video capture card. The Intel Atom processor N270 contains the processing power to efficiently support software-based video encoding. With an optimized solution, an Intel Atom processor N270-based DVR can achieve up to four channels of full D1 resolution (720 x 576) real-time (100 fps) viewing, while recording at 48 fps with MPEG4 compression. Using H.264 compression to reduce storage space, the system can support four channels of full D1 resolution real-time viewing and recording at 20 fps. The DVR is designed to be fully connected either through the 10/100/1000 LAN controller or a separate PCI Express minicard WLAN module. This provides connectivity to the central monitoring system, server, or backend storage. Figure 2.2 depicts a reference application for a mid-range surveillance DVR based on the Intel Atom processor N270. For higher resolution and higher recording frame rate DVR application, developers can consider the 1.6-GHz Dual Core Intel Atom D510.

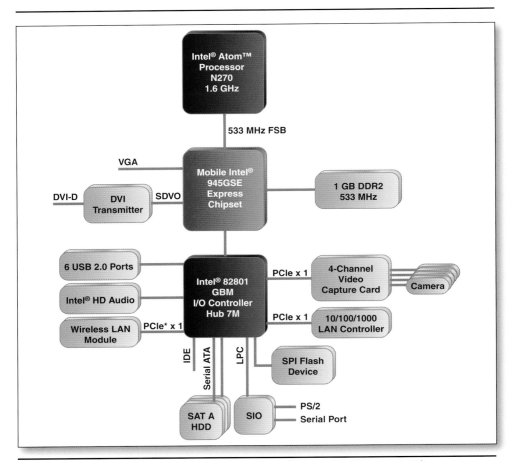

Figure 2.2   Intel® Atom™ Processor N270 Reference Application Mid-range Surveillance Digital Video Recorder

The Intel Atom processor Z5xx series can be used for an IP encoder or IP video hub device for residential, small offices, and small retail stores. The usage scenarios are up to four channels of QVGA resolution (320 x 240) real-time recording at 25/30 fps with HM-Fast compression, or up to four channels of QVGA resolution (320 x 240) real-time recording at 25/30 fps with H.264 compression. Figure 2.3 shows an Intelligent IP video detector or IP encoder block diagram based on the Intel Atom processor Z530.

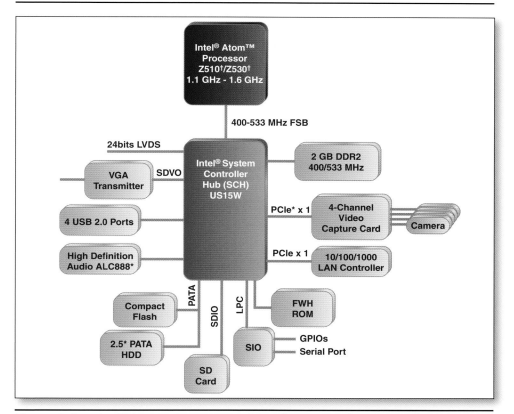

Figure 2.3   Intel® Atom™ Processor Z530 Reference Application Intelligent IP
Video Detector or IP Encoder

Software developers can optimize application performance on the Intel
Atom processors by taking advantage of the Intel SSE2, Intel SSE3 and Intel
SSSE3 instructions set, and Intel Hyper-Threading Technology. The Intel
Integrated Performance Primitives (Intel IPP) library of video codecs provides
highly optimized APIs for the Intel Atom processor. When implementing
software-based encoders, a common software coded base can be maintained
across all Intel processor-based solutions from Intel® Core™i7 to Intel Atom
processors, shortening software development cycle between generations of
product evolution.

Gaming

Within the gaming market segment, applications that are primarily based on Intel Core architecture include slot machines, lottery terminals, arcade games, and amusement with prize (AWP). Additionally, player tracking systems are used by casinos in slot machines to monitor play of casino guests and reward them with incentives for their amount of play. Player tracking systems allow players to review their play on a small video screen displayed on the slot machine driven by the Intel Atom processor. The player tracking system also benefits from the Intel Atom processor because the player tracking module normally sits in a space that is more compact than the larger motherboard, which requires a low power, fanless design.

Energy

Intel technology is playing a role in boosting intelligence in the power grid. Electrical utility operators are deploying more powerful compute and communication capability at every node throughout the network to support the growing energy demand and increasing environmental and regulatory restraints. They are seeking to do more with their existing energy capacity and improving the overall efficiency of electrical networks. For example; to benefit from distributed energy generation resources such as wind and solar the utility operators are moving control and management of the energy network from central control to a more distributed control and intelligence.

For energy generation, guide vanes tell the controller the direction of the wind. Controlling the vane's pitch, rotation and functions, the guide vanes depend on rugged embedded systems to respond, in real-time, to changing wind conditions without human intervention, and enabling maximum uptime. For energy distribution, substation control systems monitor and control all relevant operating sections of an electrical transmission and distribution network. Embedded Intel processors provide the computing horsepower required for controlling and managing these large energy systems, but another facet of this market segment, which is being enabled by the Intel low power processors, is energy consumption monitoring in the home.

Home Energy Management

Next generation In-home displays (IHDs) help customers engage and benefit from demand-response programs by making it easier to profile, monitor and manage domestic energy usage. Home energy management systems (HEMS) help both consumers and utilities realize significant energy savings through energy efficiency programs, time-of-use pricing and demand-response signals. Intel's Intelligent home energy management platform is based on the Intel Atom processor.

The Intel® Intelligent Home Energy Management Proof of Concept (PoC) is an example of a home dashboard. The concept, based on the Intel Atom processor Z530, is a low-power embedded computing panel designed to exchange monitoring and control data with smart appliances, smart plugs, smart electric utility meters and sensors located throughout the home. The concept design, pictured in Figure 2.4, is designed to be the heart of the home network. The picture shows the top-mounted Hello/Goodbye switch, which sets climate controls and security systems to pre-arranged settings while users are at home, away or sleeping. ZigBee[1] enabled smart adaptors let appliances, sensors, and smart meters communicate wirelessly with the dashboard.

---

[1] ZigBee Organization. Web site. http://www.zigbee.org

Figure 2.4   Intel® Intelligent Home Energy Management Proof of Concept Hello/
Goodbye Front Panel

Applications monitor the performance of each appliance over selected time intervals, alert users to anticipated problems, provide maintenance reminders, and make usage recommendations that can save time, money, and energy. The concept uses a touch panel display, similar to those found in today's smart phones, to access features of the system such as:

■   Current energy usage of the home

■ Daily cost to operate each of the monitored devices

■ A color-coded clock that provides a reminder of the time of day energy pricing schedule

■ A camera that can be used to allow family members to leave video messages

■ A smart thermostat that doesn't require complex programming

The Intel Home Dashboard Concept system could also allow users the ability to remotely view and control thermostats, appliances, and security systems from a mobile phone or PC while they are away from home.

The highlights for the home energy management POC based on the Intel Atom processor Z530 are shown in Table 2.1.

Table 2.1   Highlights of the Home Energy Management PoC

Highlights
• Intel® Atom™ processor Z530 1.6 GHz
• Intel® System Controller Hub US15W
• Low-energy 11.56 inch OLED capacitive touch screen
• Motion sensor support
• Video camera support
• Stereo audio
• ZigBee home area networking
• Open software API with dedicated private data access
• Wi-Fi† enabled for communications with Internet devices

Commercial Energy Management

In addition to the home, the Intel Atom processor also has a place in building energy systems (BEMS), known as commercial energy management. Figure 2.5 depicts a reference design for a commercial energy management PoC. The scalable and self-configuring system is designed to monitor power consumption in a multi-circuit power distribution system for candidate facilities, such as an engineering lab and a typical office workstation. The application reference design demonstrates the technical feasibility and benefits of wireless sensor network (WSN) solutions based on the low-power Intel Atom processor, including solutions converted from ARM† and other Intel® architecture processors. The reference design can be used as the basis for proof-of-concept platforms that apply the features and capabilities of Intel Atom processors to resource virtualization, mesh networking with multi-protocol support (802.15.4e 6LoWPAN), performance and power comparisons with ARM-based solutions, and ultra-low power management and power harvesting. The wirelessly connected reference design performs networked sub-metering, with energy use thresholds and alert triggers, in addition to environmental sensing, including temperature, humidity, light, and carbon dioxide. The system is an out-of-band solution with no dependency on legacy building management or automation systems, and the platform is based on open Information Technology (IT) standards including end-to-end IP and Web services.

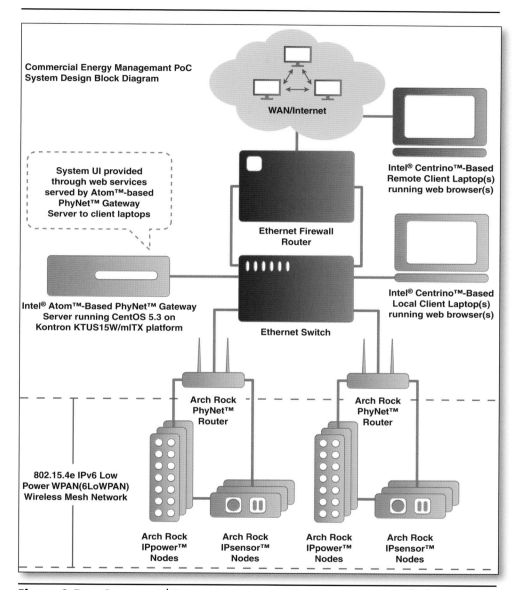

Figure 2.5 Commercial Energy Management PoC System Design Block Diagram

The specifications for the commercial energy management POC reference design are shown in Table 2.2. The reference design is based on the Intel Atom processor Z530. However, developers can use lower frequency SKUs to fit their need for performance, power, and functionality.

Table 2.2   Specifications for the Commercial Energy Management PoC Reference Design

Specification	Details
Processor	Intel® Atom™ processor Z510 1.1GHz and Z530 1.6GHz
Chipset	Intel® System Controller Hub US15W
Expansion busses	1 PCI 2 PCI Express† x1
Memory	1 DDR2 socket up to 2 GB
Graphics	Intel® GMA 500 with 2D/3D Graphics Engine Dual independent display (incl. 2 LCD) Hardware-assisted DVD/MPEG2 decoding
Storage	1 ATA100 2 Serial ATA 150/300
I/O	8 USB 2.0
LAN	1 10/100/1000 Ethernet
Sound	HD Audio and AC97 compliant
Modular Options	Wi-Fi† 802.11 b/g; Bluetooth USB port (DECT FXO) (Camera optional) 1 mini PCIe slot

Industrial

Industrial computing platforms are found in places like factories and the transportation industry, including building automation, power and energy, and process control devices. Test and measurement instrumentation within this segment such as oscilloscopes, signal generators, and spectrum analyzers require smooth inter-operation, which helps ensure scalability and software reuse, and real-time performance management and monitoring for product testing and data gathering. Human–machine interfaces rely on sophisticated functionality to enhance ease of use, localization, and responsiveness. Industrial PCs must be rugged platforms that can withstand extremes of temperature, shock, and vibration. Industrial automation designs use programmable controllers and computer numerical control equipment. Transportation systems use compute platforms to support sophisticated engine control, transmission, and braking for highest safety standards, and building automation need to efficiently control systems from climate control to security and lighting.

Industrial control systems are evolving from applications designed to control dedicated hardware towards standardized, general-purpose platforms that incorporate concepts traditionally associated with the domain of IT. The push of IT into the industrial sector is also occurring both at the field level, where sensors and actuators are becoming more Intelligent. New programmable logic controllers (PLCs) are being designed using commercial off-the-shelf (COTS) hardware based on embedded PCs. Design choices available to incorporate reliability, determinism, and control functions make the PC software extremely flexible and well suited for complex applications. These new types of industrial controllers are in effect open control platforms that bring into scope the advantages inherent in the PC industry including open programming, connectivity, and greater flexibility. For example, a highly automated factory requires seamless integration of different subsystems such as programmable controllers, testing systems, machine vision, and back-end IT infrastructure.

Industrial control systems must quickly respond to changing performance, safety, and feature requirements. An application-specific integrated circuit (ASIC) or application-specific standard product (ASSP) would need to be designed and deployed, but by using a design approach that partitions the functionality into firmware and hardware components, the flexibility, scalability, and time to market are improved and eliminate the long ASIC and ASSP design cycles. Cost-effectiveness, energy efficiency, long life availability and support, and deterministic real-time performance are all factors that are important to this segment. Multiple use cases exist within each sub-segment, and using compatible hardware and software platforms is important in reducing fragmentation that would otherwise increase the overall complexity and expense of the solution.

The Intel industrial control reference design shown in Figure 2.6 is based on the Intel Atom Z5xx processor and its associated chipset facilitates the migration to a flexible modular architecture. It's based on a platform, comprising hardware and software components from industrial market leaders Intel, Altera[2], MSC[3] and 3S-Smart Software Solutions. This reference design delivers real-time performance[4] and I/O flexibility using COTS components.

---

[2] Altera Corporation. Web site. http://www.altera.com/
[3] MSC Vertriebs GmbH and Gleichmann Electronics. Web site. http://www.mscsystems.de/en/home/home/index.html
[4] Performance results are based on certain tests measured on specific computer systems. Any difference in system hardware, software or configuration will affect actual performance. For more information go to http://www.intel.com/performance.

Real-time industrial control performance, measured by data latency and bandwidth, is achieved while satisfying aggressive power consumption and form factor requirements. This platform consumes just 4.5 watts TDP total and reduced footprint by more than 80 percent over the previous-generation three chip solution.

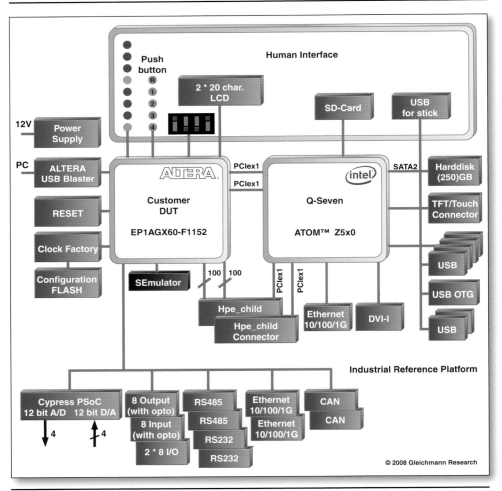

Figure 2.6　Intel® Industrial Control Reference Design

The Intel® Industrial reference design advantages for developers include:

- *Reduced Time to Market.* The reference design, supplying basic software, IP, and driver foundation, helps reduce development time and simplifies the integration of multiple fieldbus variants.

- *Scalability.* The solution can be migrated to other Intel architecture platforms, existing and future, with long term availability for all key components. MSC is planning to release a follow-on reference design in the fall of 2010 based on the Intel® Atom™ processor E6xx series.

- *Versatility.* The fanless, cost-effective design, based on well known hardware and software architectures and standard interconnects, can be applied to many different devices.

- *Flexibility.* Modular, programmable I/O components and peripherals ease customization.

The technical advantages of the Intel Industrial reference design include:

- Maximum flexibility to incorporate support for industrial I/O

- Low power that enables high performance fanless designs

- PCI Express for high performance I/O

- Extreme low power that enables rugged solutions for harsh environments

- Integrated graphics for embedded HMI

- Intel Hyper-Threading Technology that enhances real-time performance

- Power over Ethernet, including TFT-Display

- Miscellaneous functions integrated into one peripheral FPGA: LPC, FWH-I/F, keyboard touch controller, bus interface such as Ethernet, CAN, and so on

- Easy adoption of various industrial bus interfaces with standard interconnect modules

In-Vehicle Infotainment

The automotive industry is experiencing escalating demand to design and deliver in-vehicle infotainment (IVI) systems that provide seamless integration between home, office, and car multimedia capabilities. To do this, developers and auto manufacturers need an Open Infotainment Platform (OIP) that bridges the gap from generation-to-generation of product development in the form of a standards-based, low-power, scalable and highly flexible platform that enables rapid development and simplified upgrades at minimal cost.

IVI applications support telematics, navigation, and entertainment systems. Examples of IVI applications include: GPS, two-way data communications through an embedded modem or the driver's cell phone via Bluetooth, graphics, and images tied to maps stored onboard the vehicle, multiple zones for AM/FM/Satellite/HD radio, CD, digital audio, video and DVD playback, games, Internet access, satellite TV, and communications and connectivity provided by Wi-Fi, WiMAX, 3G and 4G networks. Location-based services pull destinations for places like the nearest ATM, lowest priced gasoline in three-mile radius, restaurants, and points of interest, or push information such as advertising of merchandise on sale as the vehicle passes near a certain store location. Driver safety features are provided in the form of preventative diagnostics, camera integration, driver assistance, and Human Machine Interface (HMI) voice commands. One important requirement for IVI systems is the ability to boot a graphics splash screen almost instantly after the system is powered on. For example, the system needs to boot in less than two seconds for vehicle use cases where cameras are used for viewing behind the vehicle, and be ready within five seconds total to run other applications, such as multimedia and navigation systems.

Intel Atom processors are ideal for IVI systems because of their small footprint and low-power design, and performance[5] headroom to incorporate the latest infotainment features and applications. Intel Hyper-Threading Technology increases performance and improves the user experience by allowing tasks to be processed simultaneously. Intel Virtualization Technology enables separation of mission critical and time critical applications from entertainment applications. For example, camera- and telematics-critical processing can be separated from the noncritical multimedia processing. Another advantage is

---

[5] Performance results are based on certain tests measured on specific computer systems. Any difference in system hardware, software or configuration will affect actual performance. For more information go to http://www.intel.com/performance.

the Intel Atom processor's integrated 2D and 3D graphics and video decode for 3D navigation and rear seat entertainment.

Since most consumer software is developed on and for the personal computer, developers can easily add a wide range of applications to Intel based IVI systems via software only upgrades, and developing on Intel architecture gives automakers a choice. The Microsoft Automotive and Industrial Equipment Solution Group[6] is working with their ecosystem partners to bring new capabilities and solutions to the automotive industry, and is expanding its hardware support to include the Intel Atom processor Z5xx series, which meet the industrial temperature requirements[7]. Additionally, MeeGo, Intel and Nokia's[†] open source operating system optimized for the Intel Atom processor, is expanding its reach through the development of a new IVI community. The new community will enable developers to extend their application work to the automotive industry and develop applications for OIPs. This allows car manufacturers to tap into a larger supply chain, resulting in more product choice and quicker pace of development.

The Low-Power Intel® In-Vehicle Infotainment Reference Design shown in Figure 2.7, utilizes the Xilinx Automotive Spartan[†]-3E FPGA family to extend the platform's flexibility and integrate many automotive-specific functions, including early access to video and Media Oriented Systems Transport (MOST) network connectivity. The design enables development of an OIP that addresses requirements for in-car operating conditions, as well as quality and reliability standards. The integrated platform incorporates a variety of IVI features and comes with complete schematics and bill of materials (BOM) to simplify development and speed time-to-market. The design has a small footprint, efficient thermal design, and compact I/O interfaces, which fit into a standard, single DIN slot. Low-power characteristics of the platform, based on the Intel Atom processor Z530, Intel® System Controller Hub US15W and fanless thermal solution, help eliminate noise and reliability concerns related to the use of fans and heat sinks.

---

[6] Microsoft Automotive and Industrial Equipment Solution. Web site.
   http://www.microsoft.com/industry/manufacturing/automotive/default.mspx
[7] Microsoft Corporation. 2009. *Innovation Comes "Standard" in New Microsoft Auto Platform.*
   http://download.microsoft.com/download/6/5/0/6505FA0E-1F39-4A34-BDC9-A655A5D3D2DB/
   AutoPlatformInnovationPR.pdf

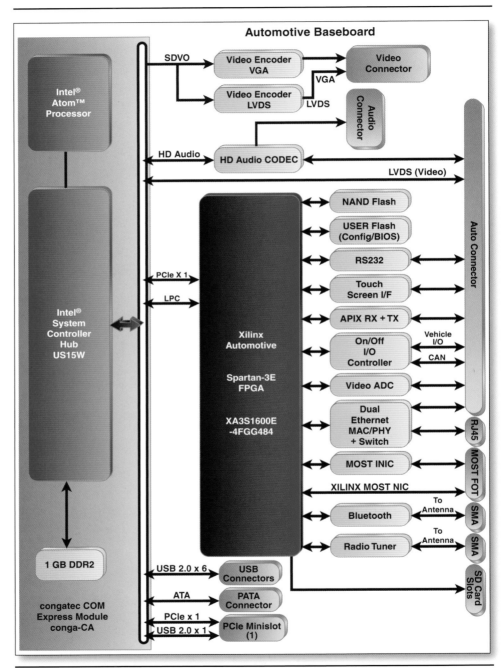

Figure 2.7 Low-Power Intel® In-Vehicle Infotainment Reference Design

Table 2.3 lists the specifications for the Low-Power Intel IVI Reference Design.

Table 2.3   Specifications: Low-Power Intel In-Vehicle Infotainment Reference Design

Specification	Details
Dimensions	165-mm wide by 175-mm deep supports standard DIN slot
Processor	Intel® Atom™ Processor Z530
Chipset	Intel® System Controller Hub US15W
Peripheral extension chip	Xilinx Spartan†-3E FPGA
Operating system	Drivers for a variety of operating systems
Memory	1 GB DDR2 533 MHz
Hard disk interface	One PATA connector supporting up to two drives
Display interface	Primary: LVDS; Secondary: LVDS or VGA
Audio interface	Through connector: Line-in L/R, Line-out L/R, SPDIF 5.1, stereo microphone
I/O connectivity	6 USB ports, 1 serial port, 1 Ethernet RJ-45 connector
Expansion card options	Wi-Fi, WiMAX, TV tuner
Power supply	Wide range (8–20V)

Media Phone

The media phone is a new category of broadband devices that will redefine the traditional home phone by combining the power of a PC with the convenience of an always-on wired telephone. The media phone is much more than a traditional phone. Think of it as a command center for the home, providing easy access to the most popular and frequently used applications that are currently scattered among several different devices. A media phone is a family device and supports visual voicemail, consolidates the family contacts list, calendar, and to-do list. It's like an iPhone† for the family and connected to a landline. Plus, during idle times the media phone can be used as a digital photo frame accessing photos from local storage or online photo sharing sites.

A media phone is a bit smaller than a laptop and has a base unit with a 6- to 9-inch color touchscreen for converged communications and at least one cordless handset for voice communications. The device is always ready to deliver the latest news, weather, and traffic, help find restaurants or movie listings, or lookup recipes. It can also be used to monitor a home and alert you when the baby is crying or when someone is at your front door. It can play MP3[†] songs, YouTube[†] videos, and can be used for social networking with sites like Facebook[†], MySpace[†], and so on. The exact design of the media phone will vary based on the manufacturer and service provider that is marketing the product, but a typical media phone device is small enough to sit comfortably on the kitchen counter, or on top of a desk or bedside table.

The requirements of the media phone are driven by consumer standards for desirability, which means it needs to be slim, lightweight, and energy efficient/cool to the touch. Further, the performance of the media phone needs to deliver responsiveness, reliability, and versatility. After all, the speed of the media phone's performance and the one-touch access to applications and services it delivers are what will attract consumers to the device.

The Intel Atom processor's new microarchitecture makes the processor ideal for small devices, supporting a board that is dense, fanless, and reliable. The design of the Intel Atom processor, which includes support for multiple threads along with Intel Smart Cache and Intel Media Boost, delivers the performance[8], responsiveness, and low power consumption requirements of the media phone market.

OEMs can build their own version of a media phone quickly and easily using either the Intel Atom processor-based media phone reference design pictured in Figure 2.8 or one of the commercially available Intel® architecture-based media phone systems.

---

[8] Performance results are based on certain tests measured on specific computer systems. Any difference in system hardware, software or configuration will affect actual performance. For more information go to http://www.intel.com/performance.

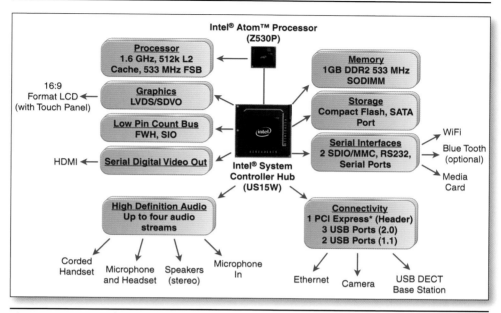

Figure 2.8　Intel® Atom™ Processor Z530P Media Phone Reference Design

The specifications for the Intel media phone reference design are shown in Table 2.4. The reference design is based on the Intel Atom processor Z530P. However, developers can use lower frequency SKUs to fit their need for performance, power, and functionality.

Table 2.4   Specifications for the Intel Media Phone Reference Design

Specification	Details
Board Dimensions	9.6 inch x 5.4 inch – 137.3 mm x 243.7 mm
Processor	Intel® Atom™ processor Z530P 533 MHz FSB
Chipset	Intel® System Controller Hub (Intel SCH) US15W
Supported OS	Moblin – www.moblin.org
Memory	1 GB DDR2 533 MHz SODIMM
Storage	8 GB Compact Flash (user removable) 1 SATA optional
Display /Video /Graphics	8.9-inch resistant-touch LCD (16:9 aspect ratio LVDS)
Audio	HD audio, up to 4 audio streams
I/O Connectivity	2 SDIO/MMC serial interfaces RS232 6 USB 1.1 and 2.0 support (5 external, 1 internal) 2X RJ45 (LAN and PC) 1 HDMI 1 RJ22 handset connector 3.0 mm audio jacks – microphone input headset output 2.0 mm phone headset jack Internal speakers and microphone
Modular Options	Wi-Fi 802.11 b/g; Bluetooth USB port (DECT FXO) (Camera optional) 1 mini PCIe slot

There are several media phone service providers, one of which is OpenPeak†. OpenPeak migrated their media phone device from ARM to the Intel Atom processor for VoIP telephony, digital, and Internet content. Figure 2.9 shows a picture of the OpenPeak OpenFrame 7 media phone device[9]. Both the base unit and cordless handset are shown.

Working with Intel has proved to be an overwhelmingly satisfying experience. Utilizing the IA-32 instruction set literally allowed us to have this board up and running in one weekend.

—Dan Gittleman, CEO, OpenPeak

---

[9] OpenPeak, Inc. 2010 Web site. http://www.openpeak.com

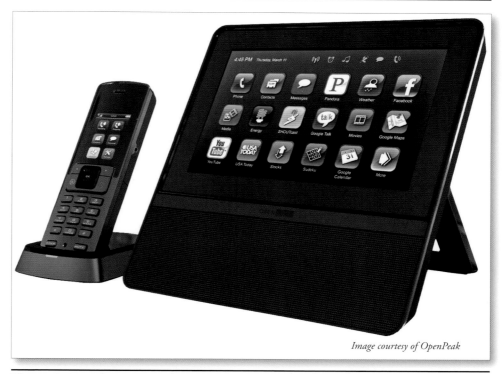

Image courtesy of OpenPeak

Figure 2.9   The OpenPeak OpenFrame 7† Media Phone for the home

For more details about the OpenPeak OpenFrame 7 device and architecture migration from the RISC architecture to Intel architecture refer to the case study[10] by Intel. For more information about OpenPeak products based on the Intel Atom processor refer to the OpenPeak Inc. Web site.

---

[10] Intel Corporation. 2010. *OpenPeak* Conversion from RISC architecture with External DSP to Intel Architecture Boosts Performance Up to 10X.* http://www.intelrethinkthepossibilities.com/Applications/Download/intel_CaseStudy_Open_Peak.pdf

Military, Aerospace, and Government

The Military, Aerospace, and Government (MAG) market segment includes government agencies and departments as well as avionics. The government agencies include the U. S. Department of Homeland Security, National Aeronautics and Space Administration (NASA), energy, justice, national labs, state agencies and the Department of Defense (DOD), which is most often engaged through its prime contractors and subcontractors. The MAG market segments include a number of diverse embedded applications. For instance, digital signal processing and image processing blades used in radar and information operations, surveillance and reconnaissance, command and control, and communications. These applications can be found in a variety of manned and unmanned airborne and ground vehicles, as well as man-packs, which are rugged compute systems that are secure, and can send and receive information under extreme environmental conditions that can include dust, humidity, drops, and spills.

Low power and small form factor requirements are found in many of these military applications. The Intel Atom processor can help meet the needs of man-pack devices not only because of their small form factor, low thermal and low power requirements, but also because they're typically fanless devices, which means that they can be sealed and protected from harsh environmental conditions.

Print Imaging

Copiers and multifunction printers (MFPs) constitute the print imaging market segment, which scale product types to suit the needs for production, enterprise, workgroup, and consumer use. Production printers are high end systems used commercially to produce books, brochures, and enterprise systems print media at local copy services stores. Workgroup printing mainly use higher volume business printers and are focused on Energy Star[†] requirements. Consumer printing targets home use and generally have an average sales price (ASP) under USD 200. Print imaging products need to be reliable and use low power for basic scan and copy type functionality.

The Intel Atom processor offers performance at a cost competitive option for workgroup printing. The Intel Atom processor increases reliability over the previous-generation processors because it uses processor sleep states that reduce power consumption when devices are idle, and does not require a fan for cooling, which would be a potential source of system failure.

Retail

The business of traditional brick and mortar establishments is being affected by all of the competition between superstores and consumers buying direct through online shopping, home shopping networks, and catalogs. Retailers need a competitive advantage, such as costs and features, to attract and retain customers. As a result, retailers are turning to scalable point of service (POS) terminals, wireless transaction devices, processor intensive kiosks, graphical displays, and digital supply chain management.

Businesses have a growing demand for innovative applications and computing power throughout the retail enterprise that offer value, space efficient designs, high reliability, and ease of use. The use of automatic teller machines is expanding for all types of locations such as indoors, outdoors, drive-up, convenience and money deposit. Paying for orders is happening via mobile devices and self-order kiosks are shortening payment transaction processing. Consumers are demanding the convenience of more self-service options such as airport check-in, postal purchases, and hospital patient tracking services that no longer require customers to wait at full-service counters.

The industry requires secure financial transactions, customer privacy, and data integrity. Self-service applications need to appear to be up and running, even when they are in an idle sleep, and need to work with consumer mobile devices as a kiosk. At the same time carbon footprints, power consumption, and overall maintenance costs need to be reduced. The Intel Atom processor solves the requirements for the electronic cash registers, offering a cost competitive option with a long life embedded roadmap and use processor sleep states that reduce power consumption when devices are idle. Reliability is increased because Intel Atom processors systems can run cooler, generating less heat than previous-generation processors, and require fewer fans, which are a potential source of system failure.

Security

People are using wireless Internet for the convenience of staying connected while on-the-go. Wireless communication allows people to stay informed and work more efficiently with the ability to access their compute networks while away from home or the office. Whether the purpose is for business, school, or leisure online connectivity, laptops and other mobile devices are susceptible to security threats since they are routinely connected to public open networks at places like airports, hotels, restaurants, bookstores, and coffee shops. These mobile devices are challenged with running robust network security software and maintaining optimum network and power performance.

The Intel Atom processor is a low power device that provides the required performance for running high-speed security content processing for smaller networks. Network security processing benefits from Intel Atom processor's low cost, low power, and small form factor, and uses the 512K on-chip L2 cache memory for optimal performance of deep packet inspection.

Sensory Networks[11] is an example of a software acceleration technology solution optimized for the Intel Atom processor and provides high-speed security content processing and support for security applications, which perform intrusion protection, deep packet inspection, application identification, and traffic management.

Storage

The popularity of digital photograph, music, video, and other large file formats is driving market demand for home servers and small office network attached storage (NAS) systems to help users store, share, and protect their content more effectively. It can also support services for advanced features such as media streaming, video conversion, and home automation control. To deliver a high-quality user experience, these systems must provide:

■ Performance to handle multiple simultaneous workloads, such as large file transfers and high-definition video streams, while the operating system and application tasks run in the background.

---

[11] Sensory Networks, Inc. Web site. http://sensorynetworks.com

- ■ Energy-efficiency to support quiet, space-efficient designs that can run continuously in any room of a home or office without disturbing occupants or running up utility bills.

- ■ Capacity, flexibility, and expandability to support growing storage needs across a variety of home and small office environments.

The Intel Atom processor, in combination with the Intel® 828001R I/O Controller, provides a foundation for addressing these requirements using a cost-effective and energy-efficient storage platform. With single-core or dual-core processor options, 64-bit architecture12 and Intel Hyper-Threading Technology13, this platform provides the performance[14] needed for a high-quality user experience under a range of workloads. It is compatible with both the Windows Home Server and Linux operating systems and provides a rich set of integrated storage and networking features. Other features and benefits include: hot plug for removing drives without powering down the system, 6 SATA II ports to support multiple internal drives, 2 with e-SATA capability and port multiplier support for adding capacity outside of the box, and Gigabit I/O connectivity to reduce I/O bottlenecks. The Intel Atom processor technology benefits enable small form factor NAS system designs, deliver the performance[14] to handle multiple applications and streaming to multiple clients, and low power, allowing systems to run cool and quiet. Figure 2.10 shows a block diagram for the Intel Atom Processor D400/D500 series-based Storage Platform.

---

[12] 64-bit computing on Intel® architecture requires a computer system with a processor, Chipset, BIOS, operating system, device drivers, and applications enabled for Intel® 64 architecture. Processors will not operate (including 32-bit operation) without an Intel 64 architecture-enabled BIOS. Performance will vary depending on your hardware and software configurations. Consult with your system vendor for more information.

[13] Intel® Hyper-Threading Technology requires a computer system with a processor supporting HT Technology and an HT Technology-enabled chipset, BIOS, and operating system. Performance will vary depending on the specific hardware and software you use. For more information including details on which processors support HT Technology, see http://www.intel.com/info/hyperthreading.

[14] Performance results are based on certain tests measured on specific computer systems. Any difference in system hardware, software or configuration will affect actual performance. For more information go to http://www.intel.com/performance.

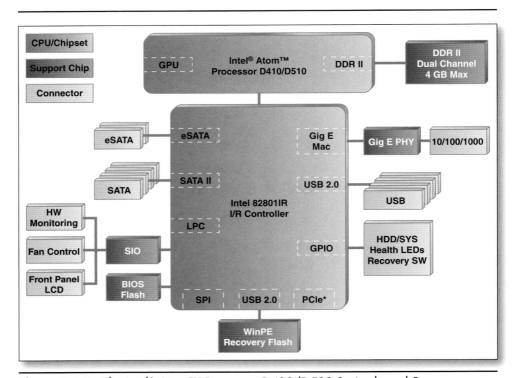

Figure 2.10 The Intel® Atom™ Processor D400/D500 Series-based Storage
Platform

The specifications for the Intel Atom processor D400/D500 series-based storage platform are shown in Table 2.5.

Table 2.5 Specifications for the Intel® Atom™ Processor D400/D500 Series-based Storage Platform

	Single Core	Dual Core
Processor Frequency	1.66 through 1.8 GHz	1.66 through 1.8 GHz
Number of Cores/Thread	1/2	2/4
Intel SMART Cache	512 KB L2	1024 KB L2
Graphic	Graphic Intel® Graphic Media Accelerator 3150	
Intel 64 Architecture	Yes	Yes
Integrated memory Controller	Yes	Yes
Memory Support	Single-channel dual-slot DDR2 or DDR3 800 MHz, up to 4 GB	
Processor Manufacturing Process	45 nm	45 nm
Processor Package Size	22 mm x 22 mm	22 mm x 22 mm
Intel I/O Controller	82801IR	82801IR
I/O Controller Package Size	31 mm x 31 mm	31 mm x 31 mm

Summary

This chapter provided an overview of several low power market segments, and examples of applications where the Intel Atom processor is already being used or could be a viable low power solution. After reading this chapter the reader should have a general understanding of the unique hardware and software requirements for these applications, trends that are shaping these market segments, and how the Intel Atom processor meets the requirements. The common trait across all of these products is the need for a low power, small footprint, and cost-effective device with seven-year lifecycle support.

Chapter 3

Intel® Atom™ Architecture for Software Developers

Simplicity is the ultimate sophistication.

—Leonardo da Vinci

If you are new to Intel® architecture and are planning or involved in a migration to an Intel® Atom™ platform, you must gain an understanding of both the basics of Intel architecture development as well as the unique features of the Intel Atom processor. The Intel Atom processor is backward-compatible with previous processors based on Intel architecture and can therefore run the same software as its predecessors. In most cases, if you have some experience with Intel architecture development then this will serve you well in your migration. Software investments on previous Intel platforms will carry over to your Intel Atom processor-based platform.

The Intel Atom processor differs from previous Intel processors so not every facet of software knowledge and experience from previous projects involving Intel architecture translates. In order to maximize the potential of the Intel Atom processor, you must understand its unique characteristics and capabilities.

This chapter provides an understanding of the Intel Atom processor so that you as a software developer can effectively develop and optimize for it. The chapter consists of four sections that cover different aspects of the Intel Atom processor:

■ Architecture

■ Platform architecture

■ Microarchitecture

■ Assembly language guidelines

First, the Intel Atom processor architecture is revealed, comparing it with previous Intel processors and discussing the high level chip features comprising its architecture such as cache sizes, memory addressability, instruction sets, and Intel technology features. Second, various Intel Atom platforms are described in detail, including the building block memory, graphics, and I/O functionality that comprise a full-fledged system. This section discusses the evolution of the Intel Atom platform from a three-chip package to a system on a chip (SoC). The section also details both the mainstream Intel Atom processors that are employed across a number of market segments besides embedded and then details the platforms and roadmap that are specific to embedded systems. The third section details the microarchitecture of the Intel Atom processor, specifically the core code-named Bonnell. Knowledge of the microarchitecture is essential for software developers such as assembly language writers concerned with optimal performance. This section serves as background information for the fourth section, which details assembly language coding guidelines. Besides the benefit of this knowledge for assembly language writers, this section enables software developers to inspect the assembly or disassembly of your application and determine if there is room for improvement.

This chapter assumes knowledge of general Intel architecture and Intel architecture assembly language programming, which can be gained by reviewing Chapter 2 of *Software Development for Embedded Multi-core Systems: A Practical Guide Using Embedded Intel® Architecture* (Domeika) and *Ensuring Development Success by Understanding and Analyzing Assembly Language* (Kreitzer and Domeika), which provide an extensive overview of historical Intel processors, processor features, and assembly language. After reading this chapter, you will have the necessary architectural knowledge to understand how these architecture features impact your software migration using the Intel Atom processor.

Intel® Atom™ Processor Architecture

The Intel Atom processor is a simpler design than the current Intel architecture processors, such as Intel® Core™ 2 processor family architecture, that target the desktop and server market segments. One of the primary considerations that went into the design of the Intel Atom processor was on minimizing power consumption compared to previous Intel processors and this focus is evident in even the most high level comparisons. Table 3.1 compares an Intel Atom processor with two other Intel architecture processors on a number of characteristics such as size and transistor count. The Intel® Pentium® processor is a much older design, but is similar to the Intel Atom processor in being what is termed an in-order, two-instruction-wide, superscalar design. The Intel Atom processors introduced in 2008 employ the same process technology as the Intel® Core™ i7 processors from the same time but employ an order of magnitude fewer transistors. The initial Intel Atom processor uses 47 million transistors in the design compared to 731 million in the Intel Core i7 processor. Processor die space is 26 mm^2 for the Intel Atom processor compared to 263 mm^2 for the Intel Core i7 processor. The design engineers that created the Intel Atom processor strove for simplicity of design and the inherent power savings in driving fewer transistors rather than focusing on absolute performance. The thermal design power (TDP) of the Intel Atom processor is much lower, 2 watts (W) compared to the 130 W TPD for the Intel Core i7 processor.

Table 3.1   Intel Processor Comparison

Processor	Intel® Atom™ processor Z530	Intel® Pentium® processor	Intel® Core™ i7 960 processor
Year introduced	2008	1993	2009
Process technology	45 nm	800 nm	45 nm
Transistor count	47 million	3.1 million	731 million
Dimensions	26 mm^2	294 mm^2	263 mm^2
Clock speed	1.6 GHz	60 MHz	3.2 GHz
Thermal Design Power (TDP)	2 W	NA	130 W

Figure 3.1 is a die photo with labeled components for the Intel Atom processor architecture, code-named Silverthorne. Unless otherwise noted, "Intel Atom processor" refers to the Bonnell core.

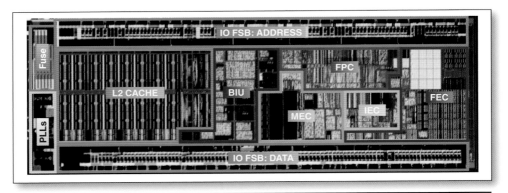

Figure 3.1   Intel® Atom™ Processor Die Photo

Caches are employed in the majority of modern processors to alleviate the difference in speed between processors and memory access. The Intel Atom processor employs two levels of caches, termed L1 and L2. The L1 caches are the closest level of cache to the processor and are comprised of a 32-kilobyte (KB) instruction cache and a 24-KB data cache. The instruction cache used in the Intel Atom processor stores predecode information alongside of the cached instructions that help delimit the boundary of individual instructions. The data cache is write-back in nature, which delays writes back to memory of modified L2 data until convenient. The L2 cache stores both instructions and data, is 512 KB in size and employs error correcting code (ECC). Both the L1 data and L2 cache employ a hardware-based L2 cache data prefetcher. A hardware-based data prefetcher analyzes memory access patterns and attempts to prefetch memory in advance of future reference to reduce memory access times.

The Intel Atom processor implements the IA-32 instruction set and Intel® MMX™, Intel® Streaming SIMD Extensions (Intel® SSE, Intel® SSE2, Intel® SSE3), and Intel® Supplemental Streaming SIMD Extensions 3 (Intel® SSSE3). Several, but not all Intel Atom processors implement the Intel® 64 Instruction Set Architecture (ISA). The IA-32 instruction set was originally introduced with the Intel386™ processor and is characterized as Complex Instruction Set Computing (CISC) with fairly verbose instructions that are variable in length. Other ISAs such as ARM† and PowerPC† employ Reduced Instruction Set Computing (RISC) where all instructions are the same size. The IA-32 architecture register set, illustrated in Figure 3.2, contains eight 32-bit integer registers. Floating point is supported via eight 80-bit floating point registers operated on as a stack. The calling convention for the IA-32 ISA is determined by the individual operating system, but in general due to the limited number of registers, function arguments are passed on the stack.

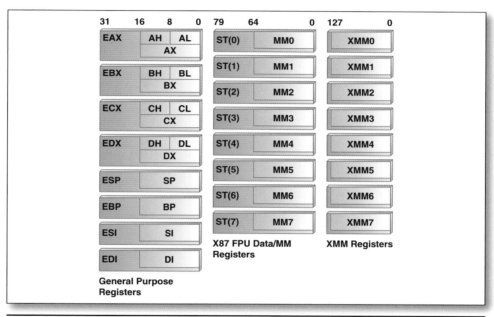

Figure 3.2 IA-32 Architecture Register Set

The Intel 64 Instruction Set Architecture was introduced in 2004 and is a natural extension of IA-32 to 64 bits. The size of registers is 64-bit, which enables direct operations on 64-bit integer values while allowing the same 8-bit, 16-bit, and 32-bit references and operations enabled by IA-32. The register set is illustrated in Figure 3.3. The Intel 64 ISA extends the number of integer registers over IA-32 from 8 to 16, which potentially increases performance as more temporary computations are stored close to the processor's computation resources. The Intel 64 ISA allows 8-bit, 16-bit, and 32-bit access to these registers enabling higher performance of algorithms that use data types that map to a smaller number of bits (`char` and `short` operations).

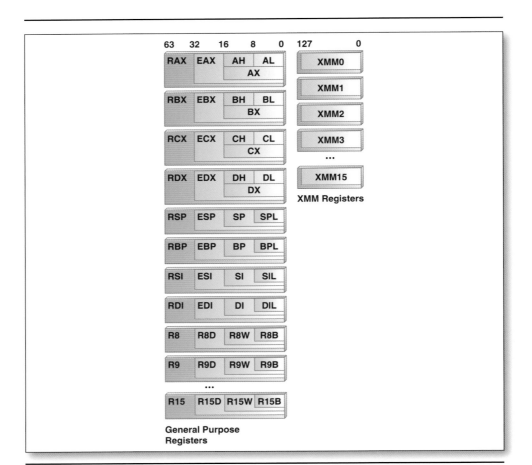

Figure 3.3   Intel® 64 Architecture Register Set

One common type of computation observed in applications is the repeated application of the same operation across different data elements such as seen in a C language for loop multiplying pairs of numbers together. One method of speeding up these types of loops is to employ Single Instruction, Multiple Data (SIMD) computation, also termed vector computing, which enables the same operation to be applied to multiple data elements. Instead of a C language for-loop that performs computation on one set per iteration, SIMD computation would enable an iteration to perform computation on two or four sets per iteration. Several processor vendors have introduced their own set of SIMD extensions to enable this style of computation. Intel has introduced multiple generations of SIMD instruction sets which are summarized in Table 3.2.

Table 3.2   SIMD Instruction Set Extensions

Instruction Set Extension	Year Introduced	Number of Instructions	Description
Intel® MMX	1996	57	SIMD operations on integers.
Intel® Streaming SIMD Extensions (Intel® SSE)	1999	70	SIMD operations on single-precision floating point, prefetch operations.
Intel® Streaming SIMD Extensions 2 (Intel® SSE2)	2001	144	SIMD operations on double-precision floating point.
Intel® Streaming SIMD Extensions 3 (Intel® SSE3)	2004	13	SIMD operations on complex data types.
Intel® Supplemental Streaming SIMD Extensions 3 (Intel® SSSE3)	2006	32	Instructions to speed up video decode.
Intel® Streaming SIMD Extensions 4 (Intel® SSE4)	2007	54	Instructions to improve performance of video encoders, image processing, and string processing.
Intel® AES New Instructions (Intel® AES-NI)	2010	6	Fast data encryption and decryption using the AES protocol.
Intel® Advanced Vector Extensions (Intel® AVX)	NA	12	256-bit registers.

In addition to the new instructions introduced with the SIMD instruction sets, new registers have been added to support operations on SIMD data. The registers, referred to as XMM registers, are 128-bit in size and support vectors of 8-bit, 16-bit, 32-bit, and 64-bit values. The IA-32 ISA enables use of 8 XMM registers while the Intel 64 ISA enables use of 16 XMM registers. The operating system is responsible for enabling use of Intel SSE instructions and ensuring that the registers are saved and restored on context switches. Most modern operating systems targeting IA-32 and Intel 64 ISAs support the registers; however this is not a safe assumption to make if you are employing or migrating a legacy operating system.

The IA-32 and Intel 64 ISA support multiple modes of operation that govern data size, memory addressing, and memory protection. The Intel Atom processor supports all modes available on IA-32 summarized as follows:

■ *Real Mode.* Sixteen-bit register access and a 20-bit address space offering no memory protection. Old operating systems created before the Intel 386 processor employed real mode. All Intel architecture processors come out of reset in real mode.

■ *Virtual x86 Mode.* Old, rarely used processor operating mode.

■ *Protected Mode.* Modern multitasking operating systems that target the IA-32 ISA run in protected mode where access to memory is protected so that one application cannot interfere with the memory used by another application. Protected mode also enables protection of kernel-level activities from user-level applications.

Under protected mode, a virtual and physical address space of 2^{32} or 4 GB is supported. A special extension of the IA-32 ISA, Physical Address Extension (PAE), is also supported, which enables a maximum physical memory of 2^{36} or 64 GB.

Intel Atom processors that enable the Intel 64 ISA support both long modes of operation, which are summarized as follows:

■ *64-Bit Mode.* Enables access to 64-bit instructions and registers and can theoretically address up to one terabyte of physical memory. However, the maximum physical address space for a given platform is much lower.

■ *Compatibility Mode.* Enables applications compiled for IA-32 protected mode to execute at the same time as other applications compiled for the Intel 64 ISA.

One fundamental architecture component necessary for memory protection is the translation lookside buffer (TLB), which caches translations of virtual to physical memory references. The Intel Atom processor features a two-level TLB with support for page sizes of 4 KB and 4 MB. The supported memory speeds are a function of the memory controller. The initial chipsets supporting the Intel Atom processor have a front side bus (FSB) speed ranging from 400 MHz to 667 MHz.

The Intel Atom processor also supports various Intel technologies that offer improvements in aspects of performance, power utilization, stability, and security. These technologies are summarized in Table 3.3. Intel Atom processors support these technologies to varying levels, so consult the processor data sheet if the technology is required in or would benefit your design.

Table 3.3   Intel Technology

Intel Technology	Description
Enhanced Intel Speedstep® Technology	Enables a deep sleep state to decrease power consumption.
Intel® Hyper-Threading Technology	Enables one processor core to appear to the operating system as two logical cores enabling greater processor resource utilization by multiple OS processes.
Intel® Turbo Boost Technology	Multi-core processor technology that enables a processor core to run at a higher clock rate for a limited period as long as thermal constraints are kept in balance.
Intel® Virtualization Technology (Intel® VT) for IA-32, Intel® 64, and Intel Architecture (Intel® VT-x)	Hardware support enabling multiple operating systems to execute concurrently on one system.
Intel Virtualization Technology (Intel® VT) for Directed I/O (Intel® VT-d)	Hardware support to increase virtualized support for I/O.
Intel® Trusted Execution Technology (Intel® TXT)	Hardware support for increased security capabilities.
Demand-based Switching	Power management technology that enables varying voltage and clock speed in response to processor load.
Intel® Burst Performance Technology (Intel® BPT)	Enables a processor core to run at a higher clock rate for a limited period as long as thermal constraints are kept in balance.

Intel® Hyper-Threading Technology (Intel HT® Technology) is a form of simultaneous multithreading (SMT) improving instruction level parallelism (ILP). The pipeline of the processor core is set up to recognize two separate streams of instructions (one for each hardware thread). Various events cause the pipeline to switch from decoding and dispatching one stream to decoding and dispatching the other stream. All of the resources in the pipeline are either shared or duplicated between the two hardware threads. For more information, see the *Intel® 64 and IA-32 Architectures Software Developer's Manual, Volume 1*, section 2.2.7. Most platforms allow you to enable or disable Intel HT

Technology as a BIOS option. In addition, the OS kernel must be built with Intel HT Technology enabled. You can view your CPU information using the Task Manager in Windows†, and /proc/cpuinfo in Linux†. If Intel HT Technology is enabled, you should see twice the number of CPUs as you have physical cores in your platform.

Enabling Intel HT Technology is part of the platform initialization process in your BIOS. Thus the number of visible cores will double once it has been switched on during the platform boot-up process. From the application standpoint, no noticeable difference exists. In fact, the processor has two sets of registers that store the current instruction, thereby creating the appearance of a multicore processor even on the register level. This creates the flexibility for the normal processor pipeline to run one thread at full speed, or two threads at the same time. In effect, employing Intel HT Technology has minimal downside. Potential performance issues are discussed in Chapter 8. Chapter 9 discusses the difference between Intel HT Technology and multi-core processing in further detail.

Figure 3.4 shows that as the instructions from thread 1 and thread 2, labeled A and B respectively, execute through the pipeline, they are temporarily stored in the queue corresponding to which virtual processor they came from. The core processor stages are shared, but each logical processor has its own pipelining queue.

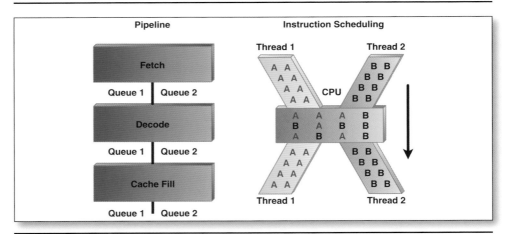

Figure 3.4   Pipeline and Instruction Scheduling with Intel Hyper-Threading Technology

Intel® Atom™ Processor Power States

The Intel Atom Processor platform supports standard mechanisms for power management. Power management is the ability of software, typically the operating system, to regulate the functioning of platform components in order to conserve the amount of power used by the system.

ACPI

Advanced Configuration and Power Interface[1] (ACPI) is an industry standard interface for operating system device configuration and power management. It enables developers a broadly supported means of controlling the power used by the device. ACPI defines several states which govern the functionality of the system across the categories described in Table 3.4. ACPI is currently enabled in many desktop and embedded operating systems such as FreeBSD, Windows Embedded, and Linux. In the table, C*n* and P*n* are vendor-defined states where *n* is a number greater than or equal to 3.

Table 3.4   ACPI Power States

State	Description
Global system states	Applies to entire system with categories such as mechanical off (G3), soft off (G2), sleeping (G1), and working (G0).
Device states	Power states of particular devices. Off (D3) to fully-on (D0).
Processor Power States	Power state of the processor. Ranges from vendor-defined low power idle (Cn) to executing instructions (C0).
Performance States	Correlates to frequency and voltage of the processor. Ranges from minimal level (Pn) to maximum performance (P0).

ACPI has some other capabilities apart from pure power management. ACPI provides the interface for Plug and Play, where the runtime docking and undocking of components occurs. ACPI is also responsible for thermal management and battery management.

---

[1] For more information on ACPI, consult http://www.acpi.info/

ACPI Component Architecture[2] (ACPICA) is an open source reference implementation of ACPI that is operating system–independent. This implementation serves as a starting point for operating systems that currently lack support for ACPI.

One reminder: a processor may implement more power states than those defined by ACPI. It is up to the BIOS to map specific processor-supported power states to those governed by ACPI. In addition, software can enable additional power states to be accessed by the operating system.

Processor States

Processor states, C-states, define just how much of the processor is on. The processor is said to be in state C0 when it is not idle and processing instructions. When the processor is idle, the processor can switch to one of its idle modes, C1 through Cn, where n is the deepest idle or sleep state supported by the processor. In these idle modes, the processor shuts down functionality and power to microarchitecture structures. This functionality and the structures comprise the following:

- Core voltage - reduced

- Core clock - stopped

- Phase Locked Loop – synchronization signal is stopped

- L1 cache – flushed and powered down

- L2 cache – flushed and powered down

In general, more structures are powered down in the deeper sleep states. Therefore, more time is required to transition from a deeper sleep state back to C0. Multiple idle modes can be supported and mapped to the ACPI C-states. The idle C-states range from C1 to C6 in some Intel Atom processors. Table 3.5 shows properties on several of the power statues available on the Intel Atom processor Z6xx series.

---

[2] For more information on ACPICA, consult http://acpica.org/

Table 3.5   Intel® Atom™ Processor Z6xx Power States

	C0 HFM	C0 LFM	C0 ULFM	C1/C2	C4	C6
Core clock	On	On	On	Off	Off	Off
PLL	On	On	On	On	Off	Off
L1 cache	Active	Active	Active	Flushed	Flushed	Off
L2 cache	Active	Active	Active	Active	Partial flush	Off
Wakeup time	Active	Active	Active	Short	Medium	Long

The states denoted C0 HFM, C0 LFM, and C0 ULFM stand for C0 high frequency mode, C0 low frequency mode, and C0 ultralow frequency mode respectively. These states correspond to the processors performance states, known as P-states. C0 HFM is equivalent to P0, C0 LFM is equivalent to P1, and C0 ULFM is equivalent to P2. On the Intel Atom processor N450, Table 3.6 shows the mapping of processor frequency to P-states.

Table 3.6   Intel® Atom™ Processor N450 P-states

Performance State	Clock Speed
P0	1.67 GHz
P1	1.33 GHz
P2	1.00 GHz

It is a function of the operating system to control the P-states. For example, on Linux, the ondemand governor is used to control P-states. The ondemand governor (Pallipadi and Starikovskiy) monitors processor utilization and dynamically adjusts P-states raising and lowering them based upon utilization checks against an up threshold value and a down threshold value.

The Intel Atom processor also supports enhanced versions of C1–C4, termed C1E, C2E, and C4E respectively. For example, C1E is similar to C1, except before the processor transitions from C0 to C1, a transition to the lowest P-state is performed, which helps reduce leakage in the idle mode. The processor implements two software interfaces for requesting these enhanced states: MWAIT instruction extensions with hints and via BIOS to automatically promote the idle states to enhanced idle states.

Intel® Hyper-Threading Technology Impact

C-state power management occurs at both the core level and the thread level when Intel HT Technology is enabled. Obviously, there needs to be some level of coordination between the C-states being requested by an individual thread and the C-state that effectively gets implemented at the core level. Table 3.7 summarizes the coordination policy which is that the processor core C-state is the more active of the two thread level C-state requests.

Table 3.7 Coordination of Thread Low-power States

Processor Core C-State		Thread 1			
		C0	**C1**	**C2**	**C4**
Thread 0	**C0**	C0	C0	C0	C0
	C1	C0	C1	C1	C1
	C2	C0	C1	C2	C2
	C4	C0	C1	C2	C4

Intel® Atom™ Processor Platform Architecture

The Intel Atom processor platform architecture is comprised of the Intel Atom processor and the supporting chips and features that enable creation of an embedded system. Figure 3.5 shows the components that typically comprise the key building blocks of a system.

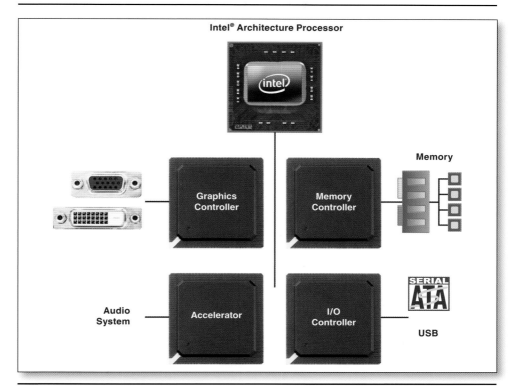

Figure 3.5   Intel® Architecture Platform Components

The components and a description of the functionality provided by these components can be summarized as follows:

■ *Central Processing Unit (CPU)*. Microprocessor providing the control and computation facilities for the platform.

■ *Memory Controller*. Provides the interface between the CPU and the memory subsystem, colloquially termed *northbridge*.

■ *I/O Controller*. Provides the interface between the CPU and the various input/output devices on the platform, colloquially termed *southbridge*.

■ *Graphics Controller*. Provides the interface between the CPU and the display and typically provides hardware support for accelerated 2D and 3D output.

■ *Custom Accelerator*. Provides hardware support for accelerated processing of application-specific algorithms.

There are many different arrangements for how this functionality can be provided in a platform. To illustrate one extreme where flexibility is paramount, consider a traditional desktop system where the functionality comprises a three chip solution: a CPU, a northbridge chip providing memory controller functionality and a southbridge providing I/O controller functionality. In addition, a discrete graphics card and a sound card can be employed to accelerate graphics and audio respectively.

On the opposite extreme, the integration of the functionality to drive a system onto one chip is termed system on a chip (SoC) and is becoming standard for embedded platforms. There is an inherent tradeoff between flexibility and complexity. Historically, Intel architecture has been employed largely in desktop and server compute environments where the flexibility of creating feature-rich platforms favored having a multichip platform solution. For embedded platforms where functionality is constrained and constraints like form factor and power become more important, integration is critical.

The roadmap for the Intel Atom processor platforms is evolving to accommodate these more highly constrained environments. The initial Intel Atom platform offerings illustrate this tradeoff between fit and functionality. The general trend will be to see more integration of functionality onto the Intel Atom processor core and facilities to enable pairing the processor with custom I/O.

Before reviewing the specific embedded platforms, you must understand the market segmentation of the broader Intel Atom platforms and the evolution plans from initial release into the future. This section details the three primary Intel Atom processor series, summarizes the evolution trends of the platform, and then shows instantiations of these and their impact in the low power embedded platforms.

Processor Series

The Intel Atom processor is offered in different classifications or series. For example the N series, the Z series, the D series, and the E series processors. These series are groupings of Intel Atom processors that target different categories of use for the processor and have slightly different combinations of processor features to optimize for the intended use. The Intel Atom processor is intended to be used across a broad range of applications, some of which would be classified as embedded and some not.

N Series

Platforms based upon N series processors primarily target application in netbooks and embedded systems where low power and mobility are important, but software compatibility and flexibility are critical. The key characteristic defining the series is its pairing of the Intel Atom processor with a traditional notebook class chipset, which offers mature functionality and software compatibility. The initial platforms are three-chip solutions. Compared to the Z series, current N series processors offer higher system bus speeds enabling faster memory performance. Current N series processors support some power savings features such as Enhanced Intel Speedstep Technology, but do not support demand-based switching.

Z Series

Platforms based upon the Z series processors primarily target application in mobile devices such as mobile phones and mobile Internet devices (MIDs). The distinguishing characteristics of platforms based upon Z series processors are higher integration; initial systems based upon Z series processors are two-chip solutions. Platforms based upon Z series processors tend to support slower bus speeds than N series and D series processors and do not support the Intel 64 ISA.

D Series

The D series of Intel Atom processors became available with the D410, D425, D510, and D525 introduced in 2010. The series is targeted to nettop devices, low-power and low-end desktop systems. The D series processors are similar to the N series processors, but target platforms tolerable of higher power utilization. Current D series processors do not support Enhanced Intel Speedstep Technology and operate at a higher TDP than the N series processors. For example, the D410, a 1.66-GHz processor, runs at the same clock speed as the N450, however is rated at 10 W versus 5.5 W.

2008 Platforms

The platforms released in 2008 and 2009 based on the Intel Atom processor were N series and Z series processors.

Intel® Atom™ Processor N270 and N280

The Intel Atom processor N270 and N280 are the initial N series offerings and employ a modified mobile chipset to provide memory, graphics, and I/O controller functionality. The chips paired with the processors are the Mobile Intel® 945GSE Express Chipset and the Intel® I/O Controller Hub 7-M (Intel® ICH7-M). Figure 3.6 summarizes the three-chip platform configuration.

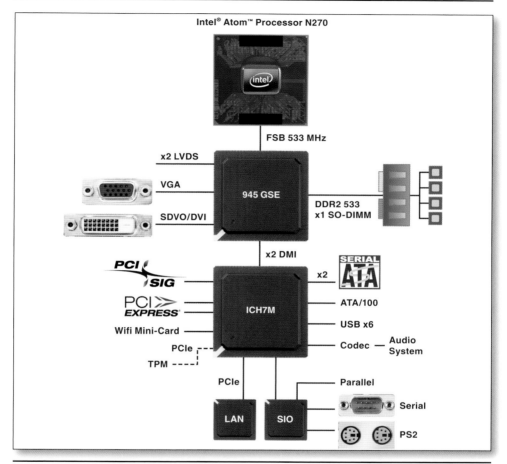

Figure 3.6   Intel Atom Processor N270

The 945GSE chipset is built on a 130-nm process and consumes an estimated 6 W of power. The chipset supports two SATA channels, one PCI Express† (PCIe), HD audio, and DDR 2 memory. The Intel ICH7-M consumes an estimated 3.3 W. Integrated 2D and 3D accelerated graphics is provided by the Intel® Graphics Media Accelerator 950. The N270 and N280 series processors support the following Intel technologies: Enhanced Intel Speedstep Technology, Intel Hyper-Threading Technology, and the Execute Disable Bit. Technologies not supported include the Intel 64 ISA, Intel VT-X, Intel VT-d, Intel TXT, Intel AES-NI, demand-based switching, and Intel BPT.

Intel® Atom™ Processor Z5xx Series

Processors in the Z5xx series comprise multiple products spanning a wide range of capabilities in terms of feature support, clock speed, and power usage. Platforms based upon these processors do not adopt a previous notebook chipset and instead employ a new chipset, called a System Controller Hub, that provides memory, graphics, and I/O controller functionality in one chip. Platforms in the Z5xx series are therefore two-chip system solutions. These Z series processors are well suited for application in low-power mobile platforms. These processors support Enhanced Intel Speedstep Technology, but lack support for the Intel 64 ISA. Figure 3.7 is a picture of a Fit-PC2 next to an Intel Atom processor-based netbook with a 10-inch screen. The Fit-PC2 employs an Intel Atom processor Z530 and with the two-chip solution enables the PC to run standard desktop operating systems in an extremely small form factor using passive cooling. The system features 1 GB of RAM and a 160-GB hard drive. The processor executes at 1.6 GHz, contains 512 KB of L2 cache, runs the system bus at 533 MHz, supports Intel VT-x and demand-based switching.

Figure 3.7   Fit-PC2 and 10.1-inch Netbook

Intel® System Controller Hub (Intel® SCH) US15W

The Intel® System Controller Hub (Intel® SCH) US15W was introduced in conjunction with the Z5xx series processors. Originally code-named Poulsbo, the chipset is built using 130 nm process technology. The chipset integrates an Intel Graphics Media Accelerator 500 graphics controller, a memory controller supporting 400 MHz and 533 MHz speeds, and an I/O controller. The chipset is rated to consume 2.3 W and is available in two sizes, 484 mm² for systems with tight form factor constraints and 1406 mm² for less constrained devices. Figure 3.8 illustrates the capabilities of the chipset. The Intel System Controller Hub US15W provides support for two-channel HD audio, eight USB connections, two x1 PCIe channels, one PATA-100 channel, and three SDIO channels.

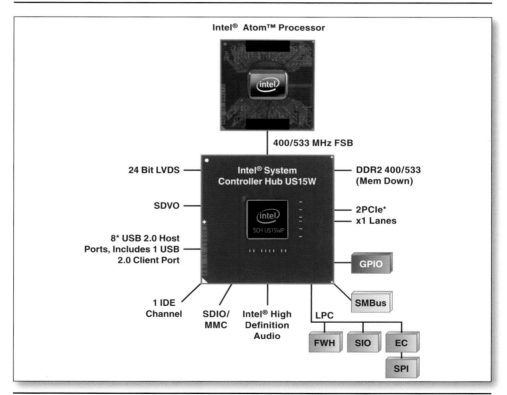

Figure 3.8   Intel® System Controller Hub (Intel® SCH) US15W

2010 Platforms

In 2010, the second generation of the Intel Atom processor and chipsets was released. The Intel® Atom™ processor Z6xx series, previously code-named Lincroft, integrates more functionality on the same die as the processor core. The integrated components include the 2D/3D graphics acceleration and display controller, memory controller, and hardware acceleration for video encode and video decode. Platforms based upon this processor require a second chip for I/O functionality so the systems are considered two-chip solutions. For nettop and netbook class systems, I/O functionality is provided by the Intel® NM10 Express Chipset. Other embedded and mobile devices can take advantage of an array of I/O controllers. Some of this flexibility appears in the embedded targeted platform, Intel® Atom™ processor E6xx series, which will be detailed later in this chapter.

Intel® NM10 Express Chipset

The Intel NM10 Express Chipset supports eight USB 2.0 ports, two 3-Gbps SATA ports, two 32-bit PCIe slots, four PCIe lanes and HD Audio. The nettop and netbook targeted processors N450, D410, D425, D510, and D525 take advantage of this chipset.

Intel® Atom™ Processor N450

The Intel Atom processor N450 was introduced in early 2010 for netbooks and features similar specifications as the previous generation N270 and N280. This processor is single core, supports Intel Hyper-Threading Technology, executes at 1.66 GHz and contains a 512-KB L2 cache. The N450 supports the Intel 64 ISA and due to integration of the graphics and memory controller generally has higher performance than the N270 and N280.

Intel® Atom™ Processors D410, D510, D425 and D525

The Intel Atom processors D410 and D510 were introduced in early 2010 and target nettop devices. The D510 is a dual-core processor that supports four logical processors in operating systems that supports Intel Hyper-Threading Technology. The dual-core part has a 1 MB L2 cache (two separate 512 KB L2 caches). Both D410 and D510 processors execute at 1.66 GHz. The key difference is that the D510 employs 176 million transistors compared to 123 million and has a higher TDP, 13 W versus 10 W.

The Intel Atom processors D425 and D525 were also introduced in 2010 and offer clock speed increases over the D410 and D510. The single core D425 and the dual core D525 both execute at 1.8 GHz.

Intel® Atom™ Processor Z6XX Series and Platform Controller Hub MP20 for MIDs

The next-generation Intel Atom processor–based platform for MIDs, formerly codenamed Moorsetown, was announced in 2010 and features the Intel Atom processor Z6xx series coupled with the Platform Controller Hub MP20. The platform targets a range of devices including high-end smart phones, tablets, and other mobile handheld devies. The platform also integrates a mixed signal IC (MSIC) that provides power delivery, battery charger capabilities, and faster transitions into and out of P-states.

Intel® Atom™ Processor Z6xx Series

The Intel Atom processor Z6xx series integrates a 45-nm Intel Atom processor core, a 3D graphics chip, hardware acceleration for video encode and decode, and an integrated memory and display controller. The processor includes a number of innovative features including:

- Intel® Burst Performance Technology (Intel® BPT), which increases frequency for short periods while staying within thermal limits.

- An integrated memory controller with support for low power DDR1 and DDR2 (LPDDR1/LPDDR2) memory; this targets extremely low power devices.

- Intel® GMA 600 Graphics enables 2D and 3D graphics with a 400-MHz graphics core. Adds support for MIPI-DSI, a display interface standard for handheld devices.

- Intel® Smart Idle Technology (Intel® SIT) enables the processor core and other components to switch off while the operating system is still executing.

- Intel HT Technology.

Intel Platform Controller Hub MP20

The Platform Controller Hub, built using 65-nm process technology, acts as an I/O hub, making the processor flexible in accommodating a wide degree of I/O functionality. The hub integrates a number of innovative features including:

■ Bus Turbo mode, which increases bus bandwidth and reduces CPU-to-memory latency when the processor is operating at higher frequencies.

■ Intel Smart Power Technology enables fine-grained power management.

■ Intel® Smart & Secure Technology (Intel® S&ST) incorporates hardware and software security architecture providing cryptographic acceleration and secure boot.

■ Intel® Smart Sound Technology (Intel® SST) incorporates a 24-bit audio DSP for voice processing and audio codec support.

Next Generation Intel® Atom™ Platform, Codenamed 'Medfield'

Medfield is the code name for Intel's next generation 32-nm SoC platform targeted at smartphones. Medfield is scheduled for 2011 and will continue substantial reductions in size and power while increasing performance compared to previous product generations.

Low Power Embedded Products

The Intel Atom processors detailed in the previous sections are adopted for use in the embedded market segments and in products such as those discussed in Chapter 2. In some cases, the processors and platforms are adopted with little modification. In other cases, the processors and platforms are supplemented to more fully target low power embedded systems. The low power embedded systems market segment is further divided into an entry performance category characterized by product offerings with system power greater than 7 W and an ultra low-power category characterized by product offerings with system power less than 7 W. The next sections detail the entry performance products followed by the ultra low-power products.

Entry Performance Products

The Intel Atom processor N270 for Embedded Computing combines the Intel Atom processor N270, the Mobile Intel 945GSE Express chipset, and the ICH7-M into a targeted platform for embedded computing. Embedded support is provided for UEFI 2.0 based BIOS, several flavors of Linux and Windows†, both the Intel Embedded Graphics Driver, Intel Graphics Media Accelerator, Intel Graphics Driver for Linux, and several I/O drivers including Intel® Matrix Storage Manager, support for the Intel 82562 Fast Ethernet Controller, and Intel HD Audio Driver.

The second generation is based upon the Intel Atom processors N450, D410, and D510 with the Intel® I/O Controller Hub 8-M (Intel® ICH8-M) chipset. The clock speed is 1.66 GHz for the N450, D410 and dual-core D510.

Ultra Low-Power Products

The initial low-power offering is the Intel Atom processor Z5xx series for Embedded Computing and comes available with either a Z510 or Z530 SC processor clocked at 1.1 GHz and 1.6 GHz respectively. The processor is a two-chip solution and offers two package sizes for the Intel SCH US15W including an industrial temperature option qualified for –40° to +85° C operation. The industrial temperature offerings are available at two clock speeds, 1.1 GHz and 1.33 GHz.

Intel® Atom™ Processor E6xx Series

In order to meet the performance, power, and form factor constraints required in embedded applications, focus and flexibility in the level of integration is required. It is challenging for one specific SoC to contain all of the features required to suit applications across multiple market segments. For example, embedded platforms targeting in-vehicle infotainment (IVI) and Internet Protocol (IP) media phones have the same general computation requirements that are met by Intel architecture; however these devices require different I/O capabilities due to user interface and connectivity requirements.

The Intel Atom processor E6xx series enables creation of embedded platforms tailored to the specific I/O requirements of the device. It does so by integrating general embedded functionality onto the processor and enabling differentiated I/O in the same package. Figure 3.9 illustrates options for pairing the Intel Atom processor E6xx series with different I/O capabilities specialized for function. For example, an IP camera can take advantage of the Intel Atom processor E6xx series paired with I/O customized to provide only USB, Gigabit Ethernet, and PCI functionality. A print imaging solution may require a proprietary I/O chip in the form of a custom ASIC. Devices requiring even more diverse I/O functionality can be paired with a more traditional I/O hub.

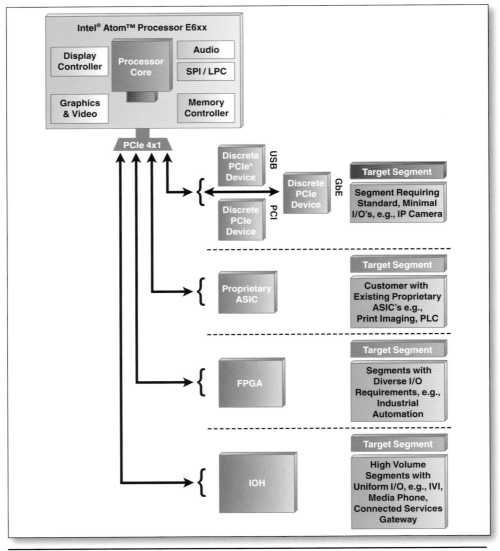

Figure 3.9   I/O Options for Intel® Atom™ Processor E6xx Series

The initial Intel Atom processor E6xx series are available at 0.6 GHz, 1.0 GHz, 1.3 GHz and 1.6 GHz. The addressable memory is 2 GB, and the integrated graphics executes at up to 400 MHz in the higher clock speed part and 320 MHz in the lower speed chips. TDP[3] ranges for the processor are between 2.7 W and 3.9 W. The Intel Atom processor E6xx series is available with temperature range options of 0 to +70° C for commercial and -40 to +85° C for industrial. The Intel Atom processor E6xx series is the first step in realizing the vision of enabling custom IOHs in the same platform.

Figure 3.10 shows the product variations for the Intel Atom processor E6xx series for embedded computing. The 'T' in the product names denotes the industrial temperature range support. Refer also to the video encode white paper (Girotra, 2010) at http://download.intel.com/design/intarch/ PAPERS/324328.pdf.

Commercial Temperature	Industrial Temperature	Core Frequency (GHz)	Graphics Frequency (GHz)	Video Encode	Estimated Thermal Design Power (W)
E680	E680T	1.6	400	Yes	3.9
E660	E660T	1.3	400	Yes	3.3
E640	E640T	1.0	320	Yes	3.3
E620	E620T	0.6	320	No	2.7

Figure 3.10 Intel® Atom™ Processor E6xx Series for Embedded Computing

Stellarton is the code name for an upcoming product based on the Intel Atom processor E6xx series that enables custom I/O or application acceleration to be integrated with the processor in one package. It enables OEMs to build customized I/O hubs or consolidate functionality of proprietary ASICs or FPGAs into the same package as the CPU. Stellarton does this with a multi-chip package.

---

[3] TDP values for Intel® Atom™ Processor E6xx Series are pre-silicon estimates.

Next Generation Embedded Platforms

Available in early 2011, the next generation Intel Atom processor–based SoC platform, codenamed Oak Trail, is optimized for sleek tablet and netbook designs, delivering up to a 50 percent reduction in average power consumption with full HD-video playback and targeting software choices including MeeGo, Microsoft Windows 7[†], and Google[†] operating systems.

Intel® Atom™ Processor Microarchitecture

The Intel Atom processor microarchitecture consists of the set of components on the processor that enables it to implement and provide support for the IA-32 and Intel 64 ISA. Embedded software developers need a basic understanding of the microarchitecture if they are engaged in low-level assembly language programming such as developers working on device drivers or performance critical portions of an application. Embedded software developers focused on utmost performance must also understand the microarchitecture and its implications on high performing assembly or machine language. The ability to inspect assembly language code or a disassembly of an application and to understand the difference between high performing and low performing code sequences when executing on the Intel Atom processor is critical for product success. This section provides the basic understanding of the microarchitecture required to do so.

Figure 3.11 is a high level depiction of the Intel Atom processor microarchitecture. At a first level, the microarchitecture of the initial Intel Atom processor is classified as an in order, superscalar pipeline. The term *in order* means the machine instructions execute in the same order as they appear in the application. The term *superscalar* means more than one instruction can execute at the same time. The Intel Atom processor is classified as *two-wide superscalar* since it has the ability to execute and retire two instructions in the same clock cycle. Modern processors are pipelined, which allows multiple instructions to be in different stages of processing at the same time.

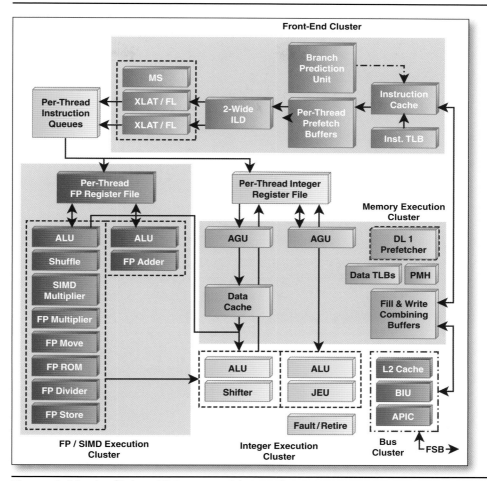

Figure 3.11   Intel® Atom™ Processor Microarchitecture

The integer pipeline for the Intel Atom processor is detailed in Figure Figure 3.12. The pipeline is divided into six phases of instruction processing:

1. Instruction Fetch
2. Instruction Decode
3. Instruction Issue
4. Data Access
5. Execute
6. Write Back

The integer pipeline consists of 16 stages and the floating point pipeline consists of 19 stages. In normal pipeline operation each stage takes one cycle to execute. The number of stages for each phase is detailed in Table 3.8. Note that each phase is pipelined; for example, it is possible for three instructions to be in the different stages of the instruction fetch phase (IF1, IF2, and IF3) at the same time.

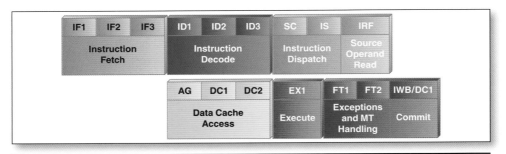

Figure 3.12   Integer Pipeline

Table 3.8   Intel Atom Processor Pipeline

Pipeline Phase	Description	Integer: Number of Stages	Floating-point: Number of Stages
Instruction Fetch	Obtain instruction from instruction cache.	3	3
Instruction Decode	Understand instruction.	3	3
Instruction Issue	Check and satisfy dependencies, read registers and issue for execution.	3	3
Data Access	Generate address if needed and access data cache.	3	3
Execute	Execution of the operation.	1	7
Write Back	Check for exceptions and commit results.	3	1

For the integer pipeline, the instruction fetch phase is 3 stages and the instruction decode is 3 stages. Instruction issue consists of 3 stages and data access consists of 3 stages. Instruction execution consists of 1 stage and write back consists of 3 stages. For floating point instructions, the instruction fetch consists of 3 stages and instruction decode consists of 3 stages. Instruction issue consists of 3 stages and data access consists of 3 stages. Instruction execution consists of 7 stages and write back consists of 1 stage. There are many exceptions for when an instruction can take longer to execute than 16 or 19 cycles; examples include division operations and instructions that decode in the microcode sequencer.

As mentioned previously, the Intel Atom processor microarchitecture is in order. You can understand what in order means by comparing it to an out-of-order microarchitecture such as the Intel Core i7 processor. Consider the sequence of instructions listed in Figure 3.13, which has the following program specified dependencies:

- Instruction 2 is dependent on the result of instruction 1.

- Instruction 3 is dependent on the result of instruction 2 and 1.

- Instruction 5 is dependent on the result of instruction 4.

- Instruction 6 is dependent on the result of instruction 5 and 4.

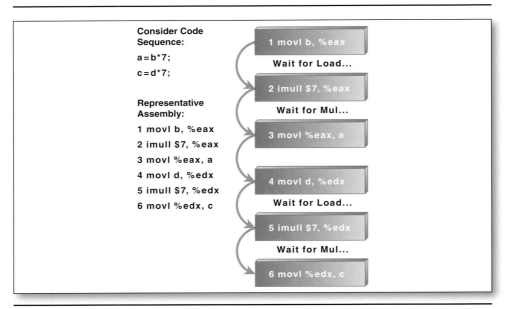

Figure 3.13 In-Order Execution

An in-order processor would execute the instructions in the order the instructions are listed. In an in-order superscalar processor such as the Intel Atom processor with two execution pipelines, instruction 2 would attempt to execute at the same time as instruction 1, but due to the dependency, the pipeline would stall until the result of instruction 1 were ready. Instruction 3 would not start executing until instruction 2 had the result from instruction 1. Instruction 4 could start execution as soon as instruction 2 finished, however instruction 5 would be stalled until instruction 4 had a result ready.

An out-of-order processor allows independent instructions to execute out of order as long as the instruction's dependencies have been fulfilled. On an out-of-order processor with sufficient execution resources the instruction schedule is more efficient. Instruction 4 can execute at the same time as instruction 1. Instruction 5 can execute at the same time as instruction 2. Instruction 6 can execute at the same time as instruction 3. The results are still written in program order; however superscalar execution enables more efficient usage of process resources.

This is a fundamental difference between the Intel Atom processor and other modern out-of-order processors. One method of addressing this disadvantage is to use a compiler that schedules for the Intel Atom processor. If the compiler laid out the instructions in the order specified in Figure 3.14, many of the same benefits of out-of-order execution would result when executing on the Intel Atom processor.

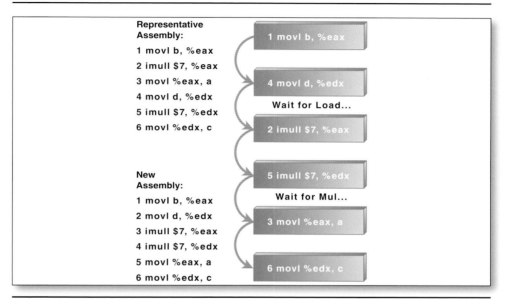

Figure 3.14 Instruction Schedule for In Order Execution

Front End

The components that comprise what is termed the front end of the processor are charged with finding and placing the instructions into the execution units. The components that comprise the front end of the processor and their functionality are:

- ■ *Branch Prediction Unit.* Predicts the target address for branches.

- ■ *Instruction TLB.* Translates virtual to physical addresses.

- ■ *Instruction Cache.* Fast access to recently executed instructions.

- ■ *Prefetch Buffer*. Holds instruction bytes ready for decoding.

- ■ *Decode*. Performs the decode.

- ■ *Microcode Sequencer*. Complex instruction decode.

The front end of the microarchitecture performs the instruction fetch and instruction issue phases of the pipeline. The first action in placing an instruction into the pipeline is to obtain the address of the instruction. This address comes from one of two places. If the current instruction that is just entering the pipeline is not a branch instruction, the next instruction is equal to the address of the current instruction plus the size of the current instruction. If the current instruction is a branch, the next instruction is determined by the branch prediction unit that caches previously seen branches and provides a prediction as to the direction and target of the branch. The instruction TLB translates the virtual address used by the program into the physical address where the instruction is actually stored. The instruction cache is used to keep recently executed instructions closer to the processor if those particular instructions are executed again. The instruction cache is 24 KB in size.

Predecode Bits

The instruction cache contains predecode bits to demarcate individual instructions to improve decode speed. One of the challenges with the IA-32 and Intel 64 ISA is that instructions are variable in length. In other words, the size of the instruction is not known until the instruction has been partially decoded. The front end contains two instruction decoders that enable up to two instructions to be decoded per cycle and this is consistent with the Intel Atom processor's dual instruction execution architecture. These decoders assume the boundary of an instruction is known, which is a change from previous decoders used in Intel architecture processors. Previous processors buffered bytes into a window that was rotated from instruction to instruction. The front end also contains two queues to temporarily hold decoded instructions until they are ready to execute. Two queues service the two threads of execution available due to support for Intel Hyper-Threading Technology.

Instruction Decode

During instruction decode, the IA-32 and Intel 64 instructions are decoded into another instruction that drives the microarchitecture. In previous IA-32 and Intel 64 architecture processors, the decode phase broke instructions into micro-operations characterized as being very simple in nature. For example, an addition operation that referenced and wrote to memory would be broken down into four micro-operations for execution by the microarchitecture. In the Intel Atom processor, the two decoders are capable of decoding most instructions in the Intel 64 and IA-32 architecture. The microarchitecture does make a distinction between instructions that are too complicated to execute in the pipeline and has a fallback mechanism, a microcode sequencer. The microcode sequencer is used to decode the more complex instruction into a number of smaller operations for execution in the pipeline. The drawback to the microcode store is that these instructions decode slower and break down into more than one operation in the pipeline.

Decode Stage to Issue Stage

The decode stages can decode up to two instructions to keep the two-issue pipeline filled; however, in some cases the decoder is limited in only being able to decode one instruction per cycle. Cases where the decoder is limited to one instruction per cycle include x87 floating point instructions and branch instructions. The Intel Atom processor is dual issue superscalar, but it is not perfectly symmetrical. Not every possible pairing of operations can execute in the pipeline at the same time. The instruction queue holds instructions until they are ready to execute in the memory execution cluster, the integer execution cluster, or the FP/SIMD execution cluster.

Memory Execution Cluster

The memory execution cluster provides the functionality for generating addresses and accessing data. Components of the memory execution cluster and their functionality include:

- *Address Generation Unit.* Generates data address composing base address, scale, and offset.

- *Data TLB.* Translates virtual address to physical address.

■ *Data Cache*. Holds recently accessed data.

■ *Prefetcher*. Predicts future access and fetches by analyzing previous accesses.

■ *Write-Combining Buffers*. Allows grouping of individual write operations before being sent on to the L2 cache; enables more efficient memory bandwidth utilization.

In the optimum case for a data access, the data is resident in the L1 cache, however if the data is not resident there, an L2 cache request is made. One architectural optimization is the inclusion of a data prefetcher that analyzes historical access patterns and attempts to fetch future data in advance of reference.

Common to many architectures, the memory subsystem supports store forwarding, which takes a result of a previous store and forwards the value internally for use in a proceeding load operation. This forwarding eliminates potential pipeline stalls because the load instruction does not need to wait until the stored value is committed to the cache. A special case of forwarding results from operations that affect the flags and instructions dependent upon them. Branch operations have an implicit one-cycle penalty. All other instructions have a two-cycle bubble.

One common occurrence in instruction sequences is the computation of address for use in subsequent instructions. For example, Figure 3.15 shows an instruction sequence where the second instruction depends on an address calculation from the previous instruction. This dependency would cause a three-cycle stall because the second instruction cannot execute until the result of the first instruction is known. Figure 3.14 shows the impact on the pipeline as there is a bubble between the AG and EX pipeline stages. Techniques to avoid this situation are discussed later in the chapter.

Instruction							
subl $4, %esp	IRF	AG	DC1	DC2	EX1	FT1	
movl %ebx, (%esp)		IRF	stall	stall	stall	AG	DC1

Figure 3.15 Address Generation Stall

Integer Execution Cluster

The integer execution cluster features two arithmetic/logic units (ALU) enabling joint execution of many instructions. Dual execution in the execution cluster has some limitations.

FP/SIMD Execution Cluster

The floating point execution cluster executes x87, SIMD, and integer multiply instructions. The cluster contains two ALUs and supports limited combinations of dual execution. The second execution unit is limited to floating point additions. Integer multiplies take more than one cycle in the execute stage and effectively stall subsequent instructions until after the multiply is finished with the execute stage. The only exceptions to this are for subsequent integer multiplies, which can be effectively pipelined in this stage.

Safe Instruction Recognition

One microarchitectural issue specific to the Intel Atom processor is that the integer pipeline is shorter than the floating point pipeline. Floating point exceptions can occur in an instruction that is programmatically before an integer instruction, but takes longer to retire. A straightforward solution would be to delay retirement of integer instructions until preceding floating point instructions in the pipeline retire. This solution would effectively add a multicycle delay to integer instruction retirement. Instead, a safe instruction recognition algorithm is employed that detects if it is possible for a floating point instruction to fault. In only those cases, a restart of proceeding integer instructions from the scheduler would be issued.

Bus Cluster

The bus cluster is the connection from the processor to the memory subsystem and contains a 512-KB, eight-way L2 cache. The bus cluster also contains the Bus Interface Unit (BIU) and Advanced Programmable Interrupt Controller (APIC).

Intel® Atom™ Processor Assembly Language Primer

Software developers typically program in higher level languages such as C and C++, which insulates them from the low level details of assembly and machine language. Optimizing compilers can go a long way towards producing high performance code for your particular embedded platform. That said, there are times when embedded developers need to concern themselves with the assembly language or disassembly of an executable. During a platform migration from one architecture to another, some embedded software may have been written in assembly language and thus require the equivalent translation into Intel architecture assembly language. Developers may wish to inspect the assembly or machine language and ascertain if the generated code has been optimized well for the Intel Atom processor. This section details assembly language tips for high performance specific to the Intel Atom processor. The previous pipeline discussion helps set the stage for this because you will now understand the reason behind these tips. Four categories of tips are presented in the following sections:

- General

- Intel Atom processor

- Effective math

- Effective stack management

General Tips

The first set of tips is general and benefits performance across a wide range of architectures. This section details why each of these general tips is beneficial to the Intel Atom processor architecture.

Optimize for the Instruction Cache

The decode phase of the pipeline benefits from the predecode information in the L1 instruction cache. If the instruction reference misses in the instruction cache, a request is sent to the L2 cache, which incurs extra latency. In addition, these instructions must be decoded using a more traditional IA-32 architecture decoder and this adds at least two cycles to instruction latency. The recommendation is therefore to employ techniques that minimize code size and to be wary of optimization techniques that increase code size. One common optimization that impacts code size is loop unrolling. Loop unrolling typically increases performance by eliminating loop dependencies on loops with high iteration counts. In addition, greater instruction level parallelism is available for scheduling by optimizing compilers. The tradeoff is that loop unrolling increases code size. Use of loop unrolling, either manual or compiler generated, must be carefully considered.

Use an Optimized Dot Product

An efficient dot product for Intel Atom processors spaces address adjustments with sufficient instructions to prevent stalls when the addresses are eventually read. In addition, loop unrolling and software pipelining could be used to hide the latency between the initial multiply operation and the subsequent add operation.

Use Optimized Libraries for Copy and String Copy

One common practice in enabling platform-independent software is creation and use of platform-independent libraries to perform low level operations such as memory copies and string copies. Another common practice is to adopt system-provided routines for these low level operations. In both cases, these libraries may not be optimized for the Intel Atom processor. A simple method of ensuring use of optimized libraries is to employ a compiler that specifically targets the Intel Atom processor. Figure 3.16 shows the assembly language listing for a straightforward unoptimized memory copy and an optimized memory copy. The optimized sequence takes advantage of the SSE registers to perform the copies. The optimized sequence shows only the inner kernel of the loop and makes some assumptions about the length of the memory copy that would be ascertained before entry into the loop.

```
#Unoptimized memcopy
..B1.1:
        movb       (%edi, %ebx), %cl
        movb       %cl, (%edi, %esi)
        incl       %edi
        cmpl       %eax, %edi
        jb         ..B1.1

#Optimized memcopy
..B1.1:
        movdqa     (%eax,%edi), %xmm0
        movdqa     %xmm0, (%eax,%esi)
        addl       $16, %eax
        cmpl       %edx, %eax
        jb         ..B1.1
```

Figure 3.16　Unoptimized Memory Copy versus Optimized Memory Copy

Use Natural Alignment

Cache lines are divided into "chunks" that are checked to ensure writes to individual chunks do not conflict with other chunks. Data that is not aligned has a greater chance of spanning multiple chunks and increases the likelihood of conflicting commits. Therefore, aligning data on natural boundaries (32-bit integers aligned on 4-byte boundaries, 128-bit Intel SSE types aligned on 16-byte boundaries) is a method to reduce the possibility.

Intel® Atom™ Processor Tips

The next set of tips is specific to the Intel Atom processor based upon unique features and in some cases tradeoffs of the microarchitecture.

Store Forwarding

A commonly observed assembly language sequence is a store to an address followed by a load from the same address. The Intel Atom processor has hardware support for store forwarding, where the store value is forwarded to the load in the processor without waiting for the memory operation to complete. Figure 3.17 shows an assembly language sequence where a value is stored to the address in the register `%ebx` and subsequently read in the two following instructions. Store forwarding is limited to integer values with the same address and same size. In the example, the store would be forwarded to the first load, but not the second.

```
movl %ecx, (%ebx)
movl %(ebx), %eax #store is forwarded
movb %(ebx), %cl  #store is not forwarded
```

Figure 3.17 Store Forwarding Example

Avoid Use of Nonzero Segment Bases

Segmented memory and use of nonzero segment bases is rare and the Intel Atom processor microarchitecture is not heavily optimized for it. Throughput of memory references that employ nonzero segment bases is limited. Therefore, it is recommended to avoid the use of nonzero segment bases. If you must use nonzero segments, ensure the segment base is 64-byte aligned.

Use a Matched Call and Return to Obtain the Instruction Pointer

Low level programmers may need to obtain the instruction pointer. One example is "thunk" code in C++ that adjusts for a call to a virtual function. For Intel Atom processors, the recommendation is to use a call matched with a return sequence instead of an unmatched call with a pop of the stack into a register. Figure 3.18 shows an assembly language sequence where the function _get_ip is called. The instruction pointer is placed into register `ecx` and control returns to the original caller for use.

```
        call _get_ip
# your code that uses the ip here

_get_ip:
        movl (%esp), %ecx
        ret
```

Figure 3.18   Obtaining the Instruction Pointer

Beware of Partial Register Dependencies

In previous Intel architecture processors, code that employed partial registers, 8-bit or 16-bit register references, where a read of a larger 16-bit or 32-bit component occurred after a write to the partial register, were subject to a multicycle partial register stall. The Intel Atom processor does not have the same partial register stalls; instead a dependency on a portion of the register is assumed to be a dependency on the entire register. Figure 3.19 shows an assembly language code sequence where the 8-bit subset of %ecx, %cl is written. In the following instruction, register %ch is read. There is no true dependency between the write of register %cl and the read of register %ch, however the Intel Atom processor acts as if that were the case. The second instruction has an assumed dependency and cannot proceed until the result in register %cl is ready.

```
        movb %bl, %cl
        movb %ch, %dh #ch is assumed dependent on cl
```

Figure 3.19   Partial Register Dependency

Flag Updates

The Intel Atom processor microarchitecture has specific issue limitations on instructions dependent on the status register. Instructions dependent on the status register cannot be issued in the same cycle as an instruction that sets the status register. In Figure 3.20, the setc is dependent on the previous instruction and has a one cycle stall. Conditional branches incur less of a penalty. In Figure 3.20, the fourth instruction is dependent on the previous instruction and thus cannot issue in the same cycle as the `addl` instruction, but can be issued in the next cycle. The recommendation is to try and place some instructions in between instructions that write the status register and instructions that read from the status register.

```
addl %ebx, %ebx
setc %ah          # 1 cycle stall

addl %ebx, %ebx
   jc       dest     # executes  one  cycle  after
previous
```

Figure 3.20　Flag Consumer Stall

Effective Math

The general mantra for effective math is to be aware of traditional methods of performing math operations that execute slowly on Intel Atom processors and to instead use more optimized sequences.

Beware of leas to Perform Additions and Subtractions

Referenced addresses that are computed by previous additions and subtractions are subject to a multicycle penalty due to the fact that those computations would be available after the execute stages of the pipeline, but are required in the earlier address generation stage for the next instruction. That next instruction would need to wait until the preceding instruction completed the execute stage before address generation could occur. To prevent this delay, the recommendation is to use `lea` for address calculation. The `lea` instruction is executed at address generation time so the result would be available for proceeding instructions in time. Be careful however, since because the `lea` instruction is executed during the AG stage, there is the potential for it to stall if it is dependent on a previous instruction's result from the EX stage. Figure 3.21 shows two different assembly language sequences. The first sequence of two instructions contains a stall; the second instruction, the `lea` will stall because the result of the previous `add` will not be known until the EX stage, but is needed in the AG stage. The second sequence of three instructions shows a better sequence where add instructions are employed. In this case, there are no pipeline stalls and the instructions execute more efficiently in the pipeline.

```
add $8, %eax
lea 16(%eax), %ebx # 3 cycle stall

add $8, %eax
mov %eax, %ebx
add $16, %ebx # fully pipelined
```

Figure 3.21 Pipeline Stalls Due to lea

Effective Scheduling of Integer Multiply

Integer multiplies take multiple cycles in the execution stage of the pipeline and prevent most other instructions from entering the execution stage. There are a few exceptions. Other integer multiplies can be pipelined and enter the execution stage in proceeding cycles in a pipeline fashion. In addition, floating point operations can take advantage of the SIMD execution cluster with no impact. Therefore, effective assembly language for the Intel Atom processor will attempt to schedule integer multiplies with other integer multiplies or floating point instructions.

Avoid Divides

On the Intel Atom processor, integer and floating point divides are particularly slow compared to other Intel architecture processors. If possible, employ techniques to reduce the use of divide instructions such as multiply shift techniques for integer divides and reciprocal multiply for floating point.

Scalar Doubles Are Faster than Packed Doubles

The architecture has less throughput on packed double operations than scalar doubles to the degree that it is more efficient to employ multiple scalar double operations than to issue a packed double operation.

Use Intel® SSE Instructions, Not x87 for Floating Point

Scalar single precision floating point Intel SSE instructions execute faster and have increased throughput compared to x87 operations. The recommendation is to favor using Intel SSE instructions for floating point operations instead of x87 instructions. If x87 is used, beware that consecutive x87 instructions incur a two-cycle penalty during instruction decode.

Use Library-based Complex Number Implementations

Computations on complex numbers are typically represented as a structure containing two floating point values, one for the real and one for the imaginary. The recommendation is to use an optimized library that takes advantage of Intel SSE instructions as opposed to x87 floating point. If you do decide to implement your complex number routines, use Intel SSE for the floating point.

Effective Stack Management

The stack is primarily used in function calls to pass arguments and to allocate temporary values associated with variables local to the function. Proper management on Intel Atom processors is essential for high performance.

Do Not Mix Implicit and Explicit Modifications to the Stack Pointer

Implicit updates to the stack pointer register (register `esp` or `rsp`) result from `push`, `pop`, `call`, and `ret` instructions. These updates occur during the address generation stage of the pipeline. Explicit stack pointer adjustments through `add` and `sub` operations execute during the execute stage. Mixing implicit and explicit adjustments result in a stall between the address generation and execution stage as discussed previously. Figure 3.22 shows two pairs of instructions. The first instruction uses an explicit adjustment to `esp` that executes during the EX stage and stalls the address generation phase of the next instruction for three cycles. The third instruction (first instruction of the second pair) employs an implicit adjustment to `esp` using the `lea` instruction that executes during the AG stage and incurs no stall on the next instruction.

```
        subl $4, %esp
        movl ebx, (%esp) # 3 cycle stall

        lea -4(%esp), %esp
        movl ebx, (%esp)  # no stall
```

Figure 3.22   Implicit and Explicit ESP Updates

Avoid Use of the leave Instruction

The leave instruction is not highly optimized for the Intel Atom processor and is decoded through the microsequencer. The recommendation is to use a sequence of pop instructions and a return instruction as these instructions execute more efficiently through the pipeline.

Use Register Forms of push and pop

Where possible, employ register forms of push and pop as the memory forms execute through the microsequencer. In Figure 3.23, the difference between a memory form of a push and the equivalent register form is highlighted.

```
        # Memory form of push
        pushl 4(%esp)

        # Register form of push
        movl 4(%esp), %eax
        pushl %eax
```

Figure 3.23   Memory and Register Form of push Instructions

Use lea to Make Other Adjustments to esp

The lea instruction executes during the address generation phase, which enables the result to be ready as soon as possible for use by other instructions.

Summary

Software developers employing the Intel Atom processor in embedded designs benefit from understanding the processor architecture, platform architecture, and microarchitecture. In addition, optimization techniques focused at the microarchitecture level are essential for performance-oriented developers such as assembly language developers.

The processor architecture is a simpler design than previous Intel architecture processors optimizing for power to a higher degree. The processor is fully compatible with IA-32 and Intel 64 ISA and offers support for instruction extensions such as Intel SSE3 as well as Intel HT Technology. ACPI support enables system developers insight and control over the processor's power utilization.

The platform architecture enables a variety of devices targeting a wide range of market segments. Trends in the platform architecture from the initial 2008 platforms to today include greater levels of integration with increasing domain-specific functionality. The Intel Atom processor E6xx series enables the combination of processor and device-specific I/O functionality in one package.

The Intel Atom processor microarchitecture is termed a dual issue pipelined superscalar processor architecture. Effective assembly language optimization requires understanding processor pipeline details and which instruction sequences perform well on the architecture. This chapter provided insight into optimizing for the Intel Atom processor at the microarchitecture level by discussing general optimization tips, processor-specific tips, effective math techniques and effective stack management techniques.

Chapter **4**

Processor Architecture Differences, Software Implications, and Tools

The best way to predict the future is to invent it.

—Alan Kay

Porting software to platforms of different processor architectures can be simple or require additional effort depending on the portability of the original source code. For software implementations that abstract away the information specific to the hardware and operating system, the port could be as simple as a recompilation of the source code. However, in cases where the software is programmed to run on a specific processor, source code updates will be required to support the target architecture. Therefore, the software effort required to migrate to Intel® architecture can vary depending on the starting point of the current source code design. In any case, completing a successful port involves assessing the current situation and understanding the goals and requirements before the migration begins.

The information covered in this chapter exposes the details of migrating software to Intel architecture processors. The chapter is organized into sections that address software solution choices related to the processor architecture differences and software development for Intel architecture. One of the usual migration considerations is the memory architecture of processors, which is covered here in depth. Other relevant factors include variations between the current and target operating systems, real-time requirements, events and interrupts, graphics and video, system initialization, and software development tools.

Software Considerations Related to Processor Architecture Differences

There are two main parts to every architecture migration. The first part involves getting the code ported and executing correctly on one processor core of the target platform. Part one includes consideration of multiple software design areas including several hardware architectural differences, operating system, system initialization, and tools for migration and development. Part two involves adopting the target platform technologies. For example, part two for Intel® Atom™ platform targets could include moving from a uniprocessor serial code design to a multi-core code design. This chapter discusses each of these areas along with various design choices. Understanding that every migration situation is different, the migration design guide at the end of this chapter guides embedded software developers step-by-step through situational decisions and solutions, which will help in crafting the overall migration plan.

Differences between other processor architectures and Intel architecture span instruction set, register, and memory categories. Although some amount of assembly language code is always required, the beauty of developing code in a high level language, such as the C programming language, is that the source code for the most part is portable between hardware architectures. This is because high level languages use compilers, which handle instruction-set and register differences and generate the machine code for the target processor architecture. And so to that end, it's reasonable to conclude that the more high level language source code your system currently includes, the easier the migration effort will be and fewer the complexities you will encounter.

Table 4.1 and Table 4.2 highlight hardware architecture differences that are commonly encountered when migrating from one processor architecture to another. Examples are given for PowerPC† ARM† and Intel architecture. Note: Architecture migrations based on other processors, such as MIPS†, could also apply the design considerations covered in this chapter, and, in fact, could adapt directly to Intel multi-core technology. Refer to Chapter 3 for details about Intel® Atom™ processor architecture.

PowerPC Compared to Intel® Architecture

Table 4.1 lists the main areas of processor architectural differences between PowerPC and Intel architecture.

Table 4.1   PowerPC and Intel® Architecture Differences

Instruction Set

Instructions	PowerPC and Intel architecture instructions are very different. For some instructions there is no one to one PowerPC to Intel architecture equivalent. Refer to the "Intel® 64 and IA-32 Architectures Software Developer's Manuals" section of this chapter, which contain the Intel architecture instruction set information, and tools that may assist the assembly code migration.
Alignment	PowerPC instructions are all four bytes in size and must be aligned on four-byte boundaries. Intel architecture instructions vary in size and therefore do not require alignment. On PowerPC a `bool` data type is four bytes. On Intel architecture, a `bool` data type is one byte. Make the code portable by changing the PowerPC Boolean data to an unsigned 32-bit `int` data type.
Vector oriented instructions	PowerPC uses AltiVec† instructions. Intel architecture uses Intel® Streaming SIMD Extensions (Intel® SSE). Refer to the "Vector Oriented Code" section of this chapter for details about migrating AltiVec to Intel® SSE instructions.

Operations

Divide-by-zero	For integer divide-by-zero, PowerPC simply returns zero. On Intel architecture, executing this operation is fatal. Code should always check the denominator for zero before executing the divide operation. There is no difference in operation between PowerPC and Intel architecture floating point divide-by-zero. Refer to the "Interrupts and Exceptions Model" section of this chapter for details on handling interrupts and exception on Intel architecture.

Hardware Devices

Drivers and libraries	If a PowerPC driver or library comes from a third party vendor, check with the vendor for equivalent Intel architecture products. If any device drivers or libraries are developed in-house, they will need to be rewritten for Intel architecture. Refer to the "Device Drivers" section of this chapter for chipset and graphics driver information and what you need to know about library support.

Registers

Calling conventions Specified by the application binary interface (ABI)	Arguments are passed in registers for PowerPC. For IA-32, in general, parameters are passed on the stack. For Intel® 64, parameters are passed in registers and on the stack, and are also dependent on how the operating system implements it. Intel architecture has fewer registers than PowerPC and therefore local variables may be stored on the stack as well.

Memory

Byte order, also referred to as endianness.	*Endianness* describes how multi-byte data is represented by a computer system and is dictated by the CPU architecture of the system. Intel architecture uses little endian and PowerPC is configurable to be either big-endian or little-endian. Any PowerPC software that is hardcoded as big-endian will need to be updated to support little-endian. Refer to the "Microprocessor Endian Architecture" section of this chapter for more information.
Bit fields	The order of bit fields in memory can be reversed between architectures. Intel® architecture uses up bit ordering, which means that bit 0 is least significant. Refer to the "Bit Fields and Bit Masks" section of this chapter for more details.

Note: Architectural Differences includes information from the *Universal Binary Programming Guidelines.* 26 Feb 2007. Apple.com. 18 Dec 2008.

ARM Compared to Intel® Architecture

Table 4.2 lists the main processor architectural differences between ARM and Intel architecture.

Table 4.2   ARM and Intel® Architecture Differences

Instruction Set

Instructions	ARM and Intel architecture instructions are very different. There is no one-to-one ARM to Intel architecture equivalent. Refer to the "Intel® 64 and IA-32 Architectures Software Developer's Manuals" section of this chapter, which contain the Intel architecture instruction set information. All ARM instructions can be predicated (conditionally executed). On Intel® architecture only `MOV` instructions are conditional; no memory operations are predicated.
Alignment	ARM has alignment restrictions and size differences, dependent on the type. A four-byte integer must be four-byte aligned. A structure with three characters on ARM will be padded to four bytes. Intel architecture instructions vary in size and therefore do not require alignment. A structure with three characters on Intel architecture may be three bytes.
Vector oriented instructions	ARM uses Vector Floating Point† (VFP) and Advanced SIMD, NEON† DSP Enhanced Instructions. Intel architecture uses Intel® Streaming SIMD Extensions (Intel® SSE). Refer to the "Vector Oriented Code" section of this chapter for more details. Note: Some ARM processors, such as XScale†, use SIMD instructions.

Operations

Divide-by-zero	For divide-by-zero and floating-point, on ARM a function is used to catch the hardware trap and then throw the exception within the same thread[1]. On Intel architecture, executing this operation is fatal. Code should always check the denominator for zero before executing the divide operation. Refer to the "Interrupts and Exceptions Model" section of this chapter for details on handling interrupts and exception on Intel architecture.

[1] Exception Handling ABI for the ARM® Architecture
   http://infocenter.arm.com/help/topic/com.arm.doc.ihi0038a/IHI0038A_ehabi.pdf

Hardware Devices

Drivers and libraries	If an ARM driver or library comes from a third party vendor, check with the vendor for equivalent Intel architecture products. If any device drivers or libraries are developed in-house, they will need to be rewritten for Intel architecture. Refer to the "Device Drivers and Libraries" section of this chapter for chipset and graphics driver information and what you need to know about library support.

Registers

Calling conventions Specified by the application binary interface (ABI)	ARM adheres to the Application Binary Interface (ABI) for ARM. Parameters are passed in registers and on the stack. For IA-32, in general, parameters are passed on the stack. For Intel® 64, parameters are passed in registers and on the stack, and are also dependent on how the operating system implements it.

Memory

Byte order, also referred to as endianness	*Endianness* describes how multi-byte data is represented by a computer system and is dictated by the CPU architecture of the system. Intel architecture uses little endian and ARM is configurable to be either big-endian or little-endian. Any ARM software that is hardcoded as big-endian will need to be updated for little-endian, Refer to the "Microprocessor Endian Architecture" section of this chapter for more information.
Bit fields	The order of bit fields in memory can be reversed between architectures. Intel architecture uses up bit ordering, which means that bit 0 is least significant. Refer to the "Bit Fields and Bit Masks" section of this chapter for more details.

The information in the remainder of this chapter discusses the software implications respective to information in Table 4.1 and Table 4.2 and their available software solution choices.

Microprocessor Endian Architecture

Endianness describes how multi-byte data is represented by a computer system and is dictated by the CPU architecture of the system. Unfortunately not all computer systems are designed with the same endian architecture. The difference in endian architecture is an issue when software or data is shared between computer systems. An analysis of the computer system and its interfaces will determine the requirements of the endian implementation of the software.

This section explains endianness and its effect on code portability. Code that follows the *Endian-neutral Coding Guidelines* discussed in this section will operate correctly on host processors of differing endian architectures, easing the effort of platform migration.

Endian-Neutral Software

Software is sometimes designed with a specific endian architecture in mind, limiting the portability of the code to other processor architectures. This type of implementation is considered to be endian-specific. However, endian-neutral software can be developed, allowing the code to be ported easily between processors of different endian architectures, and without rewriting any code. Endian-neutral software is developed by identifying system memory and external data interfaces, and using endian-neutral coding practices to implement the interfaces. Platform migration requires consideration of the endian architecture of the current and target platforms, as well as the endian architecture of the code.

Endian-specific code assumes the endianness of the underlying hardware. In a nutshell, the code is endian-specific if it contains the use of unions and type casting pointers to change the size of the data access, or does not use endian-neutral macros to access binary multi-byte data.

For architecture migrations to Intel Atom processors, no endian updates are required if the source code involved in the architecture migration is designed as little-endian or endian-neutral. In fact, designing software that abstracts the OS and hardware is common practice in modern code bases. On the other hand, for the edge cases where the software design doesn't provide the abstraction layers and is hardcoded as big-endian the code will need some amount of endian updates.

This remainder of this section establishes a set of fundamental guidelines for software developers who wish to develop endian-neutral code or convert endian-specific code. These guidelines describe the software interface information that should be considered and how to convert endian-specific code to endian-neutral code.

Note: The examples in this section are based on 32-bit processor architecture.

Analysis

There are two main areas where endianness must be considered. One area pertains to code portability. The second area pertains to sharing data between platforms.

Code Portability

It is not uncommon for software to be designed and implemented for the endian architecture of a specific processor platform, without allowing for ease of portability to other platforms.

Endian-neutral code provides flexibility for software implementations to be compiled for and operate seamlessly on processors of different endian architectures.

Shared Data

Computer systems are made up of multiple components, including computers, interfaces, data storage, and shared memory. Any time file data or memory is shared between computers, the potential for an endian architecture conflict exists. Data can be stored in ways that are not tied to endian architecture and also in ways that define the endianness of the data.

Definition of Endianness

Endianness is the byte order in which multi-byte data is stored in computer memory. It describes the location of the most significant byte (MSB) and least significant byte (LSB) of an address in memory. Endianness is dictated by the CPU architecture implementation of the system. The operating system does not dictate the endian model implemented; the endian model of the CPU architecture instead dictates how the operating system is implemented.

Representing these two storage formats are two types of endian architecture, big-endian[2] and little-endian. There are benefits to both of these endian architectures. See the section "Merits of Endian Architectures." Big-endian architecture stores the MSB at the lowest memory address. Little-endian architecture stores the LSB at the lowest memory address. The lowest memory address of multi-byte data is considered the starting address of the data. Table 4.3 depicts how the 32-bit hex value 0x12345678 is stored in memory for big-endian and little-endian architectures. The lowest memory address is represented in the leftmost position, byte 00.

Table 4.3   Example of Memory Addressing for Big- and Little-endian

Endian Order	Byte 00	Byte 01	Byte 02	Byte 03
Big-endian	12	34	56	78 (LSB)
Little-endian	78 (LSB)	56	34	12

As you can see in Table 4.3, the value of the stored multi-byte data field is the same for both types of endianness as long as the data is referenced in its native data type, in this case a long value. If this data field is referenced as individual bytes, the endianness of the data must be known. An unexpected difference in endianness will cause a computer system to interpret the data in the opposite direction, resulting in the wrong value. The difference can be correctly handled by implementing code that is aware of the endian architecture of the computer system as well as the endianness of the stored data. The details of handling the endian difference in code are thoroughly discussed in the section "Byte Swapping."

Merits of Endian Architectures

You may see a lot of discussion about the relative merits of the two formats, mostly based on the relative merits of the PC. Both formats have their advantages and disadvantages.

---

[2] The terms Big-Endian and Little-Endian were coined by Danny Cohen in reference to *Gulliver's Travels* by Jonathan Swift (1726), where the Lilliputians and Blefuscudians went to war over which end of a soft-boiled egg should be opened first, the big end or the little end. The Lilliputians believed that the little end should be opened first and the Blefuscudians believed that the big end should be opened first. The terms' applicability to computer memory architecture is in respect to byte and bit address ordering.

In little-endian form, assembly language instructions for picking up a 1, 2, 4, or longer byte number proceed in exactly the same way for all formats: first pick up the lowest order byte at offset 0. Also, because of the 1:1 relationship between the address offset and byte number, offset 0 is byte 0, multiple precision math routines are correspondingly easy to write.

In big-endian form, by having the high-order byte come first, you can always test whether the number is positive or negative by looking at the byte at offset zero. You don't have to know how long the number is, nor do you have to skip over any bytes to find the byte containing the sign information. The numbers are also stored in the order in which they are printed out, so binary to decimal routines are particularly efficient.

In the past embedded communication processors and custom solutions associated with the data plane have been designed on big-endian architectures. Because of this, legacy code on these processors is often written specifically for network byte order, which is big-endian format.

Table 4.4 lists several popular computer systems and their endian architectures. Note that some CPUs can be either big- or little-endian, referred to as bi-endian, by setting a processor register to the desired endian architecture.

Table 4.4   Computer System Endianness

Platform	Endian Architecture
ARM†	Bi-endian
DEC Alpha†	Bi-endian
HP PA-RISC 8000†	Bi-endian
IBM PowerPC†	Bi-endian
Intel® architecture	Little-endian
Intel® IXP network processors	Bi-endian
Intel® Itanium® processor family	Bi-endian
Java Virtual Machine†	Big-endian
MIPS†	Bi-endian
Motorola 68k†	Big-endian
Sun SPARC†	Big-endian
Sun SPARC V9†	Bi-endian

Relevance of Endian Order

Endian order means that any time a computer accesses a stream, such as a network tap, local file, audio, video, or multimedia stream, the software needs to understand how the file is constructed. For example: if a graphics file, such as a .BMP file, which is little-endian format, is written out to a big-endian machine, the byte order of each integer must first be reversed. Otherwise another standardized program will not be able to read the file.

How can the opposing endian data be efficiently processed? A hardware solution doesn't allow for variability in data since it expects either big-endian or little-endian formats. Also, hard-wired endian swapping typically won't suffice for a large range of networks and protocols and many of these file formats are endian specific. Software byte swapping seems to be a viable method. Several different methods are available, and are described in the following sections.

Byte Swapping

Basically, anytime multi-byte data is imported or exported between computer systems, the format of the data must be standardized. If the data format is binary, the endianness of the data must be known by both computer systems. With this knowledge, the computer systems can decide, based on their own endian architecture, whether byte swapping must be performed on the data. Byte swap methods are developed to standardize the access to the data. The byte swap methods of endian-neutral code use byte swap controls to determine whether a byte swap must be performed.

Byte Swapping Methods

Several methods are available for byte swapping. These methods perform the actual byte swapping of the given data.

- Byte swapping macros provided by an operating system's networking libraries include `ntohl` and `ntohs`, short for network-to-host long and network-to-host short.

- Optimized custom byte swap macros.

- Inline `bswap` macros.

■ Assembly language instructions such as rotate operand right (`ror`) or rotate operand left (`rol`).

■ Standard C library function `swab` can be used to swap two adjacent bytes.

■ A generic assembly language function implementing the same algorithm as the `ntohl` and `ntohs` macros.

Network Input/Output Macros

All communication protocols must define the endianness of the protocol so that there is a predefined agreement on how nodes at opposite ends know how to communicate. In the Transmission Control Protocol/Internet Protocol (TCP/IP) stack, each network host is identified by its 32-bit IP address, which is ordinarily displayed in the four numeric octets referred to as network byte order. TCP/IP defines the network byte order as big-endian and the IP header of a TCP/IP packet contains several multi-byte fields. Computers having little-endian architecture must reorder the bytes in the TCP/IP header information into big-endian format before transmitting the data and likewise need to reorder the TCP/IP information received into little-endian format.

Computers having big-endian architecture need to do nothing since their endian architecture is the same as TCP/IP.

Network input/output (I/O) macros are standardized popular macros commonly available in network libraries and are commonly used to import/export TCP/IP packet header data, which is described below, in an endian-neutral manner.

■ Length: 2 bytes

■ ID: 2 bytes

■ Offset: 2 bytes

■ Source: 4 bytes

■ Destination: 4 bytes

Table 4.5 describes network I/O macros. The term *host* is used to refer to the processor's endian architecture and the term *network* is used to refer to the TCP/IP endian architecture. Using these macros allows for the same code to work on a big-endian or little-endian processor.

Table 4.5   Network I/O Macros

Macro Name	Translation (Can be read as...)	Meaning
htons()	host to network short	Converts the unsigned short integer hostshort from host byte order to network byte order.
htonl()	host to network long	Converts the unsigned integer hostlong from host byte order to network byte order.
ntohs()	network to host short	Converts the unsigned short integer netshort from network byte order to host byte order.
ntohl()	network to host long	Converts the unsigned integer netlong from network byte order to host byte order.

The byte swap performed for TCP/IP communication on little-endian processors adds performance overhead. However, this overhead can be recovered as the processor speed increases. See the section "Recovering Byte Swap Overhead."

Custom Byte Swap Macros

Custom byte swap macros are used to wrap and standardize the code for accessing each data type. Table 4.6 shows examples of byte swap macros for each data size.

Table 4.6   Custom Byte Swap Macros

Access Size	Example Macro Name	Macro Code

16 bits	SwapTwoBytes	```#include <stdio.h>```
		
		```#define SwapTwoBytes(data) \```
		``((((data) >> 8) & 0x00FF)
			(((data) << 8) &```
			```0xFF00))```

32 bits	SwapFourBytes	```#include <stdio.h>```
		
		```#define SwapFourBytes(data) \```
		``((((data) >> 24) & 0x000000FF)
			(((data) >>```
			``8) & 0x0000FF00)
				\```
				`` (((data) << 8) & 0x00FF0000)
					(((data) <<```
					```24) & 0xFF000000))```

64 bits	SwapEightBytes	```#include <stdio.h>```
		
		```#define SwapEightBytes(data) \```
		```((((data) >> 56) & 0x00000000000000FF) |```
		``(((data) >> 40) & 0x000000000000FF00)
			\```
			``` (((data) >> 24) & 0x0000000000FF0000) |```
			``(((data) >> 8) & 0x00000000FF000000)
				\```
				``` (((data) << 8) & 0x000000FF00000000) |```
				``(((data) << 24) & 0x0000FF0000000000)
					\```
					``` (((data) << 40) & 0x00FF000000000000) |```
					```(((data) << 56) & 0xFF00000000000000))```

Byte Swap Controls

Byte swap controls are used within byte swap methods to determine when byte swapping should be performed. In normal usage, the controls add byte swap code if byte swapping is required. If byte swapping is not required the control adds no code and thus, does nothing. Byte swapping can be controlled with the following mechanisms:

- ■ Compile-time controls

- ■ Runtime controls

Compile-Time Controls

Table 4.7 is an example of how the compiler preprocessor is used within data access wrappers to control whether or not byte swapping should be performed. Note that different code is compiled in based on the preprocessor definition. This example is defined by the compiler to work for both little-endian and big-endian processors.

Table 4.7   Preprocessor Control

Access Size	Example Macro Names	Macro Code
16-bit big-endian data	MY_RD_BE_SHORT MY_WRT_BE_SHORT	`#if CPU_ARCHITECTURE == BIG_ENDIAN` `/* Do nothing */` `#else` **`SwapTwoBytes`** `(data)` `#endif`
16-bit little-endian data	MY_RD_LE_SHORT MY_WRT_LE_SHORT	`#if CPU_ARCHITECTURE == BIG_ENDIAN` **`SwapTwoBytes`** `(data)` `#else` `/* Do nothing */` `#endif`
32-bit big-endian data	MY_RD_BE_LONG MY_WRT_BE_LONG	`#if CPU_ARCHITECTURE == BIG_ENDIAN` `/* Do nothing */` `#else` **`SwapFourBytes`** `(data)` `#endif`
32-bit little-endian data	MY_RD_LE_LONG MY_WRT_LE_LONG	`#if CPU_ARCHITECTURE == BIG_ENDIAN` **`SwapFourBytes`** `(data)` `#else` `/* Do nothing */` `#endif`
64-bit big-endian data	MY_RD_BE_DOUBLE MY_WRT_BE_DOUBLE	`#if CPU_ARCHITECTURE == BIG_ENDIAN` `/* Do nothing */` `#else` **`SwapEightBytes`** `(data)` `#endif`
64-bit little-endian data	MY_RD_LE_DOUBLE MY_WRT_LE_DOUBLE	`#if CPU_ARCHITECTURE == BIG_ENDIAN` **`SwapEightBytes`** `(data)` `#else` `/* Do nothing */` `#endif`

Runtime Controls

It is possible to detect the endian architecture of a processor using runtime code. Figure 4.1 shows an example of code that performs a runtime test that checks whether the code is running on a little- or big-endian system. This allows runtime code to dynamically perform endianness processing.

```
union
{
    char Array[4];
    long Chars;
} TestUnion;

char c = 'a';

/* Test platform Endianness */
for(x = 0; x < 4; x++)
    TestUnion.Array[x] = c++;

if (TestUnion.Chars == 0x61626364)
    /* It's big endian */
```

Source code example courtesy of Mark Sullivan, 2004. Intel Corporation.

Figure 4.1   Run-Time Byte Order Test

Recovering Byte Swap Overhead

Overhead associated with byte swapping the fields in the IP header are miniscule compared to the actual propagation delay associated with even the fastest network transmission speeds available today. The byte-swapping overhead, though it undeniably exists, can be readily recovered, especially with the latest performance capabilities of today's processors. Figure 4.2 depicts a time exaggerated example of the overhead required for byte swapping, as well as the reduced processing time of current little-endian processors that recover the time.

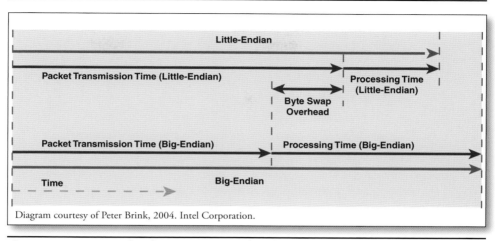

Diagram courtesy of Peter Brink, 2004. Intel Corporation.

Figure 4.2   Example of Byte Swap Overhead and Recovery

Figure 4.2 shows that some overhead is associated with swapping the bytes in the network headers. However, given a substantial increase in processor performance[3], the time associated with processing the byte swap required on the little-endian processor is recovered.

Platform Porting Considerations

If the target application is currently running on a big-endian platform and the goal is to port to a little-endian platform, or vice versa, byte ordering may become an issue. For the most part, the byte ordering within a system is self-contained and therefore not affected by endianness. However, a few cases can result in porting problems, including the use of:

■ Data storage and shared memory

■ Data transfer

■ Data types: unions, byte arrays, bit fields and bit masks, pointer casts

---

[3] Performance results are based on certain tests measured on specific computer systems. Any difference in system hardware, software or configuration will affect actual performance. For more information go to http://www.intel.com/performance.

Data Storage and Shared Memory

File system data and shared memory create a unique problem, because depending on the system design this type of data is accessible between platforms.

Problem 4.1: The endian architecture of the platforms that access the data could be different. The format in which data is written to a file or shared memory must be understood by the reading application or the content will be misinterpreted by opposite endian architecture platforms.

Example 4.1: Accessing data across platforms

The big endian system writes the value 0x11223344. The little-endian system reads the value as 0x44332211.

Solution 4.1.A: Store the data in an endian-neutral format

For example: use text files with string data format, or the External Data Representation[4] (XDR) protocol. XDR is a protocol governed by standards and formalizes a platform-independent way for computers to send data to each other.

Solution 4.1.B: Specify the endian format

Specify one endian format for the stored data and always write the data in that format. Then wrap the data access with macros that are aware of the endian format of the stored data as well as the native endian format of the host processor. The macros will perform byte swapping based on a difference in formats.

Data Transfer

Data transfer is the movement of data from one system to another across a specified transmission medium.

Problem 4.2: When transferring multi-byte data between big- and little-endian systems, the data has to be manipulated to ensure the preservation of the true meaning of the data on both systems. When transferring multi-byte data from

[4] External Data Representation. Wikipedia Web site. 2010 http://en.wikipedia.org/wiki/External_Data_Representation

a big-endian machine, the most significant byte will be in the leftmost position. When a little-endian system receives the data, however, the most significant byte will be in the rightmost position unless the bytes are swapped.

Example 4.2: Transferring data between big-endian and little-endian systems

The big-endian system transmits the value 0x11223344. The little-endian system receives the value as 0x44332211.

Solution 4.2: Byte swap the data

Whenever multi-byte data is transferred between big and little-endian systems, the bytes must be swapped in order to preserve the true meaning of the values. Use functions that swap the bytes like the network I/O macros to ensure the preservation of data in its true form on both big and little-endian systems.

Data Types

The use of certain data types, such as unions, byte arrays, bit fields, bit masks, pointer casts, can create porting problems.

Unions

A union is a data type that may hold objects of different types and sizes, with the compiler keeping track of the size and alignment requirements. Objects of dissimilar types and sizes can only be held at different times. A union provides a way to manipulate different kinds of data in a single area of storage.

Problem 4.3: Unions work fine for using the same memory to access different data. The key is to know what type of data exists in the memory before it is accessed.

Example 4.3: Accessing the same data with different types

Accessing the same data with different data types is not a valid use of unions and can cause endian issues. Although the code in Figure 4.1 suits the purpose for the runtime byte order test to check for the endianness of the machine, it is an example of an improper use of a union. Also, if data types longer than 8 bits are united with a byte array, the data becomes byte order dependent.

Solution 4.3: Always access the same data with the same data type

Only use unions for their purpose of conserving space. Ensure that unions are not used to access the same data with different data types.

Byte Arrays

A byte array is a character array that is used to hold a specified number of bytes. The size of array is always equal to the number of bytes to hold.

Problem 4.4: If data in the byte array is accessed outside of its native data type, the data becomes byte order dependent.

Example 4.4: Array initialized as a list of characters

An array that is initialized with a list of characters will be read as different values between little-endian and big-endian platforms. A byte array is initialized as "abcd". Accessing this array as a long data type on a little-endian platform results in the value 0x64636261. On a big-endian platform it results in the value 0x61626364.

Solution 4.4: Avoid accessing byte arrays outside of the byte data type.

Accessing data outside of its natural data type breaks endian neutral code. Always access byte arrays as byte values.

Bit Fields and Bit Masks

Bit operations are endian sensitive. Even a bit field defined within a single byte is endian sensitive. Code that defines bit fields is subject to endianness conflicts when porting the code to an opposite endian platform.

Problem 4.5: In the following example, the network protocol IP header contains a bit field defined within a single byte. There are two fields within the definition, each four bits long, which is a bit length also referred to as nibbles. Code that sets the value of these nibbles, `iphdr.ver = 4`, and `iphdr.ihl = 7`, will get different results if the bit field data is accessed as a byte. The result of the data read as a byte on the big-endian machine is 0x47, whereas the result of the data read as a byte on the little-endian machine is 0x74.

Also, if the data is set as a byte value, say 0x74, on the little-endian machine, the result of the data read as nibbles on the little-endian machine is a value of 4 for `iphdr.ver` field, and a value of 7 for `iphdr.ihl` field. On the big-endian machine the results would be a value of 7 for the `iphdr.ver` field, and a value of 4 for the `iphdr.ihl` field.

Example 4.5: IP Header Bit Fields

The code in Figure 4.3 illustrates how bit fields are susceptible to endian issues. The code purposefully incorrectly sets the value for the IP header version using bit fields, and then reads the data as a byte. The value of the IP header version will be 0x47 on a big-endian machine, or 0x74 on a little-endian machine.

```
struct
{
   char ver:4,
   ihl:4;
} iphdr;

/*
 * A packet header may utilize bit fields. Bit
 *order
 * within a byte is determined by the byte order
 *of the
 * processor. In this example we modify two
 *nibbles of an
 * IP header and  then access later as a byte.
 */
char ipbyte;
iphdr.ver = 0x4;
iphdr.ihl = 0x7;
ipbyte = *(char *)&iphdr;

if (ipbyte == 0x47)
{
   printf ("Big Endian\n");
}
else if (ipbyte == 0x74)
{
   printf ("Little Endian\n");
}
```
Source code example courtesy of Bob Huff, 2004. Intel Corporation.

Figure 4.3   IP Header Bit Fields

Solution 4.5: Access the entire 8-bit value in its native char data type.

Access the value as a char data type and use a mask to access the bits of each field. Table 4.8 shows how the bit mask and hex values are represented for the four bits of the version field, V, and the 4 bits of the header length field, L.

Table 4.8   IP Header Bit Masks

Data Name and Bits	Mask Value
Version field (V) bit mask	1111 0000
Version bit mask hex value	0xF0
Header Length field (L) bit mask	0000 1111
Header Length bit mask hex value	0x0F

Pointer Casts

Casting pointers changes the native meaning of the original data. Doing so will affect which data is addressed.

Problem 4.6: If the native data pointer is a 32-bit pointer and is cast to a byte pointer, depending on the endian architecture of the host, either the first byte or the last byte will be pointed to.

Example 4.6: Casting pointers

Casting a pointer that stores the 32-bit value 0x11223344 to a byte pointer, the big-endian system points to 0x11. The little-endian system points to 0x44.

Solution 4.6: Never change the native type of a pointer

Instead, get the data in its native data type format and use byte swapping macros to access the bytes individually.

Native Data Types

Whenever data is accessed outside of its native data type, conflicts can occur. It is important to note that this is true whether the size accessed is smaller or larger than the native data type.

If data is read or written outside of its native format, then the endian format of the shared data must be known and static. For example: if a big-endian computer stores data to a file in big-endian format, a little-endian computer must account for the endian difference and perform byte-swapping in order to read the data correctly. Conversely, whenever the little-endian computer writes data to that same file, it must perform byte-swapping to convert the data back to big-endian format

Table 4.9 shows the conversion action that is required when accessing data outside of its native data type and on opposite endian architectures.

Table 4.9   Data Type Conversion Actions

Native Data Type Size	Size Accessed	Conversion
short	char	Swap both bytes.
long	short	Swap both shorts end for end.
long	char	Swap bytes 0 and 3. Swap bytes 1 and 2.
double	long	Swap both longs end for end.
double	short	Swap bytes 0, 1 with 7, 6. Swap bytes 2, 3 with 5, 4.
char	short	Never. Although this may be efficient for copies, it is not a good programming practice.
short	long	Never. Although this may be efficient for copies, it is not a good programming practice.
long	double	Never. Although this may be efficient for copies, it is not a good programming practice.

Endian-Neutral Code

The goal of endian-neutral code is to provide one software source-set of files that will work correctly no matter which processor endian architecture the code is executed on, eliminating the need to rewrite the code. The way to effectively achieve this goal is by identifying the memory and external data interfaces of the system and then implementing the use of processor-independent macros to perform the interface operations. These macros automatically compile the appropriate code for the respective endian architecture.

Endian-neutral code makes no assumptions of the underlying platform in its implementation. Instead, it funnels all data and memory accesses through wrappers that decide how the accesses should be made. The decision is based on information that is defined during code compilation and specifies which endian architecture the code is being compiled to support.

To convert endian-specific code to endian-neutral code, external interfaces that use endian-specific code will need to be re-implemented using the *Endian-Neutral Coding Guidelines* in the following section.

Endian-Neutral Coding Guidelines

Endian-neutral code can be achieved by identifying the external software interfaces and following these endian-neutral coding practices to access the interfaces.

1. Data Storage and Shared Memory

    Store data in a format that is not tied to endian architecture. Choices include:

    ■ Using a format that works for all architectures, such as text files and strings, or XDR protocol.

    ■ Specifying one endian format for the stored data and always write the data in that format, or using a header that specifies the endian format.

    ■ Wrapping the data access with macros that understand the endian format of the stored data as well as the native endian format of the host processor. The macros will perform byte swapping based on a difference in formats.

2. Byte Swap Macros

    Use macros that serve as wrappers around all binary multi-byte data interfaces.

3. Data Transfer

   Use network I/O macros to read/write data from the network. The macros will determine when byte swapping should occur based on whether the format of the transferred data is in the native endian format of the processor.

4. Data Types

   Never access data outside of its native data type. Always read/write an `int` as an `int` type as opposed to reading/writing four bytes. An alternative is to use custom endian-neutral macros to access specific bytes within a multi-byte data type. Lack of conformance to this guideline will cause code compatibility problems between endian architectures. Examples of data type usages that can cause issues include:

■ Unions

   Never use unions to access the same data with dissimilar types. See Platform Porting considerations.

■ Byte Arrays

   Never access multi-byte data as a byte array. See Platform Porting considerations.

■ Pointer and Variable Typecasts

   Never use type casting to change the size of a pointer or variable. See Platform Porting considerations.

5. Bit Fields

   Never define bit fields across byte boundaries or smaller than 8 bits. If it is necessary to access bit data that is not a full byte or on byte boundaries, access the entire bit field in its native data type and use a bit mask for the bits of each fields.

6. Bit Shifts

   Use the C language << and >> constructs to move byte positions of binary multi-byte data.

7. Pointer Casts

   Never cast pointers to change the size of the data pointed to.

8. Compiler Directives

    Be careful when using compiler directives, such as those affecting storage. Example; `align` and `pack`. Directives are not always portable between compilers. The C language defined directives, such as `#include` and #define, are okay. Use the #define directive to define the platform endian architecture of the compiled code compilers.

Porting to the Target Operating System

Most architecture migrations will target the same operating system for the Intel platform as on the current platform. However, for architecture migrations that involve an in-house developed proprietary OS, a good option for the migration plan is to adopt an open source or COTS OS that already supports the Intel architecture. If the architecture migration includes a port to a new OS, check with the target OS distributor to see if an OS migration guide is available that supports the current and target OS pair used in the migration.

Considerations for porting source code to a new OS not only includes updating the OS calls, but also includes locating the correct version of all necessary third-party utilities and libraries needed to build the application. Common examples are:

- Source control system

- Developer tools

- Build utilities

- Licensing, graphics, or other third-party libraries

If the situation allows, make sure to port to the OS version that will be used for the target multi-core solution. Meaning, if symmetric multiprocessing (SMP) will be used as the target OS solution, port to the SMP version of the target OS. Refer to Chapter 6 to learn about operating system choices. Also, refer to the section in Chapter 6 titled "Porting a Proprietary Operating System."

IA-32 Interrupt and Exception Handling Model

Integral to all processors is the ability for the processor to handle events that are orthogonal to the execution flow of the program. All modern processors have a well-defined model to signal and prioritize these events. The processor can then change the flow of the executing instructions sequence to handle these events in a deterministic manner. The event is typically handled by transferring execution from the current running task to a special software routine called interrupt or exception handlers. To aid in handling exceptions and interrupts, each architecturally defined exception and each interrupt condition requiring special handling by the processor is assigned a unique identification number, called a vector.

Interrupts are divided into two types—hardware and software. Hardware interrupts are typically generated as a result of a peripheral (external to the processor core) that needs attention. Peripherals both within the SOC device and on the platform can raise an interrupt to the processor. The processor then transfers control to the appropriate interrupt handled for the specific device interrupt.

Software interrupts are typically triggered via a dedicated instruction such as INT #vector on Intel architecture processors and SWI on ARM architectures. The execution of a software interrupt instruction causes a context switch to an interrupt handler in a similar fashion to an external hardware interrupt.

Interrupts can be classed as maskable or non-maskable, though not all processors make provision for non-maskable interrupts. Non-maskable interrupts as the name suggests are interrupts that are always serviced. There is no ability to prevent or delay the recognition of a non-maskable interrupt. Non-maskable interrupts are themselves uninterruptible, with at most one non-maskable interrupt active at any time.

Exceptions are events detected by the processor. They are usually associated with the currently executing instruction. A common exception supported by all processors is "Divide by Zero" which is generated as a result of a DIV instruction with a denominator of zero. Processors detect a variety of conditions including protection violations, page faults, and invalid instructions. The processor also monitors other processor conditions that may not be strictly correlated to the current instruction being executed. On the Intel architecture platform these are known as *machine check* exceptions. Machine check exceptions include system bus errors, ECC errors, parity errors, cache errors, and translation look-aside buffer (TLB) errors. The machine check details are recorded in machine-specific registers.

Precise and Imprecise Exceptions

Exceptions can categorize as precise or imprecise. Precise exceptions are those which indicate precisely the address of the instruction that caused the exception. Again, the divide-by-zero exception is an excellent example of a precise exception because the faulting instruction can be identified. Imprecise exceptions on the other hand, cannot directly be associated with an instruction. The processor has continued execution of an indeterminate number of instructions between the time the exception was triggered and the processor processed it; alternatively, the exception was generated by an event that was not due to an instruction execution. An example of an imprecise exception is the detection of an uncorrectable ECC error discovered in a cache. Imprecise exceptions are not generally recoverable; although the Linux machine check handler does all it can to avoid a kernel panic and the resulting reboot, imprecise exceptions are referred to as *aborts* on Intel architectures. Precise exceptions fall into two categories on Intel architectures, *faults* and *traps*:

■ *Faults.* A fault is an exception that can generally be corrected and that, once corrected, allows the program to be restarted with no loss of continuity. When a fault is reported, the processor restores the machine state to the state prior to the beginning of execution of the faulting instruction. The return address (saved contents of the CS and EIP registers) for the fault handler points to the faulting instruction, rather than to the instruction following the faulting instruction.

■ *Traps.* A trap is an exception that is reported immediately following the execution of the trapping instruction. Traps allow execution of a program or task to be continued without loss of program continuity. The return address for the trap handler points to the instruction to be executed after the trapping instruction. Traps are generated by INT 3 and INTO (overflow) instructions.

The fault handler points to the faulting instruction for faults; this is because the handler is likely to rerun the faulting instruction once the underlying reason for the fault is resolved. For example, if a page fault is generated the operating system will load the page from disk, set up the page table to map the page and then rerun the instruction. Instructions that generate a trap on the other hand are not rerun. On other embedded platforms such as ARM, the fault address recorded on the exception is always that of the next instruction to run.

However when all instructions are the same size, it's a trivial matter to establish the faulting instruction; it's not quite as straightforward with a variable size instruction set.

The list of exceptions and interrupts that a processor supports is part of a processor's architecture definition. All exceptions and interrupts are assigned a vector number. The processor uses the vector assigned to the exception or interrupt as an index into a vector table. On Intel architecture this vector table is called the Interrupt Descriptor Table (IDT). The table provides the entry point to the exception or interrupt handler. IA-32 defines an allowable vector range of 0 to 255. Vectors from 0 to 121 are reserved for architecture-defined exceptions and interrupts. Vectors 32 to 255 are designed as user-defined interrupts. The user-defined vectors are typically allocated to external (to the processor) hardware generated interrupts and software interrupts. Table 4.10 is a partial list of the IA-32 Protected mode exceptions and interrupts. Refer to Chapter 5 of the *Intel® 64 and IA-32 Architectures Software Developer's Manual Volume 3A: System Programming Guide, Part 1* for more information about the Intel 64 and IA-32 protection mechanism.

Table 4.10 Abbreviated IA-32 Exceptions and Interrupts

Vector Number	Description	Type	Source
0	Divide Error	Fault	DIV and IDIV Instructions.
2	NMI	Interrupt	Non maskable external Interrupt.
3	Breakpoint	Trap	INT 3 instruction.
4	Overflow	Trap	INTO (overflow) instruction.
6	Invalid Opcode	Fault	Reserved opcodes.
13	General Protection	Fault	Any memory reference or other protection checks.
14	Page Fault	Fault	Any memory reference.
16	X87 FPU Floating Point	Fault	Exception from the FP unit.
17	Alignment Check	Fault	Misaligned data references in memory.
18	Machine Check	Abort	Model specific faults.
32–255	User-defined Interrupts	Interrupt	External interrupt or INT n instruction.

In summary, exceptions and interrupts can come from a wide range of sources from the processor core, caches, floating point units, bus interfaces, and external peripherals. Figure 4.4 shows the wide range of sources.

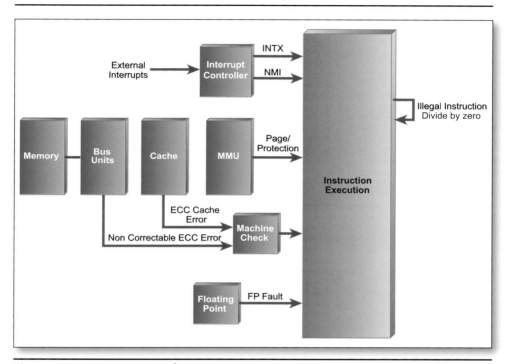

Figure 4.4   Exception and Interrupt Sources

Vector Table Structure

All processors provide mechanisms to translate an interrupt or exception into a handler for the interruption. Different processor architectures provide differing levels of hardware support in identification of the underling hardware exception. As we mentioned above, external hardware interrupts are assigned a vector. PowerPC and some ARM architectures have a single IRQ line to the processor. The exception handler must then resolve the underlying cause of the interrupt, look up a software-based vector table, and transfer control to the interrupt handler. On Intel architecture processors, the processor hardware itself identifies the underlying cause of the interrupt and transfers control to the exception handler without software intervention. An Intel processor takes a number of steps in the transition to the interrupt handler. Figure 4.5 shows the structures and registers that are used in the process.

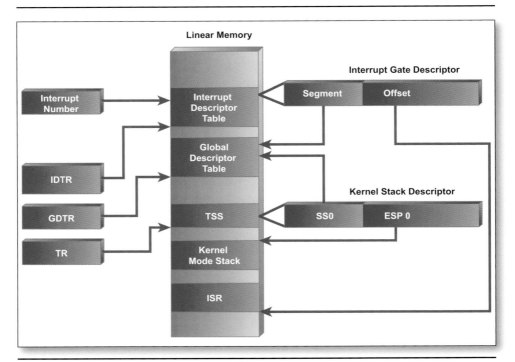

Figure 4.5 Interrupt Descriptor Dereferencing

The Intel architecture processor automatically takes several steps in transfer of control to the exception function handler. The hardware interrupt controller sends an interrupt N message to the CPU. The interrupt controller is called the Local Advanced Peripheral Interrupt Controller (Local APIC) on Intel architecture processors. The CPU reads the interrupt descriptor from the Interrupt descriptor table (IDT). The Interrupt descriptor table is located in system memory. The IDT stores a collection of gate descriptors that provide access to interrupt and exception handlers. The linear address for the base of the IDT is contained in the Interrupt Descriptor Table Register (IDTR). The IDT descriptor can contain one of three types of descriptor: task gate, interrupt gate, and trap gate. The IDT contains either an interrupt gate or trap gate descriptor for external interrupts. The difference between an interrupt gate and a trap gate is its effect on the IF flag: using an interrupt gate clears the IF flag, which prevents other interrupts from interfering with the current interrupt handler. The interrupt gate contains the following information:

- *Segment selector.* The segment selector selects a segment in the global or local descriptor table; this provides a base address for the IRQ handler table.

- *Segment offset.* This offset is added to the based address found in by the referencing of the segment selector to produce the linear address of the ISR handler.

- *Privilege level.* This is usually set to zero (same privilege level as kernel mode code.)

The address of the actual interrupt service routine is

```
ISR Linear Address =
        GDT[(IDTR[Vector
          Number].SegmentSelector)].BaseAddress +
          IDTR[Vector Number].SegmentOffset
```

For Linux the values populated in the tables degenerate to the following (the processor still performs the lookups but the value returned is zero):

```
ISR Linear Address =
        IDTR[Vector Number].SegmentOffset
```

Before the processor transfers control to the ISR, it must identify the appropriate stack to use to save registers two situations can occur. The first situation can occur when the interrupt privilege is the same level as the currently executing code. This can happen when an interrupt occurs while the processor is running kernel mode software. In this scenario the processor saves the EFLAGS, CS, and EIP registers on the current stack. The other situation can occur when the interrupt privilege level is lower than the currently executing code. An example is when the processor is interrupted while running user mode application code. In this case the segment selector and stack pointer for the stack to be used by the handler are obtained from the Task State Segment (TSS) for the currently executing task. On this new stack, the processor pushes the stack segment selector and stack pointer of the interrupted procedure. The processor then saves the current state of the EFLAGS, CS, and EIP registers on the new stack. The processor then transfers control to the interrupt service routine. The following sections describe the stack frame established by the processor and the resulting software handlers.

Exception Frame

A considerable amount of data must be saved when an exception occurs. The state is saved on a stack, and the format of the saved data is known as an *exception frame*, as shown in Figure 4.6. The exception frame can be split into two distinct portions: the first is the portion saved automatically by the processor, and the second is the set of additional registers that are saved by operating system interrupt service routine before it loads the software handler that deals with the actual device interrupt.

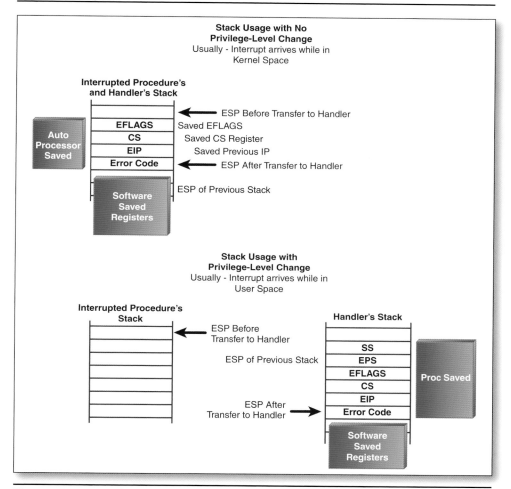

Figure 4.6   Stack Frames

Some processor-generated exception frames include an error number on the stack. For example, a page fault will provide an error code on the stack frame. These error codes provide additional information such as whether the fault was due to a page not being present or a page-level protection violation.

The actual IRQ function call is usually written in assembly language. The function is then responsible for saving the registers that may be destroyed in the handling of the interrupt. For example, the MACRO SAVE_ALL defined in the Linux kernel file entry_32.s saves all the required registers as part of interrupt handler call. Once the interrupt has been processed the system must return to normal execution. The IRET instruction will restore the processor to the same state prior to the interrupt (once the software saved state is also unrolled). In a simple embedded system this is the normal mechanism used to return to the pre-interrupt operation; however in a multitasking operating system environment, the operating system may not necessarily return directly to the task that was interrupted. Take for example, if the operating system timer IRQ *fires* while a user process is running. The operating system will save the user space process registers into a process-specific storage area, execute the interrupt handler, and then identify what code should run next. It most likely will execute the kernel scheduler function. The kernel scheduler identifies the process to continue with and transfers control to that process.

Masking Interrupts

As mentioned earlier, interrupts fall into two classes, maskable and non-maskable interrupts. Processors provide a control mechanism to disable the servicing of interrupts received by the processor core. For Intel architecture CPUs the Interrupt Enable (IF) flag in the EFLAGs register provides the control. If the flag is set then the processor will service interrupts. If the flag is cleared, the processor will not service maskable interrupts. A number of mechanisms can be used to control the state of the IF flag. First there is an instruction specifically assigned to allow you to set and clear the flag directly. The set interrupt enable flag instruction (STI) sets the flag, and the clear interrupt enable flag instruction (CLI) clears the flag.

The use of STI/CLI (or its equivalent on other processors) has been quite prevalent in embedded systems to provide a low cost method of mutual exclusion. For instance, if two threads are working with a linked list, it was quite common to disable interrupts while the pointer updates associated with link element insertion took place. Afterwards, re-enable the interrupts. This allows the multiple pointer updates associated with a linked list insertion to be atomic. The mechanism can also be used between interrupt handlers and threads used for deferred processing. However, two issues arise with this approach.

The first issue relates to the introduction of multiple hardware threads in processors (multiple processor cores, or hardware threading on a single core). The STI/CLI instructions mask interrupts on the hardware thread that issued the instruction (the local CPU). Interrupts can be processed by other hardware threads. As a result, the guarantee of atomicity has been lost. In this case other synchronization mechanisms such as locks may be needed to ensure there are no race conditions.

The second issue arises because masking of interrupts can affect the real-time behavior of the platform. Masking interrupts introduces non-determinism associated with the overall interrupt latency performance. In embedded systems, having a deterministic latency time to service some specific interrupts can be very important. For both these reasons and others, directly enabling and disabling of interrupts to provide mutual exclusion should be avoided. A case in point: the Linux kernel 2.4 had a significant number of `sti()/cli()` calls in the device drivers. The version 2.6 Linux kernel, which was aligned with multi-core processors is becoming more prevalent, has few `sti()/cli()` calls remaining in its drivers for direct enabling and disabling of interrupts. In fact, function wrappers for `sti()/cli()` have been removed from the kernel.

The interrupt flags can also be affected by the following operations: the PUSHF instruction saves the flags register onto the stack where it can be examined, POPF and IRET instructions load the Flags register from the stack, and as a result can be used to modify the interrupt enable flag.

The interrupts are automatically masked when you enter an interrupt handler, and the driver or operating system will re-enable interrupts.

Acknowledging Interrupts

When a device indicates an interrupt request to the interrupt controller, the interrupt controller typically latches the request in an interrupt status pending register. The interrupt handling software must eventually clear the interrupt in the device and also indicate to the interrupt controller that the interrupt has been serviced. The device driver is typically responsible to consume all events that are associated with the interrupt and explicitly clear the source on the device. The interrupt controller (such as 8259/IOAPIC) must also be notified that an interrupt has been processed so the interrupt controller state can be updated.

The device interrupts on Intel architecture systems may be presented to the interrupt controller as either edge- or level-triggered interrupts. For level-based interrupts, the device will de-assert the interrupt line once the underlying device event has been acknowledged. Level-triggered interrupts consist of a message sent to the interrupt controller that an interrupt has been raised. The actual interrupt line is now represented by a message being routed on a bus.

There is no message signal to indicate that the interrupt has been cleared. The legacy (8259) interrupt controller has a register known as the End Of Interrupt (EOI) register. The system interrupt handler may have to write to this register depending on the configuration.

Interrupt Latency

It is important to understand both the latency and the jitter associated with interrupt latency on embedded systems, as shown in Figure 4.7. The interrupt latency is defined as the time when the hardware event occurred to the time when the software handler starts to execute. The contributions to the overall latency (and its variability) are:

- Hardware detection of the interrupt and its propagation to the processor core.

- Waiting for the interrupt to be at the appropriate level, such as, for example, waiting for a current interrupt handler to complete.

- Recognition by the processor either by waiting for the current instruction to complete or by interrupting the current instruction at the next available cycle.

- The processor must identify the linear address of the interrupt handler. On Intel architecture processors this requires reading the GDT and IDT tables, which could result in cache and translation look-aside buffer misses.

- The processor saves critical registers and transfers control to the interrupt handler.

- The interrupt handler then saves the remaining registers before the traditional C interrupt handler is called.

It's evident that quite a few steps are involved between the interrupt event and the actual transfer of control to the handler. In most operating systems the first handler must do very little work to process interrupts directly. Typically the interrupt is just acknowledged and a signal to another thread or context is generated. The rest of the interrupt processing then takes place in the signaled task. The latency before this next task executes is generally larger than the original latency between events and interrupt handler. At the platform level additional latencies such system management interrupts, power saving sleep states, and CPU frequency throttling can all affect the jitter of the interrupt response.

The definition of real-time can differ for every application, and it's not unusual for the question of real-time behavior to pop up whenever interrupt latencies in a system are discussed, Is the system hard real-time or soft real-time, for instance? It really depends on the target application, and the expected deadlines imposed by the application and how it interacts with the interrupt events. For real-time platforms, the actual delay between interrupt and service routine (latency), consistency of time delay (jitter), and a maximum upper bound are all important criteria. Figure 4.7 shows a number of delays that can occur before the interrupt is called. The nominal interrupt latency delay between the raising of an interrupt to the execution of the handler is in the order of microseconds.

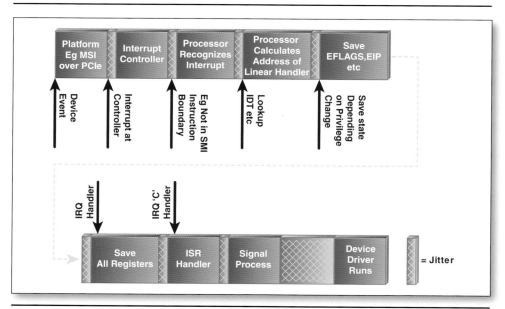

Figure 4.7   Components of Interrupt Latency

Real-Time and Interrupt Latency

Architectural migration for real-time control applications requires a thorough understanding of the targeted processor architecture. Despite having relatively complex CISC architecture, Intel Atom processors are capable of handling real-time tasks within deterministic bounded time.

The following are interrupt types supported by platforms featuring the Intel Atom processor, specifically the Intel® Z5xx Atom™ processor and Intel® System Controller Hub US15W (Intel SCH) platform:

■ *Peripheral Interrupt Request (PIRQ/INTR/INTx)*: Interrupt request source from peripherals, such as PCI devices, serial peripheral devices, etc.

■ *Serial Interrupt Request (SERIRQ)*: Interrupt request from low pin count (LPC) peripherals.

■ *Non-Maskable Interrupt (NMI)*: The highest level of severity that will cause a system halt, such as memory corruption.

■ *System Management Interrupt (SMI)*: Typically used for system or platform level management without OS awareness, such as thermal sensor events, system management RAM access, and chassis open.

■ *System Control Interrupts (SCI)*: Generally used by hardware to notify the OS about ACPI state events.

In general, interrupt events can be delivered from peripherals to the CPU through either (1) legacy interrupts, or (2) Message Signaled Interrupts (MSI) generated by the IOxAPIC controller, or delivered from (3) a PCIe device in-band MSI message to the CPU.

The legacy interrupt delivery method is implemented through a "side-band" INTR pin, which is connected to the CPU through a pair of 8259 PIC controllers. In order to determine the ISR vector, the CPU has to acknowledge the 8259 PIC controller upon receiving INTR signal.

The MSI delivery method as specified by the PCI Special Interest Group (SIG) task force is an in-band message write by a PCIe device. This method is realized by IOxAPIC or PCIe devices. Since it is in-band in nature, the ISR vector is carried as part of the message written by the peripheral, and acknowledgment cycles involved. The Intel Atom platform interrupt architecture is shown in Figure 4.8.

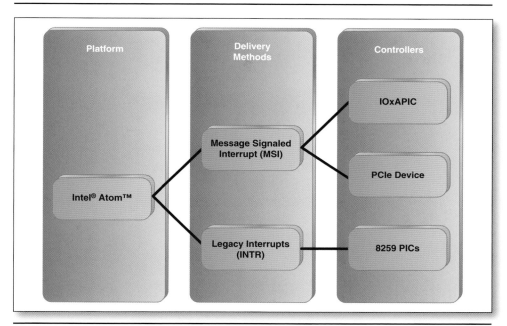

Figure 4.8   Intel® Atom™ Platform Interrupt Architecture

There are three methods for interrupt flows. The Legacy interrupt flow is shown in Figure 4.9, the IOxAPIC-MSI interrupt flow is shown in Figure 4.10, and the PCIe-MSI interrupt flow is shown in Figure 4.11.

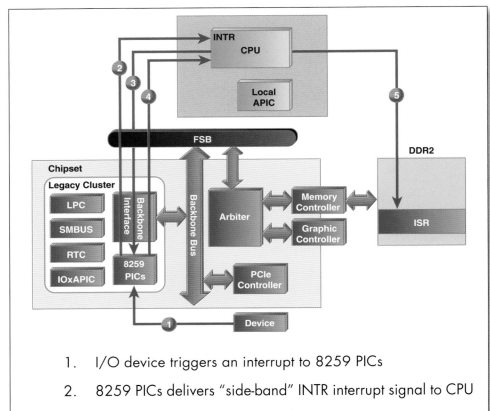

1. I/O device triggers an interrupt to 8259 PICs

2. 8259 PICs delivers "side-band" INTR interrupt signal to CPU

3. CPU sends interrupt acknowledge to 8259 PICs

4. 8259 PICs sends 8-bit interrupt vector to CPU

5. CPU pushes current states into stack and fetches ISR instructions from memory based on interrupt vector

Figure 4.9 Method 1: Legacy Interrupt Flow

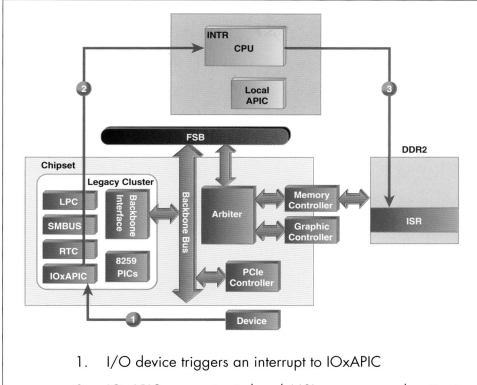

1. I/O device triggers an interrupt to IOxAPIC

2. IOxAPIC generates in-band MSI message and writes to CPU through backbone bus

3. CPU pushes current states onto the stack and fetches the ISR instructions from memory based on the interrupt vector

Figure 4.10 Method 2: IOxAPIC-MSI Interrupt Flow

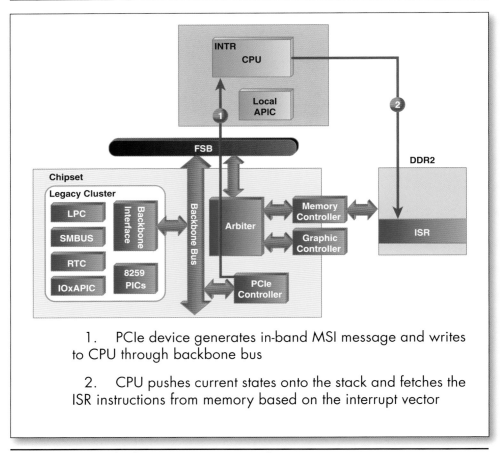

1. PCIe device generates in-band MSI message and writes to CPU through backbone bus

2. CPU pushes current states onto the stack and fetches the ISR instructions from memory based on the interrupt vector

Figure 4.11 Method 3: PCIe-MSI Interrupt Flow

Interrupt Latency Comparison

Out of all three methods, method 3 takes the simplest path and averaged interrupt latencies measured at less than 2 μs (Kean, 2010[5]). Furthermore, in-band MSI carries the interrupt vector in the MSI message packet and eliminates unnecessary cycles to fetch the interrupt vector. Therefore, for best real-time latency performance, MSI is the recommended choice for interrupt

[5] L. E. Kean, "Microcontroller to Intel® Architecture Conversion: Programmable Logic Controller (PLC) Using Intel® Atom™ Processor", 2010. http://download.intel.com/design/intarch/papers/323213.pdf

implementation. Method 2 is similar and may be considered as an alternative for legacy PCI devices that do not support MSI.

Local Interrupts (LINT0/LINT1) Usage

The Local APIC handles local interrupts including Local Interrupt pins (LINT0 and LINT1), APIC timer, performance monitoring counters, thermal sensor, and internal APIC error detector. This section focuses on Local Interrupt pins LINT0 and LINT1.

Apart from interrupt delivery methods discussed in the preceding section, the Intel Atom processor offers external devices direct interrupt pins into the CPU through Local APIC controller, namely LINT0 and LINT1 pins.

The mapping structure of Local Interrupts is different than the 8259 PICs and IOxAPIC. Vectors for LINT0 and LINT1 can be statically fixed by programming the Local Vector Table (LVT). Due to static interrupt vector assignment, Local Interrupts do not require additional cycles for vector fetching, for which "side-band" signals are used. Thus, LINT0 or LINT1 pins are expected to deliver interrupts with lower and more consistent latency. Moreover, it reduces backbone bus traffic and arbitration because the need for vector fetching is eliminated in this case.

Real-Time Operation and Power Management

Some embedded applications depend on predictable response times and therefore run on operating systems offering real-time support. In a real-time environment, it's critical for an OS to be able to guarantee certain time slices. Additionally, it's important that time slice measurements remain consistent. This should be taken into consideration whenever power management is enabled. For example: If a high end platform response should happen within a certain number of microseconds, with power management enabled it could require some of that time for the processor to wake up, which affects the amount of time left for the response.

Speculative prefetch memory accesses can also cause real-time issues in tight loops. Intel architecture power management and speculative prefetch features should be disabled for requirements of real-time operating system (RTOS) guaranteed response times.

Furthermore, the manner in which software is written can affect real-time operation and power management. For example, polling might be used for real-time events. However, polling keeps the processor active, preventing sleep state opportunities. Consequently, power-efficient code should avoid polling and should instead use an event-driven software design. Refer to Chapter 8 for power optimization examples.

Device Drivers

For any device driver that is developed in-house, the low level initialization needs to be updated for Intel architecture. Open source versions of the driver may help guide the changes that are required.

Intel Chipset Drivers

Standard desktop, mobile, and server chipset drivers for Microsoft Windows XP[†] or Microsoft Windows Vista[†] can be downloaded at: http://downloadcenter.intel.com/.

Intel Embedded and Communications Chipset Drivers

The Intel architecture chipset data sheets contain information about registers that need to be programmed. Technical information about the Intel embedded and communications chipsets can be found at: http://www.intel.com/products/embedded/.

Depending on the OS, Intel architecture device drivers are available from various providers. The RTOS board support packages for Intel embedded chipset drivers are available from the RTOS vendors. Board support packages for Microsoft Windows CE[†] can be downloaded from these third party vendor sites:

■ Adeneo Corporation[†]

■ BSQUARE[†]

■ Wipro Technologies[†]

Intel® Graphics Drivers

Intel provides graphics drivers to support both mainstream PC and embedded solutions for Intel's integrated graphics controllers. While the mainstream PC drivers can be used in embedded devices, the embedded-specific drivers are implemented to address capabilities and usages for embedded applications.

The Intel® Graphics Media Accelerator (Intel GMA) drivers are the mainstream PC drivers for the Intel Atom platforms, and are available for Microsoft Windows XP[†], Microsoft Vista[†], and Microsoft Windows 7[†] operating systems. Additionally, PC/laptop graphics drivers are implemented for MeeGo, and are fully integrated into the MeeGo distribution, and not distributed as a separate driver component.

Solutions for Embedded Systems

The Intel® Embedded Graphics Drivers are the graphics solution developed to support embedded focused operating systems, such as Microsoft Windows XP Embedded, Microsoft Windows CE, MeeGo, and various Linux distributions. These drivers are developed to be more flexible to address the plethora of display variations found in the embedded market segments, versus the fairly standard display usage models for PCs and laptops. The Intel Embedded Graphics Drivers were also developed to be a cross-platform solution supporting the Intel Atom platforms, as well as many of the desktop and mobile Intel platforms.

A recent evolution to the embedded graphics solution is the Intel® Embedded Media and Graphics Driver (Intel EMGD). This driver has many of the same features as the Intel Embedded Graphics Drivers for the embedded applications, but is developed to be optimized for the PowerVR SGX[†] graphics cores, which are used on many of the Intel Atom platforms. Table 4.11 shows the association of Intel Atom platforms to the graphics cores and associated graphics drivers, for embedded and mainstream PC drivers.

Table 4.11   Intel® Atom™ Platform to Intel® Graphics Drivers Matrix

CPU	Chipset	Intel® Atom™ Platform Codename	Graphics Controller	Embedded Driver	Mobile Driver
Intel® Atom™ Processor Z5xx Series	Intel® System Controller Hub US15W	Menlow	PowerVR SGX 535	Intel® Embedded Graphics Drivers, transitioning to Intel EMGD	Intel GMA 500
Intel® Atom™ Processor N270	Intel® 945GSE Chipset	Navy Pier	Intel GMA 950	Intel® Embedded Graphics Drivers	Intel GMA 950
Intel® Atom™ Processor N450/D410 /D510	Intel® 82801HBM I/O Controller Hub (ICH8M)	Luna Pier	Intel GMA 3150	Intel® Embedded Graphics Drivers	Intel GMA 3150
Intel® Atom™ Processor E6xx Series	Inte®l Platform Controller Hub EG20T	Queens Bay	PowerVR SGX 535	Intel EMGD	N/A

Note: The Intel® Embedded Graphics Drivers and Intel EMGD are not included with packaged chipset drivers or board support packages, and must be downloaded separately from the EDC. However, Moblin and MeeGo distributions targeted specifically for embedded usage models and some Microsoft embedded operating system distributions have the Intel® Embedded Graphics Drivers and Intel EMGD integrated into the OS.

Refer to the Intel® Embedded Graphics Drivers[6] and Intel EMGD[7] Web sites for downloads and details about embedded graphic solutions for Intel Atom platforms.

---

[6] Intel® Embedded Graphics Drivers, Web site. 2010. http://edc.intel.com/Software/Downloads/IEGD/
[7] Intel® Embedded Media and Graphics Drivers. Web site. 2010. http://edc.intel.com/Software/Downloads/EMGD

System Initialization Firmware

Every embedded design must include a firmware stack that initializes the processor, memory, I/O, peripherals, and may include diagnostic routines. Firmware initializes the system to a point where the operating system can load and take control. Other architectures, such as PowerPC or ARM, are accustomed to getting the boot logic solution as an ingredient for free; either homegrown, through open source or the ecosystem, or from their silicon vendor. Achieving system initialization on Intel architecture is just as easy for closed box and open box designs. Refer to Chapter 5, "Boot Loader Choices for Small and Fast System Initialization Requirements" for a complete overview about system initialization solutions for Intel architecture.

Migrating to the Intel® Architecture Instruction Set

For the most part, migration will need to be done manually. However, there are a few migration tools that can provide some help. These tools are described below.

Intel® Architecture and Instruction Set

Compiler languages provide abstraction for the underlying hardware instruction set. Therefore code written in high level languages, such as the C language, will require a simple recompile for the Intel Atom processor. We must consider that there will always be a portion of assembly code either contained in assembly source files or inline assembly used within C source files. Assembly code is not portable and will need to be updated to target Intel architecture processor instructions. If the code was originally written in assembly for performance reasons, hardware and compiler improvements may now permit it to be rewritten in C or C++.

Intel® 64 and IA-32 Architectures Software Developer's Manuals

The Intel® 64 and IA-32 Architectures Software Developer's Manuals contain the details for each Intel architecture instruction, including the Intel® Streaming SIMD Extensions instructions. Use this set of manuals as a reference for converting assembly code instructions to equivalent functionality with Intel architecture instructions.

Vector Oriented Code

Single Instruction, Multiple Data (SIMD) is a technology used for vector oriented code. AltiVec[†] and Intel Streaming SIMD Extensions (Intel SSE) are extensions to the fundamental processor architecture instruction set. PowerPC uses AltiVec assembly instructions. ARM uses Vector Floating Point, (VFP) and NEON DSP enhanced instructions, while Intel architecture uses Intel SSE instructions. All vector code must be rewritten or translated to Intel SSE instructions and optimized for Intel architecture. Libraries such as the Intel® Performance Primitives support APIs that are highly tuned for Intel architecture and SSE instructions. Refer to Chapter 7 for more details about performance libraries for Intel architecture.

Manual Vector Oriented Code Migration

For information on translating AltiVec to SSE instructions see the AltiVec/SSE Migration Guide at: http://developer.apple.com/documentation/Performance/Conceptual/Accelerate_sse_migration/Accelerate_sse_migration.pdf.

N.A. Software[†] Vector Oriented Code Conversion Tools

Manually converting existing, highly optimized AltiVec software to Intel SSE can be a daunting task. Intel has been working with N. A. Software to bring three tools to market for Linux and Wind River VxWorks[†] operating systems, which will reduce the DSP software conversion effort.

1. *Vector Signal Image Processing Library. The Vector Signal Image Processing Library (VSIPL)* is highly efficient computational middleware for signal and image processing applications. VSIPL is an open standard for embedded signal and image processing software and hardware vendors. It abstracts hardware implementation details; applications are portable across processor types and generations without rewriting the software. This tool will be available as the VSIPL library, or as C-VSIPL, the plain C language equivalent for in house libraries that need to be converted. N. A. Software will also port custom in-house DSP libraries to Intel architecture.

2. *The altivec.h include file for Intel architecture.* This `altivec.h` include file for Intel architecture is the same as the PowerPC `altivec.h`

file, but targets the Intel SSE instruction set instead of AltiVec. An application's DSP code remains unchanged.

3. *AltiVec Assembler to Intel® Assembler-Compiler.* The AltiVec Assembler to Intel® Assembler-Compiler converts small blocks of PowerPC/AltiVec assembler into C code, which can then be compiled into Intel SSE assembler code. This tool is currently under development, and should be available for beta in the fall of 2010 with product availability in January of 2011.

N.A. Software measured the Intel Atom processor performance[8] for DSP and documented the study in a 2009 white paper[9]. The study compared the performance of several low power processors and concluded that the Intel Atom processors used in the study were viable for certain DSP scenarios. Refer to the white paper for all of the details of the performance comparisons.

Software Development Tools

Software tools are important for any architecture migration. Understanding the needs and availability of tools for the new platform is important when investigating the requirements of the port. Keep in mind that software development tools have system requirements, as with all software applications. This means that the tool must support the target processor and operating system. Thus, a tool that is used on the current pre-port system may not be available for the target system. In contrast, it wouldn't be a surprise to find that developing on Intel architecture opens new doors to tools and software that were not available for other platforms. These considerations may affect the OS and tools choice for your migration plan. Check with the OS and tools providers to determine their tools product availability for the target Intel processor. Besides the vast set of COTS and Intel® Software Development Products support for Intel architecture, architecture migrations currently based

---

[8] Results have been estimated based on internal Intel analysis and are provided for informational purposes only. Any difference in system hardware or software design or configuration may affect actual performance.

Intel does not control or audit the design or implementation of third party benchmark data or Web sites referenced in this document. Intel encourages all of its customers to visit the referenced Web sites or others where similar performance benchmark data are reported and confirm whether the referenced benchmark data are accurate and reflect performance of systems available for purchase.

[9] Tim Freeman and Dave Murray. "Intel® Atom™ Processor Performance for DSP Applications". 2009
http://www.nasoftware.co.uk/home/attachments/019_Atom_benchmarks.pdf

on open source tools will likely find the same tools available that target Intel Atom processor-based platforms. Furthermore, Intel, Green Hills Software[†], and Wind River Systems[†] all provide embedded compilers and other software development products for the Intel Atom processor.

On-Chip Debugging Tools

Joint Test Action Group (JTAG) is a transport system used for in-circuit emulators, which are useful for debugging embedded systems. An on-chip debugger is a combination of hardware and software, both on and off the chip. The part that resides on the chip is implemented in various ways, and is commonly referred to as On-Chip-Debug (OCD). The part that resides off chip is often referred to as an In-Circuit-Emulator (ICE) or as a JTAG adapter. JTAG adapters are, in effect, PC peripherals, and need a Linux or Windows-based PC to control them, and to present a user interface. Figure 4.12 shows a typical development system.

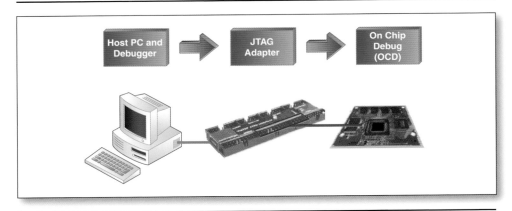

Figure 4.12 A Complete Debug Solution Consisting of Three Distinct Components[10]

The JTAG debugger is a handy tool to have when powering up a new board design for the first time, since no code would be available in ROM or RAM at that time to initialize peripherals. A JTAG system can be used therefore to initialize devices connected to the processor, debug and test the RAM initialization code and parameters, and even to program a boot loader

[10] R. Johnson and S. Christie, "JTAG 101; IEEE 1149.x and Software Debug", 2009
http://download.intel.com/design/intarch/papers/321095.pdf

into ROM. Similarly, device driver developers and OS developers use JTAG, especially in the initial stages. For example: without a JTAG it can be extremely difficult to get the debug messages out an Ethernet port, or just maintain a link, while you are still debugging the TCP/IP stack. Refer to Chapter 10 for complete details about JTAG and embedded debugging.

For embedded device developers, as opposed to desktop programmers, a JTAG connection is often the only debug channel that can be relied upon because it will not interfere with the regular devices' operational mode. JTAG vendors that support Intel Atom platforms include:

- Arium[†]
- Green Hills Software[†]
- Intel
- Lauterbach[†]
- Macraigor Systems LLC[†]
- Wind River Systems[†]

Choosing Between JTAG Products

Choosing between JTAG products depends on the project requirements, such as whether an end-to-end, standalone, or low cost solution is preferred. Arium, Green Hills, and Wind River provide end-to-end software development solutions that cover the board to operating system and application layers, including a JTAG debugger and an integrated development environment (IDE). Lower cost standalone solutions are available from Lauterbach and Macraigor Systems, and Arium also provides a standalone solution. An in-depth comparison of JTAG tools for the Intel Atom processor was recently documented by Felix McNulty[11], an EDC community moderator, and this comparison is updated in the following pages:

Arium. Arium has been supplying Intel developers JTAG debug tools since 1992, and currently focuses on host and target products for Intel and ARM.

---

[11] F. McNulty, "New offerings extend JTAG debug support for Intel® Architecture", 2009
http://community.edc.intel.com/t5/New-to-Intel-Architecture-Blog/New-offerings-extend-JTAG-debug-support-for-Intel-Architecture/ba-p/1426

Arium offers two products, the ECM-XDP3[12] for standard JTAG run-control and the LX-1000[13], which provides run-control as well as processor event trace (off the XDP debug port) in a trace buffer up to 8 GB deep. Arium pioneered BIOS development through JTAG and now fully supports all UEFI debug paradigms. In addition, Arium, provides key features such as code execution trace using Cache-as-RAM as a trace buffer, as well as using DRAM providing developers with on-board trace solutions. The LX-1000 stores trace information in an external trace buffer. Another key feature is Linux OS-aware debugging where developers can debug BIOS, UEFI, boot loaders, kernel, KMODS, and applications all in one JTAG interface.

The ECM-XDP3 pictured in Figure 4.13 and LX-1000 pictured in Figure 4.14 include Arium's SourcePoint† debugging software for SoC design, run on Microsoft Windows and Linux hosts, and support targets running various operating systems. The hardware emulators are platform-specific, but the software is common. So, for developers who are used to developing with ARM it should be an easy transition for them to debug Intel architecture because the user interface to the core debug functions like setting breakpoints, inspecting registers and memory, and writing flash will be virtually identical.

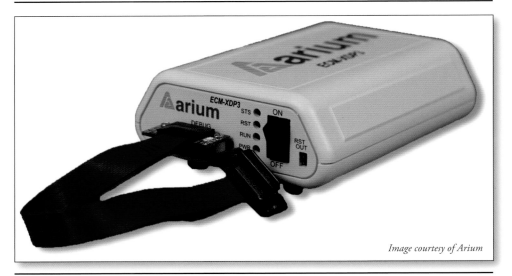

Image courtesy of Arium

Figure 4.13   Arium ECM-XDP3 Intel JTAG Debugger

[12] Arium ECM-XDP3 Intel JTAG Debugger. Web site. 2010
    http://www.arium.com/product/55/ECM-XDP3-Intel-JTAG-Debugger.html
[13] Arium LX-1000 JTAG Debugger. Web site. 2010
    http://www.arium.com/product/55/ECM-XDP3-Intel-JTAG-Debugger.html

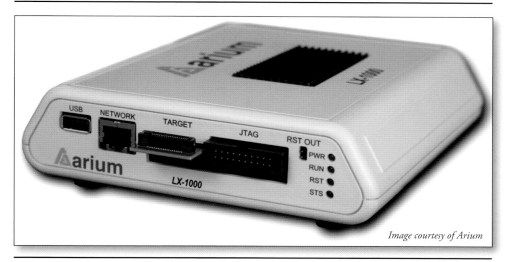

Image courtesy of Arium

Figure 4.14 Arium LX-1000 JTAG Debugger

Green Hills Software. Green Hills Software's support for Intel architecture debug comes in the form of an upgrade to the Green Hills Probe†. According to their published specifications[14], the Probe debugger supports over 1,000 devices from over 30 manufacturers. Embedded Intel architecture processors supported are Intel Atom processors, Intel® Core™ 2 processors, Intel® Core™ i3, Intel® Core™ i5, Intel® Core™ i7, and Intel® Xeon® 5500 (Nehalem). Multi-core and Intel® Hyper-Threading Technology debug of all supported processors are supported as well. The Green Hills Probe is shown in Figure 4.15.

[14] Greens Hills Probe. Web site. 2010. http://www.greenhillssoftware.com/products/probe.html

Image courtesy of Green Hills Software

Figure 4.15   Green Hills Probe

Key features of the Probe include:

■ 100+ MHz sustained JTAG TCK rates (not all boards and CPUs can support this clock rate)

■ 10+ MB/second sustained download speeds (not all boards and CPUs can support these download speeds)

■ Gigabit Ethernet

■ USB 2.0 High Speed

■ RoHS, PSE, and CEC compliance

The Probe device is tightly integrated with the Green Hills MULTI Integrated Development Environment (IDE). The company claims that MULTI supports more target processors, operating systems, and third-party tools than any other IDE, including target configurations with home-grown proprietary OS or even no OS. As shown in Figure 4.16 the Green Hills Probe supports three host interfaces, multi-core debugging, ultra-high download speeds, and an on-board 32-bit CPU, which is configurable for different targets.

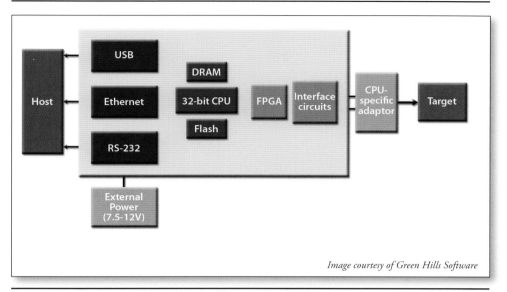

Image courtesy of Green Hills Software

Figure 4.16   Green Hills Probe Configuration

Intel® JTAG Debugger for Intel Atom Processor. The Intel JTAG Debugger is a component of the Intel Embedded Software Development Tool Suite for Intel Atom processor[15], and is a fully OS-aware Eclipse† RCP GUI based JTAG debug solution. The Intel JTAG debugger allows in-depth access of Intel architecture-specific features (execution trace support), as well as access to system-on-chip and chipset peripheral register content. This feature is unique and makes it valuable for driver development and debugging. Even the entire processor and peripheral registers are fully documented in the JTAG debugger solution. Supported JTAG devices:

■   Third party vendor JTAG interface support available at Macraigor. Get hardware device through www.macraigor.com/intel.

■   Intel® XDP3 JTAG interface. Note: This is an enabling product only. There is no public product available. Please contact Intel at MIDDevTools@intel.com if you are a hardware manufacturer.

15   Intel® Tools for Intel® Atom™ Processors. Web site. 2010
http://software.intel.com/en-us/articles/intel-tools-for-intel-atom-processors/

The Intel JTAG Debugger provides vital features for the system developer, such as:

■ Bit field editor views of chipset, processor model and core registers with documentation

■ On-chip instruction trace view

■ Detailed page translation table and descriptor table views

■ Flashing capabilities

■ Linux kernel module and kernel thread awareness

■ Remote cross-debugging support

Lauterbach. Lauterbach's entry into the Intel architecture space is support for Intel Atom processors added to their Trace32[16] product line. The modular product is configured by combining a universal PowerDebug[†] base module that is used for all supported processors with a processor-specific interface module for Intel Atom processors. Two base modules are available, with USB only or USB plus Ethernet host connections. The base modules are priced at USD 2,010 and USD 4,000, respectively, and the Intel Atom processor interface costs USD 3,000. Lauterbach users who already have the base module from another project need only swap in the new Intel Atom processor interface to get up and running on Intel Atom. Everything else is the same. The Lauterbach Trace32 PowerDebug product for Intel Atom processors is shown in Figure 4.17.

[16] Lauterbach Trace32. Web site. 2010. http://www.lauterbach.com/frames.html.

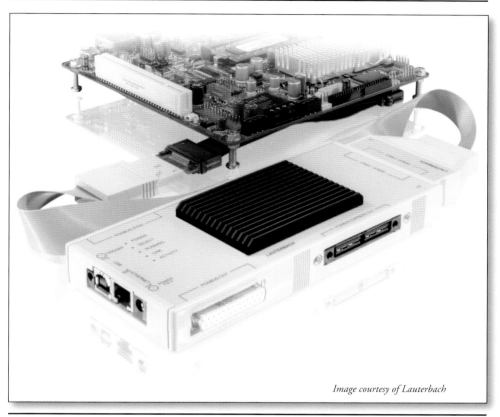

Image courtesy of Lauterbach

Figure 4.17   Lauterbach Trace32 PowerDebug for Intel® Atom™ Processor

Lauterbach's Web site highlights the following features:

■   SMP debugging (including Intel Hyper-Threading Technology)

■   Fast high-level and assembler debugging

■   Intelligent loader to boost download speed

■   Interface to all compilers

■   Linux- and WindowsCE[†]-aware debugging

■ User-configurable display system for internal and external peripherals at a logical level

■ Flash programming

■ Powerful script language

■ Lauterbach does not offer their own compilers or RTOS, but Lauterbach contends that their compiler support is more open and that RTOS awareness is a strength.

■ Ability to set breakpoints at the thread, process, or kernel level and examine stacks and task control blocks, kernel resources, status of all loaded threads, and look at contexts other than the current one.

■ Fast target download, which is achieved by operating at up to 80 MHz JTAG speed (204 KB/s using 20 MHz JTAG frequency) combined with TRACE32's intelligent loader, utilizing techniques like compression and differential loading, that is, loading only those parts of the image that changed since the last build. These features are in part enabled by a high performance CPU onboard the main debug module. All of this results in achievable intelligent downloads to ~4 MB/s.

Lauterbach[17] stated that if they don't already support your commercial RTOS, they'll add it at no charge, typically in two or three month's time, and you can add support for a custom RTOS yourself using an available kit. Additionally, Lauterbach includes a flash programmer and, similar to their RTOS posture, if your device isn't already supported they will add it at no charge in a short period of time.

Macraigor Systems LLC. Macraigor's entry into the Intel architecture space is support for Intel Atom processors added to their core product line usb2Demon[18], which is shown in Figure 4.18. One side of the usb2Demon interfaces to a USB 1.1 or USB 2.0 port of a host PC and the other side connects to an OCD (On-Chip Debug) port on the target system. The list price of usb2Demon listed at the product's Web site at the time of writing

17 Norbert Weiss (International Sales & Marketing Manager). Lauterbach GmbH, 2010
18 Macraigor usb2Demon for Intel® Atom™ Processors. Web site. 2010. http://www.macraigor.com/Intel/index.htm

this is USD 799, which includes various free software components. A flash programmer comes at additional cost. The debugger's capabilities listed at the product's Web site include the following:

- When connected to a USB 2.0 port on your PC, the usb2Demon will run up to Hi-Speed USB rates (480Mb/s). For the Intel Atom processor on the Crown Beach board, the download rate is 35KB/s (with JTAG clocked at 24 MHz).

- Power is supplied by the USB interface so that no external supply is necessary.

- The buffers that interface to the target OCD signals are powered by the target itself, allowing the usb2Demon to automatically match target voltages between 5.0 V and 2.2 V.

- As with all Macraigor interface devices, the usb2Demon can simultaneously debug up to 255 devices on a single scan chain.

- Up to 16 usb2Demons can be connected to a single host machine.

- It supports configurable JTAG/BDM clock rates up to 24 MHz.

- The usb2Demon is compatible with Windows and Linux hosts. Supported versions of Linux are Red Hat 7.2 – 9 and Fedora Core 2 - 12.

- It is available now with a 24, 31, or 60 pin interface.

Macraigor[19] claims that their tool can do everything that the others do with one exception, which is the runtime trace. Macraigor's take is that trace isn't all that necessary if the primary task is software bring-up rather than hardware debug, and that their breakpoint functionality is a suitable alternative. Macraigor recently added support for the Intel Atom D5xx and D4xx Moon Creek board and also provides an example GNU/Eclipse[†] project for it.

---

[19] James MacGregor. Macraigor Systems LLC. 2010

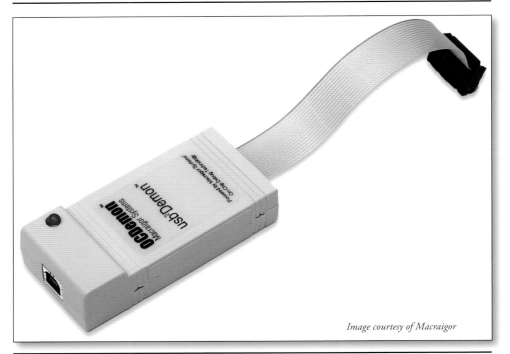

Figure 4.18 Macraigor usb2Demon JTAG

Wind River. Wind River started providing JTAG tools for the Intel Atom processor in June 2009. Wind River's solution integrates JTAG debug hardware with their Eclipse†-based integrated development environment (IDE) known as Wind River Workbench†. Debug hardware is available in two configurations, an entry-level "portable" unit, and one that is multi-core, multithread capable. Consistent with Wind River's legacy of cross-platform support, their JTAG offering covers most popular embedded architectures including ARM, MIPS†, Power Architecture†, and now Intel architecture. So, developers who are familiar with Wind River JTAG on one of their other supported processors should find an easy transition to Intel architecture. The Wind River ICE 2[20] JTAG emulator shown in Figure 4.19 provides visibility to all CPU cores simultaneously within a single window, and supports Intel Hyper-Threading Technology, and 60-pin XDP, 31-pin XDP-SSA, 24-pin XDP-SFF, and 28-pin

---

[20] Wind River On Chip Debugging. Web site. 2010
http://www.windriver.com/products/OCD

ITP-700 connectors (Finkel, 2010[21]). The Wind River Probe[†], not shown, is also available as their entry level USB-based portable JTAG solution.

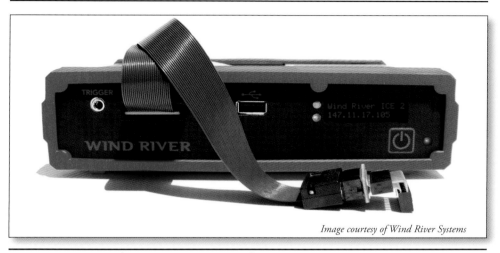

Image courtesy of Wind River Systems

Figure 4.19 Wind River ICE 2 JTAG Emulator

Intel® Software Development Products

Intel supports a wide variety of software development products, which help developers unleash the performance of their software on Intel platforms. The Intel software tools product line includes compilers and debuggers, performance analyzers, performance libraries, and threading tools. These tools are highly optimized for multi-core Intel architecture. The products are extremely helpful when implementing threads and even more important when tuning the performance of the application and optimizing the software for Intel architecture multi-core platforms. The products are available for a variety of operating systems. For more details about each product and a current listing of processor and OS support, refer to the products' Web sites at http://software.intel.com/en-us/articles/buy-or-renew/.

[21] B. Finkel, Wind River Systems, 2010.

Intel® Compilers

Intel® compilers are compatible with other tools you might use, integrate into popular development environments, and are source and binary compatible with other widely-used compilers. The Intel® compilers offer the support for creating multithreaded applications and includes features for advanced optimization, automatic processor dispatch, vectorization, auto-parallelization, multithreading, OpenMP†, data prefetching, and loop unrolling, along with highly optimized libraries.

OpenMP is a standard for compiler based multiprocessing features. To learn more about OpenMP and the specification refer to the OpenMP specification web site at: http://openmp.org/wp/.

Refer to Chapter 8 for details about using the Intel Compiler for performance optimization and to Chapter 9 for details about multithreading applications with OpenMP.

Intel® VTune™ Performance Analyzer

The Intel® VTune™ Performance Analyzer provides application performance tuning with a graphical user interface and no recompiles required. It is compiler and language independent so it works with C, C++, and more. Unlike some products that offer only call graph analysis or only a limited set of sampling events, Intel® VTune analyzer offers both with an extensive set of tuning events for all the latest Intel processors. This performance analyzer can locate hotspots in the code, identifying the lines of code where the hotspot exists. Refer to Chapter 8 for details about performance optimization using Intel VTune.

Intel® Performance Libraries

Intel® Performance Libraries are foundation level building blocks for high-performance threading, math and multimedia applications, and provide consistent performance across all Intel microprocessors. Use the performance libraries to get the most out of today's new multi-core and multi-processor systems. Refer to Chapter 7 for information about Intel performance libraries.

■ Intel® Integrated Performance Primitives. This highly optimized Intel software library contains audio, video, imaging, cryptography, speech recognition, and signal processing functions and codec component functions for digital media and data-processing applications. Refer to

Chapter 7 for details about the Intel Integrated Performance Primitives functions and optimizations for the Intel Atom processor.

■ The Intel® Math Kernel Library. This library contains highly optimized, extensively threaded, mathematical functions for engineering, scientific, and financial applications that require maximum performance.

Intel® Threading Tools

Intel® Thread Checker, Intel® Thread Profiler and Intel® Threading Building Blocks (Intel® TBB) help to thread applications correctly and optimize performance on Intel multi-core processor systems.

■ *Intel® Thread Checker.* The Intel Thread Checker facilitates debugging of multithreaded programs by automatically finding common errors such as storage conflicts, deadlock, API violations, inconsistent variable scope, and thread stack overflows. The nondeterministic nature of concurrency errors makes them particularly difficult to find with traditional debuggers. The Intel Thread Checker pinpoints error locations down to the source lines involved and provides stack traces showing the paths taken by the threads to reach the error. It also identifies the variables involved.

■ *Intel® Thread Profiler.* The Intel® Thread Profiler facilitates analysis of applications written using Windows and POSIX threading APIs or OpenMP pragmas. The OpenMP Thread Profiler provides details on the time spent in serial regions, parallel regions, and critical sections. It also graphically displays performance bottlenecks due to load imbalance, lock contention, and parallel overhead in OpenMP applications. Performance data can be displayed for the whole program, by region, and even down to individual threads. The Windows API or POSIX Threads API Thread Profiler facilitates understanding the threading patterns in multithreaded software by visual depiction of thread hierarchies and their interactions. It will also help identify and compare the performance impact of different synchronization methods, different numbers of threads, or different algorithms.

Since Thread Profiler plugs-in to the Intel VTune Performance Analyzer, multiple runs across different number of processors can be compared to determine the scalability profile. It also helps locate synchronization constructs that directly impact execution time and correlates to the corresponding source line in the application. Intel Thread Profiler is packaged with the Intel VTune Performance Analyzer. Refer to Chapter 8 for details about performance optimization using Intel Thread Profiler.

■ *Intel® Threading Building Blocks.* Intel® TBB is a C++ runtime library that abstracts the low-level threading details necessary for multi-core performance. It uses common C++ templates and coding style to eliminate tedious threading implementation work. Intel TBB requires fewer lines of code to achieve parallelism than other threading models. Applications written with Intel TBB are portable across platforms. Since the library is also inherently scalable, no code maintenance is required as more processor cores become available. Refer to Chapter 9 for details about multithreading applications with Intel TBB.

An open source version of Intel® Threading Building Blocks is available at: http://www.threadingbuildingblocks.org/.

James Reinders has also written a book, *Intel® Threading Building Blocks: Outfitting C++ for Multi-core Processor Parallelism.* Go to the Intel® Threading Building Blocks product Web site for directions on ordering the book.

Intel® Tools for Intel® Atom™ Processors

Specifically targeting the Intel Atom processor with a set of Linux hosted tool suites, Intel provides solutions for software development using many levels of cross development methodologies. These tool suites bundle some of the individual tools mentioned previously and add features and installation options tailored for the Intel Atom processor as shown in Figure 4.20.

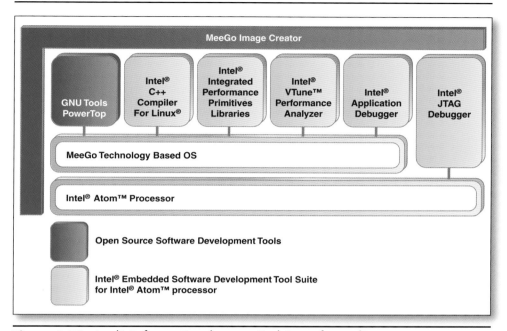

Figure 4.20 Intel® Software Development Tool Suites for Intel® Atom™ Processor

Intel® Application Software Development Tool Suite for Intel® Atom™ Processor

The Intel® Application Software Development Tool Suite targets Linux hosted software development. This tool suite has a special focus on porting applications to Intel Atom processor based small form-factor devices running compatible software stacks for the Moblin or MeeGo operating systems. In all, this tool suite addresses the entire software development cycle from coding, through debugging and establishing software maturity and reliability, to performance tuning and final adjustments.

Intel Application Software Development Tool Suite for Intel Atom processor includes:

- The Intel® C++ Compiler with the latest Intel Atom processor specific optimization options.

- The Intel® Integrated Performance Primitives for Linux in a release that is targeted and optimized especially for low-power Intel architecture.

■ The Intel® Application Debugger. This debugger solution has a rich Eclipse RCP† based user interface. The debugger is tailored for TCP/IP based remote cross-debug of an application running on an Intel Atom processor based device or in a virtual machine.

■ The Intel® VTune™ Performance Analyzer for Linux with a small command line sampling data collector, intended to be run with little overhead on an Intel Atom processor based embedded device, handheld device or consumer electronics device. This Intel VTune release comes with prebuilt kernel modules to collect event-based performance data from the processor's Performance Monitoring Unit (PMU) for a set of common Moblin or MeeGo compatible OS releases, as well as the Linux base installation used on the Intel® Media Processor CE3100 and Intel® Atom™ processor CE4100.

Intel® Embedded Software Development Tool Suite for Intel® Atom™ processor.

The Intel® Embedded Software Development Tool Suite targets system and device driver software development. This embedded tool suite adds features for testing and developing the platform and OS software stack and device drivers by including the Intel JTAG Debugger. Refer to the "On-Chip Debugging Tools" section in this chapter for more information about the Intel JTAG Debugger.

Tool Suite Usage Models

The Intel® Application Software Development Tool Suite and Intel® Embedded Software Development Tool Suite both support a wide variety of Intel Atom processor based devices. No single use case or single usage model will fit the needs of every developer. However, software development for Intel Atom processor based devices tends to have one aspect in common. In most cases you will want to take advantage of the performance and the high screen resolution of your regular software development environment, and only deploy your build to the real hardware for validation and analysis. In short, the most common usage model will be one of cross development.

The Intel Embedded Software Development Tool Suite for Intel Atom processor addresses cross development in multiple ways:

■ The Intel C++ Compiler and the Intel Integrated Performance Primitives will, by default, be installed on the software development host system. However, to provide a protected build environment without host system library pollution it is also supported to install these components into the Moblin Image Creator 2 jailroot system or to install them into a Moblin 2 developer image running inside a KVM virtual machine or even on a real target. For the installation into Moblin Image Creator 2 or into a KVM image, it is recommended to do this following the yum rpm repository based installation process outlined in the Moblin Integration Guide.

   ■ Moblin Image Creator 2 kickstart scripts can be found at http:// software.intel.com/en-us/articles/moblin-integration-software-development-tool-suite-atom/

   ■ A template rpm repository definition file for the direct KVM image installation of the Intel C++ Compiler and Intel IPP can be found at http://software.intel.com/en-us/articles/installing-compiler-into-kvm-atom/.

■ The Intel Application Debugger with the standard installation package will be installed on the software development host system. Via TCP/IP the host system can connect to and debug a process running on the actual Intel Atom processor based target hardware, or on a KVM virtual machine or another virtualization. For further details on the Intel Application Debugger usage, refer to the tool's Getting Started Guide.

■ The Intel JTAG Debugger with the standard installation package will be installed on the software development host system. The host system can connect to the target platforms eXtended Debug Port (XDP) using the JTAG device, which provides the ability to perform remote cross-debugging of the entire platform and system level software.

■ The Intel VTune Performance Analyzer performs event based and time based sampling data on the development host. The data is collected on an Intel Atom processor based target platform with low overhead, which results in accurate sampling data. The analysis can be done within the standard KDE† or Gnome† based standard Linux GUI.

More information about the Intel Tools for Intel Atom Processors can be found at http://software.intel.com/en-us/articles/intel-tools-for-intel-atom-processors/

CriticalBlue Prism†

CriticalBlue Prism[22] is a tool suite aimed at multithreaded and multi-core software development, and includes a spectrum of activities needed to migrate existing sequential single core software onto a multi-core platform. Prism supports 32-bit and 64-bit Intel architecture processors, including the Intel Atom processors. The tool provides performance analysis with extended capabilities for exploring the affect of new software design strategies and helping the developer understand their affect before changing any code.

Prism's features are listed here and more details about Prism's performance tuning capabilities are covered in Chapter 8.

■ *Analyze.* Prism integrates with Eclipse and allows the use of familiar software development tools and libraries. Prism's analysis feature can identify program hotspots, call graph trees, data flow patterns and data dependencies, which will shape achievable parallelism.

■ *Exploration.* Prism allows developers to explore different parallel scenarios to help select the best strategy before modifying any code. For example, what if a function ran in a separate thread, or what if certain dependencies were removed? Understanding which scenario is the best strategy is valuable information because it allows the developer to model all of the thread design possibilities, but only implement code that results in a material benefit.

22 CriticalBlue Prism. Web site. 2010. http://www.criticalblue.com/criticalblue_products/prism.shtml

■   *Implementation, verification, and tuning.* Prism can create trial schedules across a varying number of cores. Using the explore feature, any number of cores can be modeled to understand their affect even though the system under analysis may have fewer cores than the models. This helps the developer understand the level of scalability designed into the code and to ensure that the cores present are utilized efficiently. The verification capabilities of Prism allow the user to ensure that their multithreaded code will work under all scheduling conditions, and that no potential data race conditions exist in the code that could cause failures in the field at some unknown point in the future.

Refer to Chapter 8 for examples of Prism and performance optimization.

National Instruments LabVIEW†

National Instruments' LabVIEW[23] graphical development environment is a high-level software development tool that enables scientists and software engineers to create their applications using graphical icons connected by wires indicating the flow of data. The graphical nature of LabVIEW makes it more intuitive for developers to quickly develop their application using a method closer to their natural method of expressing solutions to problems.

The LabVIEW environment offers many of the same programming constructs found in traditional text-based programming such as conditional execution, looping, and complex data types, however the fundamental difference is that the code is developed using diagrams. Function calls are represented by hierarchical blocks called virtual instruments (VIs). Data is passed into and out of each VI via wires that represent the inputs and outputs of the system. Developers create their applications by connecting the necessary blocks to define their algorithm. Graphical programming offers programmers a level of abstraction in both developing their algorithms as well as targeting their hardware platform. Figure 4.21 shows an example of graphical and data flow programming with LabVIEW.

---

[23] National Instruments LabVIEW. Web site. 2010 http://www.ni.com/labview/

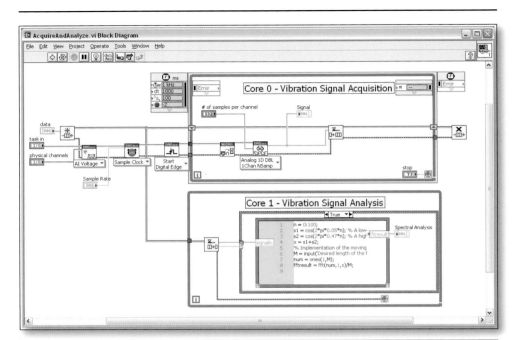

Figure 4.21   Example of Graphical and Data Flow Programming with National Instruments LabVIEW

Graphical Programming with National Instruments LabVIEW allows developers to easily parallelize applications across multi-core Intel prcoessors. Software developed with LabVIEW is portable across multiple operating systems and processors including Intel architecture, ARM, and PowerPC. Developers are provided a system level abstraction of the underlying processor architecture as LabVIEW compiles the developer's code into a native binary specific the chosen platform. Because of the system level abstraction and the portable machine code that LabVIEW generates, migrating to the Intel architecture allows developers to easily take advantage of multi-core systems, including Intel Hyper-Threading Technology. The LabVIEW compiler is optimized to be able to automatically spawn threads from orthogonal operations on a LabVIEW diagram, and then schedule the threads across multiple Intel processor cores. The data flow nature of LabVIEW code described earlier allows for data dependencies to be seen visually and reduce the time spent tracking race conditions. This combination of graphical abstraction combined with high-performance Intel multi-core processors enables engineers to reduce their development time, while still maximizing their system resource usage[24].

Product Technologies

Part of migrating software to the Intel Atom processor regards consideration of how the software and end product can benefit the Intel Atom product technologies such as Intel Hyper-Threading Technology, Intel® Virtualization Technology, and more.

For example, for Intel Atom processors that provide multiple cores, how can the software and end product benefit from the additional cores? Maybe higher performance is desirable, in which case a symmetric multiprocessing design methodology would be implemented. Possibly virtualization would be implemented to execute legacy software with little or no modification, or for platform consolidation, or to run OS co-location, which provides the ability for real-time and general-purpose operating systems to run simultaneously. Other technologies included Intel 64 and Intel Graphics Technology. Refer to Chapter 9 to learn about design choices and techniques for adopting Intel Atom product technologies.

Training and Design Information

The Intel® Embedded Design Center[25] (EDC) provides information about designing for embedded Intel architecture systems. The site includes information ranging from embedded hardware platforms and schematics to software solutions and white papers. The EDC provides online training for a number of hardware and software modules, and references to other resources including books and training services such as Mindshare†, Mindshare is a training services company that provides classroom, virtual, and eLearning training for Intel architecture, including the Intel Atom processor and other Intel architecture platform topics.

---

[24] J. Brettle, National Instruments. 2010
[25] Intel® Embedded Design Center. Web Site. http://edc.intel.com

Migration Design Guide

Up to this point, this chapter discussed the software design areas that need to be considered when migrating from other architectures to Intel architecture. The migration methodology provides guidelines for the procedures of the migration. The guide steps through situational decisions, resulting in an outline for the overall migration solution and plan. There are two parts to every architecture migration. The first part includes steps 1, 2, and 3, which involves getting the code ported and executing correctly on the target platform. Part two includes steps 4 and 5, which involves adopting the target platform technologies that may apply.

There are five ordered steps for the migration and cover OS requirements, hardware differences, and software optimization on the target Intel architecture platform:

1. Port the code to the target operating system

2. Execute the code correctly on one Intel architecture core

3. Optimize the code for performance on one Intel architecture core

4. Apply multi-core software design updates

5. Optimize the software design for multi-core Intel architecture performance

Step 1: Port the Code to the Target Operating System

If the architecture migration includes a port to a different operating system, complete the port to the new operating system before starting the migration of the current software to the Intel architecture hardware. The goal in this step is to ensure that the software performs as expected and correctly on the new OS. Since this step requires stability of the same code running on the target OS, do not make other software design changes in this step. Refer to Chapter 6 for information about operating systems enabled for Intel architecture.

Step 2: Execute the Code Correctly on One Intel® Architecture Core

In order to ensure success with this step, follow this checklist:

1. Update the operating system related code for Intel architecture. Whether the current and target OS are the same or different, device drivers, libraries, and software development tools need to be surveyed and availability for Intel architecture determined.

    a. If any device drivers or libraries are developed in-house, they will need to be rewritten for Intel architecture.

    b. If any third party drivers or libraries are required, check with the third party vendor for equivalent Intel architecture products.

    c. Intel® Graphics Drivers: Refer to the section titled "Intel® Graphics Drivers" in this chapter.

    d. Intel embedded chipset drivers: Refer to the section titled "Intel Chipset Drivers" in this chapter.

2. Choose the method for system initialization. Refer to Chapter 5 for the details.

    Solutions:

    a. BIOS

    b. Boot loader for Intel Architecture

3. If any part of the code is written in assembly language it will need to be updated for Intel architecture instructions: Refer to the section titled "Migrating to the Intel® Architecture Instruction Set" in this chapter.

    Solutions:

    a. Basic assembly instructions – Manually update the basic assembly instructions using the Intel® 64 and IA-32 Architectures Software Developer's Manuals and Intel Assembly Code Conversion Tool as a reference.

    b. Vector oriented instructions - Vector oriented code will need to be updated to use Intel SSE instructions. Refer to the section titled "Vector Oriented Code" in this chapter.

4. Does the software abstract the endian architecture of the processor?

■ Yes – The code is endian-neutral. No changes are required.

■ No – The code will need to be updated for little-endian memory architecture. Manually update the endianness differences in the code. Refer to the information in the section "Microprocessor Endian Architecture" in this chapter as a guide to the required changes.

5. Refer to the respective Architecture Differences tables in this chapter for any other architecture differences that may need software updates.

6. Build, test, and debug the code using one Intel architecture core. Refer to the section titled "Software Development Tools" in this chapter.

Step 3: Optimize the Code for Performance on One Intel® Architecture Core

When step 3 is accomplished successfully, the migration is potentially completed, because the remaining steps 4, and 5 are only necessary for adoption of multi-core updates.

Although the end product will run on multi-core architecture, performance tuning methodology first requires that serial code be optimized for serial performance. Use performance libraries that are already optimized for Intel architecture. Refer to Chapter 7 for information about Intel architecture performance libraries and Chapter 8 for Intel Atom processor performance optimization.

Use the top-down, closed-end loop performance methodology, and when applicable use the Intel Software Development Products. Understand the performance requirements and baseline before making any changes. Make one change at a time. The methodology is explained in the article titled "De-Mystifying Software Performance Optimization" (Vecchio, 2008[26]),

1. Analyze the performance:

a. Measure the performance results and compare against the baseline and requirements. Stop making changes when the performance requirements are achieved, because there could be diminishing returns on further tuning efforts.

---

[26] P. Vecchio, "De-Mystifying Software Performance Optimization", 2008 http://software.intel.com/en-us/articles/de-mystifying-software-performance-optimization/

b. Use the Intel VTune Performance Analyzer or other performance analysis tools to pinpoint hotspots in the code where the processing could be distributed between the available cores.

c. Use the Intel Thread Profiler or other thread analysis tools to identify any thread imbalances for multithreaded designs.

2. Generate alternatives and implement code changes:

a. For advanced optimizations, use the Intel C++ Compiler and select features to implement advanced optimizations using Profile Guided Optimization (PGO), executable size, and power consumption.

b. Use the Intel Performance Libraries, or other performance libraries enabled for Intel architecture, to increase performance with a variety of APIs that are highly tuned for Intel architecture. Functions include video, imaging, compression, cryptography, audio, speech recognition, and signal processing functions and codec component functions for digital media and data-processing applications.

3. Debug the code - Build, debug, and test the change. Refer to the section titled "Software Development Tools" in this chapter.

4. Back to procedure 1. Analyze Performance.

Step 4: Apply Multi-core Software Design Updates

There are several ways to benefit from multi-core processors. It's not unusual for architecture migrations to start from serial code bases. Therefore, the target software design needs to identify the solution to meet the migration requirements. SMP can improve application performance and can be designed to scale as the number of processors increase. However, SMP requires analysis to identify opportunities for parallelism in the code and updating the source code to introduce the parallelism using multithreading. For CPU intensive code, which is difficult to redesign for parallel processing using SMP and multithreading, AMP could be a good alternative solution. Choose the multi-core design. Refer to Chapter 9 for more information about adopting Intel Atom product technologies:

■ *AMP.* Choose AMP if the migration requirements specify that no changes can be made to the application or operating system.

■ *SMP.* Choose SMP if one operating system will be run, using all of the cores as equal processing resources, and the applications can be parallelized to benefit from SMP systems. SMP affinity can sometimes improve cache hit rates on multiprocessor systems by pinning certain tasks to certain cores to improve data locality. Use multi-core enabled performance libraries. Refer to Chapter 7 for more information about performance libraries for Intel architecture.

■ *Virtualization.* Choose virtualization for system consolidation, OS co-location, and the additional benefits of features such as security, QoS, HA, and load distribution.

Step 5: Optimize the Software Design for Multi-core Performance

Whether the design is SMP or AMP, multi-core software designs require specialized software development tools. For SMP the tools help identify and implement parallelism into the code and pinpoint threading issues such as race conditions, deadlocks, and thread load imbalances. The tuning methodology is the same as for a uniprocessor in step 3, except that the goal is to correctly and efficiently execute multiple processes or threads simultaneously across multiple cores. Multi-core tools help implement parallelism and help tune and debug the parallelized code. Use performance libraries that are already optimized for Intel multi-core processors. Refer to Chapter 7 for information about Intel architecture performance libraries and Chapter 8 for Intel architecture performance optimization.

1. Intel VTune Performance Analyzer – Pinpoints hotspots in the code where the processing could be distributed between the available cores.

2. Intel C++ Compiler – Multi-core features include OpenMP and auto-parallelization.

3. Use Intel Performance Libraries or other performance libraries to increase parallelism with performance threaded APIs that are already highly tuned for Intel multi-core architecture.

4. Implement threads with threading APIs such as Windows and POSIX[†] thread APIs, and Intel Thread Building Blocks. Debug threads with Intel Thread Checker or other thread debugging tools. Identify thread workload imbalances and lock contention of the threads with Intel Thread Profiler or other thread profiling tools.

5. The OSV should also provide a set of multi-core development tools. Check with the OSV to understand which tools are available.

Summary

This chapter provided an overview of the software considerations and guidelines for completing a successful software architecture migration to Intel architecture, as well as resources that can assist during the migration software design and implementation. The information included processor architecture differences, Intel architecture system initialization choices, operating system porting considerations, interrupts and real-time considerations, graphics driver choices, software development tools, and migration guidelines. Remember, each situation is different and the effort required for the migration depends on the amount of abstraction that is already programmed into the code. Follow the five steps of the Migration Design Guide to assess and understand the current software migration situation and requirements, and plan each step before the migration begins.

Boot Loader Choices for Small and Fast System Initialization Requirements

---

If GM had kept up with technology like the computer industry has, we would all be driving $25 cars that got 1000 MPG.

—Bill Gates

There are several system initialization solutions for Intel architecture. Choosing the solution that is best for a given architecture migration depends on requirements such as boot speed, boot loader size, and the amount of configurability that the system needs to support. With these factors in mind, boot loaders either target closed box designs or open box designs. Other architectures, such as PowerPC[†] or ARM[†], are accustomed to getting the boot logic solution through open source or from their silicon vendor. This chapter provides an overview of the Intel architecture system initialization solutions, which include custom boot loaders and Basic Input/Output System (BIOS).

System Initialization Roles and Responsibilities

The system firmware is a layer between the hardware and the operating system that maintains platform hardware data for the operating system. The system firmware is customized for the specific hardware requirements of the platform and perhaps for a given application. Traditionally, platforms based on Intel architecture boot in three steps:

1. System firmware

2. Operating system loader

3. Operating system

As part of the power on self test (POST), the system firmware begins to execute out of flash memory to initialize all the necessary silicon components including the CPU itself and the memory subsystem. Once main memory is initialized, the system firmware is shadowed from ROM into RAM and the initialization continues. As part of the advanced initialization stages the system firmware creates tables of hardware information in main memory for the operating system to utilize during its installation, loading, and runtime execution. Hardware workarounds are often implemented during the power-on self-test (POST) to avoid changing silicon or hardware during later design phases. There may be an element of the system firmware that remains active during later stages to allow for responses to various operating system function calls.

The last task that the system firmware performs is a handoff of control to the operating system loader. The operating system loader does exactly what its name implies. It is customized with knowledge about the specific operating system, how it is ordered, and which blocks of the operating system to pull from the OS storage location. The operating system loader may be configured to extend the platform initialization beyond the system firmware's scope in order to allow for additional boot options. Depending on the system architecture and the firmware solutions that are adopted, the operating system loader and the system firmware could be part of the same binary.

The operating system completes the initialization of the hardware as it executes the software stack and device drivers. It potentially loads the human/machine interface and finally begins the applications. Care should be taken when considering combining elements of various components together as licenses may prohibit linking the objects together in various ways.

Boot Loaders for Closed Box Designs

Some embedded systems use minimized specialized (custom) firmware stacks created for fast speed, small size, and specific system requirements. These boot loaders perform static hardware configurations and only initialize critical hardware features prior to handoff to an operating system. They are tuned to a targeted OS, specific application, or function set, and support minimal upgrade and expansion capabilities.

QNX† Fastboot Technology for Intel® Atom™ Processors

QNX fastboot technology integrates system initialization into the QNX Neutrino† RTOS, eliminating the need for BIOS or other boot loader. It was developed specifically for use in the QNX Neutrino RTOS, for Intel® Atom™ processor Z5xx series platforms. Systems using QNX fastboot can achieve boot times of milliseconds while eliminating the BIOS royalty from their bill of materials. More information about QNX fastboot technology may be found at http://www.qnx.com/news/pr_3024_1.html.

Develop a Custom Boot Loader for Intel® Architecture

A custom boot loader may be developed for the Intel platform for architecture migrations where more time and effort is available and a do-it-yourself model is preferred. Developing your own boot loader requires a special set of software and hardware knowledge, and you'll need certain documents respective to the Intel architecture processor, chipset, motherboard, and other platform hardware. Additional information that will be needed includes operating system requirements, industry standards and exceptions, silicon-specific eccentricities beyond the standards, basic configuration, along with compiler and linker details, and software debug tools. Gather the appropriate documents at the start of the project.

Motherboard schematics are an absolute must. If the design is reusing an off-the-shelf solution from a vendor it could be more difficult to obtain the required information. In some cases confidential nondisclosure agreements (CNDAs) and perhaps restricted secret nondisclosure agreements (RSNDAs) with the various silicon vendors or motherboard vendors must be signed. The nondisclosure agreements (NDAs) will require some level of legal advice. Further, Memory Reference Code (MRC) requires an RSNDA agreement with Intel.

Until recently, no single document existed that described all of the steps and documents required to boot an Intel architecture system. Many developers will be pleased to know that this mystery is now documented in the section titled "Intel® Atom™ Processor System Boot Flow" later in this chapter.

Refer to the EDC software Web site for other boot loader technology options.

Intel® Architecture System BIOS for Open Box Designs

A common requirement for open, expandable system designs is to provide the broadest possible system initialization solution, allowing the flexibility to load a wide range of off-the-shelf operating systems and methodical, dynamic hardware configurations. These designs will support multiple standard interfaces and expansion slots, and host mainstream operating systems with a broad set of pre-OS features and are ready to run multiple applications. On Intel architecture designs that require the flexibility, developers can choose from vendor-provided firmware.

Legacy Basic Input/Output System

The legacy Basic Input/Output System (BIOS) initializes the hardware and boots it to a point where the operating system can load, and it also abstracts the hardware from the operating system through various industry standard tables (ACPI, SMBIOS, IRQ routing, memory maps, and so on). Access to the hardware is directly made through silicon-specific BIOS commands or industry standards interfaces. Intel architecture has commonly used BIOS for over twenty years to support designs with multiple use cases, customizable services, multiple boot paths, native operating systems, or that are rich in features. BIOS is a common choice for legacy Intel architecture software design support. Major BIOS vendors include:

■ American Megatrends Inc.[†]

■ Insyde Software Corp.[†]

■ Nanjing Byosoft Co., Ltd.[†]

■ Phoenix Technologies, Ltd.[†]

Talking to a BIOS vendor is a great idea when the situation demands ready solutions and the return on investment merits the costs. The BIOS solution provides everything needed to get the system initialized and to a successful production cycle. Obtaining starter code from a BIOS vendor normally requires various levels of licenses and agreements for evaluation, production, and follow-on support. Additionally, a commercial BIOS usually includes a varying amount of nonrecurring engineering (NRE), and/or royalties per unit or subscription costs.

Many successful and established computer OEM development teams utilize BIOS vendors to provide a base level of software core competency, basic OS support, tools, and on-call support. Smaller companies can take advantage of BIOS starter kits, which consists of a lesser number of features and limited support.

Unified Extensible Firmware Interface

Unified Extensible Firmware Interface (UEFI) specifications define an interface layer between the operating system and the platform firmware. Intel developed the original Extensible Firmware Interface (EFI[1]) as a C language based firmware alternative to BIOS, and donated it to the UEFI forum as a starting point for the creation of the industry specifications, including UEFI and Platform Interface (PI). The interface and all of the platform-related information provide a standard environment for booting an operating system and running pre-boot applications. Additionally, UEFI addresses the limitations inherit with BIOS implementations such as 16-bit addressing mode, 1 MB addressable space, PC AT hardware dependencies and upper memory block (UMB) dependencies.

In 2005, the Unified EFI Forum, Inc. was formed as a nonprofit corporation whose goal is to manage and promote a set of UEFI standard specifications. The UEFI Forum is governed by a board of directors from eleven promoter companies including AMD, AMI, Apple, Dell, HP, IBM, Insyde, Intel, Lenovo, Microsoft and Phoenix, and 120 contributor and adopter member companies (MacInnis, 2009[2]). The UEFI Forum is responsible for two specifications:

---

[1]Extensible Firmware Interface (EFI) and Unified EFI (UEFI) Web site. 2010. Intel Corporation.

[2]J. MacInnis, "Implementing Firmware on Embedded Intel Architecture Design", 2009
  http://download.intel.com/design/intarch/papers/321072.pdf

1. Unified Extensible Firmware Interface specification

    The UEFI specification defines interfaces between OS, add-in firmware drivers, and system firmware where the OS and other high-level software should *only* interact with exposed interfaces and services defined by the UEFI specification. It includes the EFI Byte Code (EBC) specification, which defines an interpretive layer for portable component drivers.

2. Platform Initialization Interface specifications

    The PI specification defines the core code and services that are required for an implementation of the PI specifications, hereafter referred to as the PI architecture. These are the interoperability standards between firmware phases and pre-OS components from different providers.

Figure 5.1 is a block diagram that illustrates the UEFI software and specification interfaces.

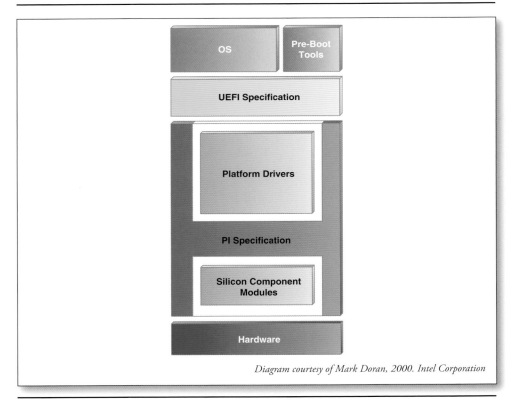

Diagram courtesy of Mark Doran, 2000. Intel Corporation

Figure 5.1   Unified Extensible Firmware Interface

For more details about the UEFI specifications, writing UEFI drivers, and how to use the UEFI Sample Implementation and UEFI Application Toolkit, see the UEFI Web site at http://www.uefi.org/.

Intel® Platform Innovation Framework for EFI

The Intel® Platform Innovation Framework for EFI is referred to as the Framework, and previously code-named Tiano, is a reference code implementation of UEFI and PI specifications developed by Intel.

The Intel® Platform Innovation Framework for UEFI Web site describes the Framework as:

> "…a set of robust architectural interfaces, implemented in C, which has been designed to enable the firmware industry and our customers to accelerate the evolution of innovative, differentiated, platform designs. The framework is the Intel recommended implementation of the UEFI specification for platforms based on all members of the Intel® architecture family" (Intel Corporation Web site. 2010).

BIOS vendors provide a Compatibility Support Module (CSM), which is used to connect operating systems to the Framework that require legacy BIOS interfaces. The Framework firmware implementation includes support for UEFI without the CSM, but does provide interfaces that support adding a CSM supplied by a BIOS vendor. The Framework is a good solution for architecture conversions, since these designs would not already use legacy BIOS interfaces, but can take advantage of the benefits of UEFI, which include:

- Locate option ROMS above 1 MB – Legacy option ROMs have been constrained for many years by having to reside below the 1-MB boundary of 16-bit code, between C0000h and FFFFFh in system memory. In server platforms, this limited the number of add-in cards that could be plugged in. The ability to move the option ROMs above 1 MB enhances their capabilities and size.

- Faster boot – Initialize only the option ROMs needed to boot the OS and load the rest later through EFI function calls from the OS.

- Faster integration – The modularity of the PEI and DXE modules allow for faster integration of differing code modules. In some cases the faster adoption of the code bases' newer technologies into the platform.

The EFI Developer Kit is the open source portion of the Framework code base, referred to as the Foundation, and is available from the TianoCore project at http://www.tianocore.org/.

A complete Framework implementation is not generally available directly from Intel, but is offered by participating vendors as products and services based on the Framework for both Intel and non-Intel silicon. These Framework products and vendors include:

■ Aptio† by American Megatrends Inc.

■ InsydeH2O† by Insyde Software Corp.

■ Nanjing Byosoft Co., Ltd.

■ SecureCore Tiano† by Phoenix Technologies, Ltd.

For more information about implementing firmware for embedded Intel architecture systems see the Intel white paper titled "Implementing Firmware on Embedded Intel architecture Designs" at http://download.intel.com/design/intarch/papers/321072.pdf.

Intel Press has also published the book *Beyond BIOS: Implementing the Unified Extensible Firmware Interface with Intel's Framework*[3], which contains examples for implementing the EFI specification

Intel® Atom™ Processor System Boot Flow

Intel architecture is a very powerful computing architecture that lends itself to all sorts of applications, from smart phones to entertainment consoles to desktop computers to blade servers. When powered on, there's so much hardware at your disposal, but since the hardware can be used for so many compute purposes, there's a bit of work involved to make it function to meet your system requirements.

The only authoritative source that provides firmware development guidance for Intel architecture platforms is the recently published Intel white paper titled *Minimal Intel Architecture Boot Loader: Bare Bones Functionality Required for*

---

[3]Vincent Zimmer, Michael Rothman, and Robert Hale. Beyond BIOS: Implementing the Unified Extensible Firmware Interface with Intel's Framework. 2006. http://www.intel.com/intelpress/sum_efi.htm

Booting an Intel Architecture Platform[4]. This section extends the information from the white paper by stepping the reader through a minimal initialization sequence for an Intel Atom based system.

> **Note:** The system boot flow diagram for the Intel® Atom™ processor, which depicts the following steps, is documented at the end of this section.

Initializing an Intel® Architecture Platform from System Reset

Upon coming out of reset, the Intel Atom processor is placed in a well-defined architectural state. All processor resources are reset. The MMU and caches are disabled, and all register contents are undefined. This state is a special subset of real mode. The top 12 address lines are held high, thus allowing the processor to execute code from the nonvolatile storage (such as flash) located within one megabyte from the top of memory.

The processor starts executing instructions at a fixed memory location near the top of the 32-bit addressable physical memory map, called the *reset vector*. Physically, this is address 0xFFFFFFF0. Therefore, in order for Intel architecture firmware to have any effect on the hardware, meaningful and valid instructions must exist at this location in the memory map. Typically this will be firmware programmed in NOR or NAND nonvolatile RAM (NVRAM).

Figure 5.2 shows the typical Intel architecture memory map at power on.

---

[4]Jenny M. Pelner, Jim A. Pelner. Implementing Firmware on Embedded Intel Architecture Design, 2010
   http://download.intel.com/design/intarch/papers/323246.pdf

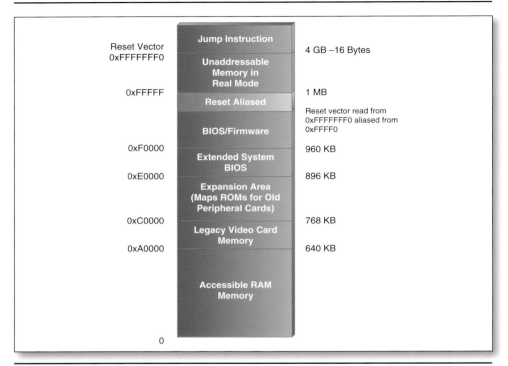

Figure 5.2   Typical Intel® Architecture Memory Map at Power On

Since there are only 16 bytes of addressability from the reset vector to the top of the 32-bit address space, not much can be done within that limited memory space. Therefore, the usual content of the reset vector is simply a jump to the beginning of firmware initialization code somewhere other than the top of the address map. The choice of what kind of jump is dependent on the architecture of the firmware as well as the capabilities of the platform.

CPU Operational Mode

First, we need to understand how the processor views the memory map. Upon reset, Intel architecture processors execute in a mode that resembles real mode, with the exception that its frame of reference is not based off the beginning of the address map (address 0). Rather, the base of operation is at 0xFFF00000, utilizing the top 1 MB of the 32-bit address map instead of the usual bottom. It continues to use this mode until it executes its first long jump, at which time it enters the mode dictated by the setting of the Protected Mode Enable bit (control register CR0) and the contents of the Global Descriptor Table (GDT). If the Protected Mode Enable bit is not set, the processor enters real mode where the address range is restricted to 1 MB starting at linear address 0. If the Protected Mode Enable bit is set, the processor enters protected mode, using the GDT entry determined by the code selector (CS) used in the long jump. Of course, if there isn't a valid GDT or if a bad selector is used, the system promptly generates an unrecoverable or fatal exception.

CPU Mode Selection

Whether a developer chooses to boot up a system in real mode or protected mode really comes down to the hardware capabilities and the firmware requirements.

1. If the hardware forwards accesses below 1 MB to NVRAM where the firmware is stored before memory is initialized, real mode may be used.

2. If the hardware does not forward accesses below 1 MB to NVRAM, protected mode must be used for 32-bit addressability.

3. If addressability above 1 MB is required in firmware, protected mode must be used.

If protected mode is chosen, the easiest mode to use is the protected flat model. Protected flat mode maps all of memory 1 to 1, meaning that all logical addresses are equivalent to physical addresses. Typically there is one data and one code GDT entry with a base of 0 and size of 4 GB. The protected flat model is typically the preferred mode among firmware developers.

Figure 5.3 shows an example GDT in AT&T[†] syntax that contains the NULL descriptor and a 32-bit code selector (0x08) and 32-bit data selector (0x10).

```
fw_gdt_start:
    # NULL descriptor                    (00)
    .byte    0x00, 0x00, 0x00, 0x00
    .byte    0x00, 0x00, 0x00, 0x00
    # 32 bit-code segment                (08)
code32_desc_start:
    .byte    0xFF, 0xFF, 0x00, 0x00
    .byte    0x00, 0x9B, 0xCF, 0x00
    # 32-bit data segment                (10)
data32_desc_start:
    .byte    0xFF, 0xFF, 0x00, 0x00
    .byte    0x00, 0x93, 0xCF, 0x00
```

Figure 5.3   NVRAM-based Protected Flat Model GDT

Note: Using a protected memory model prior to memory requires that the GDT resides in cache or in NVRAM. If it resides in NVRAM, the accessed attribute of each non-NULL descriptor must be set when building your NVRAM-based GDT, as the processor expects to be able to write to those attribute bits when those regions are accessed.

Switching to Protected Mode

Before the processor can be switched to protected mode, the software initialization code must load a minimum number of protected mode data structures and code modules into memory to support reliable operation of the processor in protected mode. These data structures include the following:

■ (Optional) Interrupt Descriptor Table (IDT).

■ GDT.

■ Code segment that contains the code to be executed when the processor switches to protected mode.

■ (Optional) One or more code modules that contain the necessary interrupt and exception handlers.

Software initialization code must also initialize the following system registers before a processor can be switched to protected mode.

- ■ Global Descriptor Table Registers (GDTRs).

- ■ (Optional) The Interrupt Descriptor Table Registers (IDTRs). This register can also be initialized immediately after switching to protected mode prior to enabling interrupts.

- ■ Control registers CR1 through CR4.

- ■ Memory Type Range Registers (MTRRs).

With these data structures, code modules, and system registers initialized, the processor can be switched to protected mode by following these steps:

1. Disable interrupts. A CLI instruction disables maskable hardware interrupts. Non-maskable interrupts (NMIs) can be disabled with external circuitry. (Software must guarantee that no exceptions or interrupts are generated during the mode switching operation.)

2. Execute the LGDT instruction to load the GDTR with the base address of the GDT.

3. Execute a MOV CR0 instruction that sets the PE flag.

4. Immediately following the MOV CR0 instruction, execute a far JMP or far CALL instruction. This operation is typically a far jump or call to the next instruction in the instruction stream.

5. After entering protected mode, the segment registers continue to hold the contents they had in real-address mode. The JMP or CALL instruction in step 4 resets the CS register. Reload segment registers DS, SS, ES, FS, and GS. If the ES, FS, and/or GS registers are not going to be used, load them with a null selector.

6. (Optional) Execute the LIDT instruction to load the IDTR with the address and limit of the protected-mode IDT.

7. Execute the STI instruction to enable maskable hardware interrupts and perform the necessary hardware operation to enable NMIs.

Switching Back to Real Mode

The boot loader may need to switch from protected mode back to real mode in order to run legacy option ROMs or to jump to a legacy OS loader. In order to switch back to real mode, perform the following steps:

1. Disable interrupts. A CLI instruction disables maskable hardware interrupts. Non-maskable interrupts can be disabled with external circuitry.

2. Transfer program control to a readable segment that has a limit of 64 Kbytes (0xFFFF). This operation loads the CS register with the segment limit required in real mode.

3. Load segment registers SS, DS, ES, FS, and GS with a selector for a descriptor containing the following values, which are appropriate for read mode:

   ■ Limit = 64 Kbytes (0xFFFF)

   ■ Byte granular (G = 0)

   ■ Expand up (E = 0)

   ■ Writable (W = 1)

   ■ Present (P = 1)

   ■ Base = any value

4. The segment registers must be loaded with non-null segment selectors or the segment registers will be unusable in read mode. Note that if the segment registers are not reloaded, execution continues using the descriptor attributes loaded during protected mode.

5. Clear the PE flag in the CR0 register to switch to real mode.

6. Execute a far JMP instruction to jump to a real mode program. This operation flushes the instruction queue and loads the appropriate base and access rights value into the CS register.

7. Load the SS, DS, ES, FS, and GS registers as needed by real mode code. If any of the registers are not going to be used in real mode, then write 0s to them.

8. Execute the STI instruction to enable maskable hardware interrupts and perform the necessary hardware operation to enable NMIs.

Detailed descriptions on how modes may be entered are documented in the *Intel® 64 and IA-32 Architectures Software Developer's Manual.*

Preparation for Memory Initialization

The following code is executed from the ROM/flash because memory is not available yet. It's desirable to have a small amount of code in this section, since executing from ROM is slow.

The following steps are taken to get the system ready to initialize memory:

■ Processor microcode update

■ Processor initialization

■ Chipset initialization

Processor Microcode Update

Intel architecture processors have the capability to correct errata by loading an Intel-supplied data block into the processor. The data block is called a microcode update. This section describes the mechanisms required to provide this feature during system initialization.

Each microcode update is designed for a specific processor or set of processors. To determine the correct microcode update to load, software must ensure that one of the processor signatures embedded in the microcode update matches the 32-bit processor signature returned by the CPUID instruction when executed by the target processor with EAX = 1. Attempting to load a microcode update that does not match a processor signature embedded in the microcode update with the processor signature returned by CPUID causes the processor to reject the update.

Processor Microcode Checksum

Each microcode update contains a checksum located in the update header. It is software's responsibility to ensure that a microcode update is not corrupt. To check for a corrupt microcode update, software must perform a checksum of the microcode update. For more details, see the *Intel® 64 and IA-32 Architectures Software Developer's Manual*.

Memory Initialization

Initialization of the memory subsystem is one of the most important tasks in the role of Intel architecture firmware. Execution out of NVRAM is slow; execution out of DRAM is fast.

MRC Technical Resources

Memory initialization for Intel platforms differs widely from chipset to chipset. The details about how to initialize the memory subsystem is considered restricted collateral. It comes in two forms:

■ Documentation (*BIOS/Firmware Writer's Guide*)

■ Memory initialization reference code (MRC)

The *BIOS/Firmware Writer's Guide* documents the steps required to initialize the memory subsystem as well as the boundaries/restrictions of the subsystem. This is useful for vendors that choose to write the memory initialization code themselves.

The MRC is distributed in different forms depending on the owning Intel division and the platform. Each form that may be available is a fully-functioning implementation of the algorithm in the *BIOS/Firmware Writer's Guide*. The MRC may be ported into any firmware stack with a minimal amount of effort. Since the MRC supports all technologies and configurations allowed on a platform, it is possible to trim down the MRC to fit a vendor's design in a minimal amount of code space. This is the vendor's responsibility and not directly supported by Intel.

MRC Dependencies

In order to use MRC distributed by Intel, care needs to be taken to provide the appropriate operating environment for the code. The operating environment requirements may include, but may not be limited to:

■ Processor operating mode

■ Cache configuration

■ Memory geometry information

MRC may be written to run in 16-bit real mode, 32-bit flat mode, or (unlikely) a 32-bit segmented mode. If the adopted code does not have the appropriate operating environment, performance cannot be guaranteed.

With the higher DRAM speeds and the need for chipset impedance and slew rate adjustments (RCOMP) and delay locked loop (DLL) calibration, typical chipsets do not have enough scratchpad space to use for calculations and bookkeeping in the register sets. Therefore, it is common for MRC to have cache configuration requirements, such that the MRC has a chalkboard to write these calculations on during initialization.

PC-based memory configurations are based on dual inline memory modules (DIMMs). These configurations are dynamically detectable through tiny EPROM chips on the DIMMs. These chips contain specification-defined information about the capability of the DRAM configuration on the DIMM, such as Serial Presence Detect (SPD) data, which is readable through an I2C interface. For chipsets that are intended to be used in PC-based systems and support DIMMs, the MRC usually has native SPD detection support included. For non-PC-based systems, it may not be present. In these configurations, it is required to hardcode the memory configuration or to provide access to the memory geometry information through any vendor-defined mechanism. For memory-down designs, it may be necessary to generate several bytes of SPD data based on the DRAM datasheets and the schematics for the platform, and provide that to the MRC.

All of these dependencies should be documented along with the code that comprises the MRC.

Post Memory Initialization

Certain initializations must be completed after MRC, but before jumping to and executing from memory. The following is a list of the initializations that should be performed:

■ Memory test

■ Shadow firmware

■ Memory transaction redirection (programmable attribute maps or PAMs)

■ Stack setup

■ Transfer to DRAM

Memory Test

The perfect time to attempt to perform some kind of memory integrity test is at the end of memory initialization. Some releases of MRC contain a memory test and some do not. BIOS vendors typically provide a memory test on a cold boot as well. Writing custom firmware requires the developer to choose a balance between thoroughness and speed since highly embedded/mobile devices require extremely fast boot times.

The reason why this is the best time to perform memory tests is because memory errors manifest themselves in very random ways, sometimes very inconsistently. If the memory integrity is not checked immediately after initializing memory the complexity of firmware debug increases immensely. The added complexity is caused by memory manipulation steps or firmware execution from DRAM, which is subject to corruption.

If a memory test is performed as part of the normal boot sequence, consideration should be given to the type of memory test that is executed. For systems that must have a very quick boot time, it doesn't make sense to exhaustively test all of memory. A light memory test that picks "smart" locations in memory to test, or maybe a memory test that tests signal-stressing patterns on physical DRAM device boundaries may be sufficient. It makes more sense to sacrifice boot time to perform a thorough stress test on all memory locations for server-based platforms that are used in mission-critical applications.

Firmware Shadow

The concept of shadowing is simple: take code from slow nonvolatile storage and copy it to DRAM because executing from DRAM is much faster. Cache misses, which cause frequent fetches to nonvolatile storage slow systems down greatly. Therefore, it is recommended that system firmware is copied from nonvolatile storage to DRAM as soon as possible, after memory is initialized. This way the nonvolatile latency hit only occurs once.

For PC-based systems, the shadow must be from nonvolatile storage to somewhere in the upper part of the lower 1 MB of system memory. For non-PC systems, the end location is arbitrary, and up to the vendor and the requirements of the overlying software stack. For most applications, it's recommended to keep firmware code below 1 MB.

Memory Transaction Redirection

Intel chipsets usually come with memory aliasing capabilities that allow reads and writes to sections of memory below 1 MB to be either routed to/from DRAM or nonvolatile storage located just under 4 GB. The registers that control this aliasing are typically referred to as programmable attribute maps (PAMs). Manipulation of these registers may be required before, during, and after firmware shadowing. The control over the redirection of memory access varies from chipset to chipset. For example, some chipsets allow control over reads and writes, while others only allow control over reads. Consult the chipset datasheet for details on the memory redirection feature controls applicable to the target platform.

Stack Setup

The stack must be set up before jumping into memory. A memory location must be chosen for stack space. The stack counts down so the top of the stack must be entered and enough memory must be allocated for the maximum stack.

If the system is in real mode, then SS:SP must be set with the appropriate values. If Protected Flat Mode is used, then SS:ESP must be set to the correct memory location.

Transfer to DRAM

This is where the code makes the jump into memory. As mentioned before, if a memory test has not been performed up until this point, the jump could very well be to uninitialized memory location. System failures indicated by a POST code (an I/O write to port 0x80 that displays the hexadecimal value on a seven segment display) between "end of memory initialization" and the first POST code that follows almost always indicates a catastrophic memory initialization problem.

Memory Caching Control

As opposed to simply being on or off, processor caches on Intel architecture platforms may be highly configured based on design needs. The layout of the cache configuration could be as simple or as complex as required. Regions may be discrete or overlapped. Care should be taken in setting up this cache configuration, because incorrect configuration is often the cause of obtuse errors that are difficult to debug.

Memory Type Range Registers (MTRRs)

The memory type range registers (MTRRs) control the caching characteristics of the regions of physical memory. They allow the type of caching (or no caching) to be specified in system memory for selected physical address ranges. They allow memory accesses to be optimized for various types of memory such as RAM, ROM, frame buffer memory, and memory-mapped I/O devices.

The MTRR mechanism allows up to 96 memory ranges to be defined in physical memory, and it defines a set of model-specific registers (MSRs) for specifying the type of memory that is contained in each range. Table 5.1 shows the memory types that can be specified and their properties.

Table 5.1   Memory Types That Can Be Encoded in MTRRs

Memory Type and Mnemonic	Encoding in MTRR
Uncacheable (UC)	00H
Write Combining (WC)	01H
Reserved*	02H
Reserved*	03H
Write-through (WT)	04H
Write-protected (WP)	05H
Writeback (WB)	06H
Reserved*	07H – FFH

Note:*Use of these encodings results in a general-protection exception (#GP).

The memory ranges and the types of memory specified in each range are set by three groups of registers: the IA32_MTRR_DEF_TYPE MSR, the fixed-range MTRRs, and the variable range MTRRs. These registers can be read and written to using the RDMSR and WRMSR instructions, respectively.

IA32_MTRR_DEF_TYPE MSR

The IA32_MTRR_DEF_TYPE MSR sets the default properties of the regions of physical memory that are not encompassed by MTRRs. The IA32_MTRR_DEF_TYPE MSR contains a fixed-range MTRR enable, an MTRR enable, and a default memory type.

Fixed Range MTRRs

The fixed memory ranges are mapped with 11 fixed-range registers of 64 bits each. Each of these registers is divided into 8-bit fields that are used to specify the memory type for each of the sub-ranges the register controls:

- *Register IA32_MTRR_FIX64K_00000.* Maps the 512-Kbyte address range from 0H to 7FFFFH. This range is divided into eight 64-KB sub-ranges.

- *Registers IA32_MTRR_FIX16K_80000 and IA32_MTRR_FIX16K_80000.* Map the two 128-KB address range from 80000H to BFFFFH. This range is divided into eight 16-Kbyte sub-ranges, 8 ranges per register.

■ *Registers IA32_MTRR_FIX4K_C0000 through IA32_MTRR_ FIX16K_F8000.* Map the eight 32-KB address range from C0000H to FFFFFH. This range is divided into sixty-four 4-KB sub-ranges, 8 ranges per register.

Variable Range MTRRs

The variable memory MTRRs permit software to specify the memory type for eight variable-size address ranges, using a pair of MTRRs for each range. The first entry in each pair (IA32_MTRR_PHYSBASEn) defines the base address and memory type for the range; the second entry (IA32_MTRR_ PHYSMASKn) contains a mask used to determine the address range. The *n* suffix indicates register pairs 0 through 7.

The *Intel® 64 and IA-32 Architectures Software Developer's Manual, Volume 3A* section "Memory Cache Control" contains all the details on configuring caching for all memory regions.

Safe Cache Setting

As stated before, memory regions that must have different caching behaviors applied will vary from design to design. In the absence of detailed caching requirements for a platform, the following guidelines in Table 5.2 provide a somewhat safe caching environment for typical systems:

Table 5.2   Safe Caching Configuration

Cache Region	Safe Rule
Default	Uncacheable (UC)
00000000-0009FFFF	Writeback (WB)
000A0000-000BFFFF	Write Combining (WC) or Uncacheable (UC)
000C0000-000FFFFF	Writeback (WB) or Write-protected (WP)
00100000-TopOfMemory	Writeback (WB)
TSEG	Uncacheable (UC)
Graphics Stolen Memory	Write Combining (WC) or Uncacheable (UC)
Hardware Memory-Mapped I/O	Uncacheable (UC)

See the appropriate chipset *BIOS/Firmware Writer's Guide* for caching control guidelines specific to the chipset.

Processor Discovery and Initialization

In order for the OS to be able to utilize all processors in the system, the firmware must detect and initialize them appropriately.

CPUID – Hardware Threads and Cores

Since Intel processors are packaged in various configurations, there are different terms that must be understood when considering processor initialization:

- *Hardware thread.* A logical processor that shares resources with another logical processor in the same physical package. This is also known as simultaneous multithreading (SMT). Intel's implementation of SMT is named Intel® Hyper-Threading Technology.

- *Core.* A processor that coexists with another processor in the same physical package that does not share any resources with other processors.

- *Package.* A "chip" that contains any number of cores and threads.

Hardware threads and cores on the same package are detectable by executing the CPUID instruction. See the *Intel® 64 and IA-32 Architectures Software Developer's Manual, Volume 2A* for details on the information available with the CPUID instruction on various processor families. Following a power-up or reset of a multiprocessor (MP) system, system hardware dynamically selects one of the processors on the system bus as the boot strap processor. The remaining processors are designated as application processors (APs).

The boot strap processor executes the BIOS / boot loader boot-strap code to configure the Advanced Programmable Interrupt Controller (APIC) environment, sets up system-wide data structures, and starts and initializes the APs. When the boot strap processorand APs are initialized, the boot strap processor then begins executing the operating-system initialization code.

Detection of additional packages may need to be done "blindly." If a design must accommodate more than one physical package, the boot strap processor needs to wait a certain amount of time for all potential APs in the system to "log in." Once a timeout occurs or the maximum expected number of processors "log in," it can be assumed that there are no more processors in the system.

Startup Inter-Processor Interrupt (SIPI)

In order to wake up secondary hardware threads or cores, the boot strap processor sends a SIPI to each hardware thread and core. This SIPI is sent by using the boot strap processor's LAPIC, indicating the physical address from which the application processor (AP) should start executing. This address must be below 1 MB of memory and be aligned on a 4-KB boundary.

AP Wakeup State

Upon receipt of the SIPI, the AP starts executing the code pointed to by the SIPI message. As opposed to the boot strap processor, when the AP starts code execution it is in real mode. This requires that the location of the code that the AP starts executing is located below 1 MB.

Wakeup Vector Alignment

The starting execution point of the AP has another architectural restriction that is very important and is commonly forgotten. The entry point to the AP initialization code must be aligned on a 4-KB boundary. For more details, refer to the *Intel® 64 and IA-32 Architectures Software Developer's Manual, Volume 3A* section "MP Initialization Protocol Algorithm for Intel Xeon Processors."

The *Intel® 64 and IA-32 Architectures Software Developer's Manual, Volume 3A* section "Typical AP Initialization Sequence" illustrates what is typically done by the APs after receiving the SIPI.

Caching Considerations

Because of the different types of processor combinations and different attributes of shared processing registers between hardware threads, care must be taken to ensure that the caching layout of all processors in the entire system remain consistent such that there are no caching conflicts.

The *Intel® 64 and IA-32 Architectures Software Developer's Manual, Volume 3A* contains a section labeled "MTRR Considerations in MP Systems" that outlines a safe mechanism for changing the cache configuration in all systems that contain more than one processor. It is recommended that this be used for any system with more than one processor present.

AP Idle State

Behavior of APs during firmware initialization is dependent on the firmware implementation, but is most commonly restricted to short durations of initialization followed by entering a halt state with a HLT instruction, awaiting direction from the boot strap processor for another operation.

Initialization

For most of the boot process, the APs don't really do all that much. What they have to do is program themselves to a desired configuration when it can't be done by another processor (the boot strap processor). Some processor resources are shared between hardware threads and some are not. Therefore, each AP needs to wake up to at least program the subset of desired platform features that it has control over. The processor *BIOS / Firmware Writer's Guides* document the topology/ownership of these features between hardware threads and cores in a single package. Separate packages must all be initialized as the package containing the boot strap processor.

Once the firmware is ready to attempt to boot an OS, all APs must be placed back in their power-on state ("Wait-for-SIPI"), which can be accomplished by the boot strap processor sending an INIT ASSERT IPI followed by an INIT DEASSERT IPI to all APs in the system (all except self). See the *Intel® 64 and IA-32 Architectures Software Developer's Manual, Volume 3A* for details on the INIT IPI, and the MultiProcessor Specification 1.4 for details on BIOS AP requirements.

Miscellaneous Platform Initialization

Miscellaneous things in the system must be configured in the boot loader for proper operation. The only way to know what has to be programmed is to review the schematics. The following things are typically required to be programmed, but it is platform dependent:

■ Clock chip programming

■ General purpose I/O (GPIO) Configuration

■ Interrupt routing

Clock Chip Programming

Refer to the schematics to determine the clock chip used and acquire the datasheet for that clock chip. Typically the clock chip is programmed through the SMBus. Refer to the SMBus controller for details on programming through the SMBus interface. The SMBus is typically found in the chipset on Intel architecture platforms.

GPIO Configuration

General purpose input/output (GPIO) pins are typically found inside an Intel chipset or in a super input/output (SIO) device.

In Intel chipsets, several functions can be multiplexed to a particular I/O pin. The configuration of the pins must be set before use. The pins are configured to be either a specific function or a general purpose I/O pin. I/O pins on the device are used to control logic/behavior on the device. General purpose I/O pins can be configured as input or output pins. On the Intel® System Controller Hub, for example, a GPIO may be used for a native for PROCHOT#.

The GPIO level may be configured for pins that are configured as outputs. Refer to the schematics to determine how to set the GPIOs for your specific platform.

Interrupt Routing

Interrupt routing is dependent on the platform. A white paper on Intel architecture IRQ routing is in the process of being authored and will be posted on the Intel® Embedded Design Center when it's finalized. Refer to this white paper for more details on interrupt routing when it becomes available.

Interrupt Enabling

Intel architecture has several different methods of interrupt handing. The following or a combination of the following can be used to handle interrupts:

- ■ Programmable Interrupt Controller (PIC) or 8259

- ■ Local Advanced Programmable Interrupt Controller (LAPIC)

- ■ Input/Output Advanced Programmable Interrupt Controller (IOxAPIC)

- ■ Messaged Signaled Interrupt (MSI)

Programmable Interrupt Controller (PIC)

Most Intel chipsets contain two cascaded 8259s with fifteen available IRQs. IRQ2 is not available since it is used to connect the 8259s.

Both PICs must be initialized by writing a four-byte sequence, Initialization Control Words (ICWs), to I/O memory location 20h for the master controller and A0h for the slave controller. For specifics on the values to be written refer to the appropriate Intel chipset datasheet.

Local Advanced Programmable Interrupt Controller (LAPIC)

The local APIC is contained inside the processor and controls the interrupt delivery to the processor. Each local APIC contains is own set of associated registers as well as a Local Vector Table (LVT). The LVT specifies the manner in which the interrupts are delivered to each processor core. Refer to the *Intel® 64 and IA-32 Architectures Software Developer's Manual* for more information on initializing the local APIC.

I/O Advanced Programmable Interrupt Controller (IOxAPIC)

The IOxAPIC is contained in the Integrated Controller Hub (ICH) / Integrated Output Hub (IOH) and expands the number of IRQs available to 24. Each IRQ has an associated redirection table entry that can be enabled/disabled and selects the IDT vector for the associated IRQ. This mode is only available when running in protected mode. Refer to the *Chipset BIOS / Firmware Writers Guide* for more information on initializing the IOxPIC.

Message Signaled Interrupt (MSI)

The boot loader does not typically use MSI for interrupt handling.

Processor Interrupt Modes

Intel architecture has several different interrupt modes that can be used for operation.

- PIC Mode

- Virtual Wire Mode

- Symmetric Mode

PIC Mode

When the PIC is the only interrupt device enabled, it is referred to as PIC Mode. This is the simplest mode where the PIC handles all the interrupts. All APIC components are bypassed and the system operates in single-thread mode using LINT0.

Virtual Wire Mode

Virtual Wire Mode uses one of the LAPICs to create a virtual wire and operates the same as PIC mode. Refer to the *Intel® 64 and IA-32 Architectures Software Developer's Manual, Volume 3A* for more details.

Symmetric Mode

Symmetric Mode uses both the I/OxAPIC and LAPICs to handle interrupts. This mode is not recommended for BIOS / boot loader. Refer to the *Intel® 64 and IA-32 Architectures Software Developer's Manual, Volume 3A* for more details and the *Chipset BIOS / Firmware Writer's Guide* for more details.

Interrupt Tables

On Intel architecture platforms, the interrupt table that will be used depends on whether the platform is in protected mode or real mode. When operating in real mode, the Interrupt Vector Table (IVT) is used. When operating in protected mode, the Interrupt Descriptor Table (IDT) is used.

Interrupt Vector Table

The Interrupt Vector Table is located at physical memory location 0x0 and contains 256 interrupt vectors. The IVT is used in real mode. Each vector address is 32 bits and consists of the CS:IP for the interrupt vector.

Interrupt Descriptor Table

The Interrupt Descriptor Table contains the exceptions/interrupts in protected mode. There are also 256 interrupt vectors and the exceptions/interrupts defined in the same locations as the IVT. Refer to the *Intel® 64 and IA-32 Architectures Software Developer's Manual, Volume 3A* for a detailed description of the IDT.

Interrupt Entries

On Intel architecture platforms, an IDT and an IVT are filled out with exception handlers and interrupt service routines. When using an IVT, real mode interrupt service routines are used. When operating in protected mode, the IDT is utilized and 32-bit interrupt service routines are used.

Exceptions

Exceptions are routines that run to handle error conditions. Examples include page faults and general protection faults. At a minimum placeholders (dummy functions) should be used for each exception handler. Otherwise the system could exhibit unwanted behavior if an exception is encountered that isn't handled. Refer to the *Intel® 64 and IA-32 Architectures Software Developer's Manual, Volume 3A* section "Exception and Interrupt Reference" for a list of real mode interrupts and exceptions.

Real Mode Interrupt Service Routines (ISRs)

Real mode ISRs are used to communicate information between the boot loader and the OS. For example INT10h is used for video services such as changing video modes, and resolution. Some legacy programs and drivers assume these real mode ISRs are available and directly call the INT routine.

Video Output Selection

Several options are available for video output selection. The features desired and speed requirements vary among the different options. The sections below provide more details.

Splash Screen Support

A splash screen is a bit image that hides the diagnostic information behind a bitmap during the boot process. The image is commonly a company logo or any other image that the product vendor deems suitable. It is common for firmware to use splash screens in order to give the user something to look at during the boot process.

Splash screens are popular for embedded systems where the user is accustomed to some type of feedback as soon as the system is turned on. A set top box is an example of this. If the user does not get almost immediate visual feedback that indicates the system is starting up they might assume that something is wrong. The Embedded Pre-OS Graphics† (EPOG) video driver provides splash screen functionality for system initialization designs based on Intel architecture custom boot loaders.

Information about which platforms support splash screens is documented at the Intel® Embedded Design Center (EDC) in the *Intel® Embedded Graphics Drivers Version 10.3.1 Feature Matrix*.

Embedded Pre-OS Graphics (EPOG) Driver

EPOG is a graphics driver that provides a graphics initialization and configuration option for the Intel architecture custom boot loader environment. EPOG is a driver built from the Intel® Embedded Graphics Driver (IEGD) family of drivers. EPOG is a lightweight fast graphics initialization driver. It fully initializes the graphics chipset to allow frame buffer access and use (that is, set display modes, draw graphics, and so on). EPOG is similar to traditional Intel architecture Video BIOS (vBIOS) such that they both initialize the graphics devices and make the ability available for the rest of the system (such as the BIOS, boot loader, and operating system). EPOG is different in that, unlike vBIOS, it's 32-bit, it does not support vBIOS style INT 10h handlers, and it's been developed to allow for quick initialization for embedded markets. EPOG's primary objectives are to support the Intel architecture custom boot loader environment and provide a speedy graphics option, which embedded developers can use to quickly set up output to their graphics device.

Additionally, like other IEGD drivers, EPOG is highly configurable using the Configuration Editor (CED) tool. Using CED, EPOG can be tweaked to create a custom driver. Options can be configured such that:

- Display can be configured to single, twin, or clone support.

- Panel timings can be adjusted to use extended display identification data (EDID) or custom detailed timing descriptors (DTDs).

- Enabled ports and port order can be configured, such as low-voltage differential signaling (LVDS), Serial Digital Video Out (SDVO), and Analog.

- Panel attributes such as intensity, backlight, and customer panel specifics can be modified.

- Splash screen support can also be enabled, utilizing a custom user-specified bitmap.

EPOG is available to the Intel architecture custom boot loaders in the form of a library (libepog.a). This library is created from configuration utilities in the Intel® Embedded Media and Graphics Driver package.

Extensible Firmware Interface Graphics Output Protocol

Extensible Firmware Interface (EFI) Graphics Output Protocol (GOP) is an EFI-based graphics initialization and configuration option also available via the IEGD family of drivers. EFI GOP provides similar functionality to the EPOG except that it supports EFI. Like EPOG, EFI provides what is called a Fast Boot option for speedier boot execution. EFI would be the option to consider for EFI-based environments. In contrast, EPOG would be used for Intel architecture custom boot loader based environments. EFI GOP is just as configurable as EPOG, with some additional EFI specific options. Configuration is also available through CED.

Video BIOS (vBIOS)

Video BIOS (vBIOS) is the traditional graphics initialization and configuration that has existed on PC platforms for years. Similar to EFI and EPOG, vBIOS is highly configurable via the CED tool, and is also available as part of the IEGD family of drivers. However, unlike EPOG or EFI, vBIOS is 16-bit code. Additionally, it does provide INT 10h support for many current and legacy operating systems, which expect to draw text and accomplish pre-driver graphics manipulation.

Headless Operation

Headless operation is when a system does not have a use for video output display. The system could be remotely managed and therefore providing video output at the system itself would be unnecessary. In this instance, no vBIOS or splash screen is necessary. This may result in both a smaller image size and faster boot speed.

Timers

Intel architecture contains several timers that can be used for many purposes and depend on the functions and features of a particular platform. The following are the different timers that are available on current Intel architecture platforms.

■ Programmable Interrupt Timer (PIT)

■ High Precision Event Timer (HPET)

■ Real-Time Clock (RTC)

■ System Management TCO Timer

Programmable Interrupt Timer (PIT)

The PIT (8254) resides in the chipset and contains the system timer also referred to as IRQ0. Refer to the chipset datasheet for more details.

High Precision Event Timer (HPET)

HPET resides in the chipset and contains three timers. Typically the boot loader does not need to do any initialization of High Precision Event Timer (HPET) and the functionality is used only by the OS. Refer to the *Chipset BIOS Writers Guide* for more details.

Real -Time Clock (RTC)

The RTC resides in the chipset and contains the system time (seconds, minutes, hours, and so on). These values are contained in a complimentary metal-oxide semiconductor (CMOS) circuit, which is explained later in the chapter. The RTC also contains a timer that can be utilized by Firmware. Refer to the appropriate chipset datasheet for more details.

System Management TCO Timer

The TCO timers reside in the chipset and contain the Watch Dog Timer (WDT). The WDT can be used to detect system hangs and will reset the system.

Note: It is important to note that for debugging any type of firmware on Intel architecture chipsets that implement a TCO Watch Dog Timer that it should be disabled by firmware as soon as possible coming out of reset. Halting the system, for debug prior to disabling this Watch Dog Timer on chipsets that power-on with this timer enabled, will result in system resets, which doesn't allow firmware debug. The OS will re-enable the Watch Dog if it so desires. Consult the chipset datasheet for details on the specific implementation of the TCO Watch Dog Timer.

Refer to the *Chipset BIOS Writers Guide* for more details.

Local APIC (LAPIC) Timer

The Local APIC contains a timer that can be used by firmware. Refer to the *Intel® 64 and IA-32 Architectures Software Developer's Manual, Volume 3A* for a detailed description of the Local APIC timer.

I/O Devices

Refer to the board schematics to determine which I/O devices are in the system. Typically a system contains one or more of the following devices.

Embedded Controller (EC)

An embedded controller is typically used in mobile or low power systems. The EC contains separate firmware that controls the power management functions for the system as well as PS2 keyboard functionality. Refer to the specific embedded controller (EC) data sheet for more details.

Super I/O (SIO)

An SIO typically controls the PS2, serial, parallel, and other such interfaces. Most systems still support some of the legacy interfaces rather than implementing a legacy-free system. Refer to the specific SIO datasheet for details on programming information.

Legacy Free Systems

Legacy free systems use Universal Serial Bus (USB) as the input device. If pre-OS keyboard support is required, then the legacy keyboard interfaces must be trapped. Refer to the *BIOS / Firmware Writer's Guide* for more details on legacy-free systems.

Miscellaneous I/O Devices

There may be other I/O devices that require initialization by the boot loader. Refer to the datasheets of those devices for programming information.

Peripheral Component Interconnect (PCI) Device Discovery

PCI device discovery is a generic term that refers to detecting which PCI compliant devices are in the system. The discovery process assigns the resources needed by each device including the following:

- I/O space

- Memory mapped I/O (MMIO) space

■   IRQ assignment

■   Expansion ROM detection and execution

PCI device discovery applies to all the newer (non-legacy) interfaces such as PCI Express (PCIe), USB, Serial ATA (SATA), and Serial Peripheral Interface (SPI) devices. These newer interfaces are controlled by controllers that comply with the PCI specification.

Refer to the PCI Specification for more details. A list of all the applicable specifications is in the References section.

Resource Allocation

Resource allocation is the method of searching through the possible range of buses, devices, and functions.

When a Vendor ID (VID) or Device ID (DID) is found that is not all 0xFFFFs, then resources are defined as follows:

1.   Write all 0xFFFFFFFFs to all Base Address Registers (BARs). Read the BAR back. Bit 0 will give an indication as to whether this is an MMIO or I/O request.

   a.   If MMIO is requested (bit 0 is a 0), then the value read back indicates how much memory is requested. Reserve the appropriate memory and write the address assigned into the BAR.

   b.   If I/O is requested (bit 0 is a 1), then the value read back indicates how many bytes of I/O are requested. Reserve that amount of I/O and write the I/O address assigned to the BAR.

2.   IRQs

   a.   Refer to the schematics to determine how the IRQ routing should occur for any PCI or PCIe slots or onboard devices.

   b.   For chipset PCI devices, the routing may be pre-determined in the chipset datasheet. Some chipsets allow control of the internal routing as well. Refer to the chipset datasheet for more details.

    c.   There are multiple things involved in IRQ routing when using the PIC. The devices are assigned to INTA–INTD, which in turn gets assigned to PIRQA–PIRQH, which gets mapped to IRQs in chipset-specific registers (0x60–0x63, 0x68–0x6B). Refer to the chipset *BIOS Writers Guide* and chipset datasheet for more details.

3.   Read the expansion ROM address register. If it is nonzero, then there is an expansion ROM (also referred to as an option ROM, or OROM) that needs to be executed. An option ROM is an executable binary written in real mode provided by hardware vendors. Some PCI or PCIe cards contain option ROMs that must be executed by the boot loader in order for the hardware to work once the OS loads. In some cases, an option ROM may need to be included as part of the boot loader image. This is necessary if hardware requiring an option ROM is designed on the board. In order to save cost, the board manufacturer may decide not to include ROM storage.

    a.   Video BIOS (vBIOS) is handled differently than typical OROMs. Typically it is executed prior to PCI enumeration in order to give certain display devices time to warm up. The vBIOS is 16-bit code that needs to run in real mode. The boot loader loads the vBIOS at C000:0 and jumps to address C000:3.

    b.   Typical OROMs get loaded after the vBIOS starting at C800:0 and can continue up to E000:0. This limits the number and size of OROMs that can exist in a particular system.

    c.   There are OROMs that are also bootable, such as Ethernet OROMs that have PXE support.

Booting a Legacy OS

Booting a legacy OS (non-EFI) consists of loading the first stage OS or OS boot loader in to memory location 0x07C0:0000 and jumping to that location while the processor is in real mode. The BIOS Boot Specification specifies the handoff behavior for legacy BIOS in great detail.

Master Boot Record (MBR)

The MBR is located on the first sector of a partitioned mass storage device. The first 446 bytes of the MBR contain the OS loader, which contains both executable code and error message text. The next 64 bytes are the partition table, which contains a record for each of four partitions (sixteen bytes each). The MBR ends with two bytes that are defined as the magic number (0xAA55). The magic number serves as a validation check of the MBR.

OS Handover Requirements

Depending on the desired features that are enabled by the boot loader, there are different tables that the OS needs. The following is a list of those tables:

- Memory map (INT15h / Function E820h)

- Programmable Interrupt Routing ($PIR) Table

- Multi-Processor Specification (_MP_) Table

- Simple Firmware Interface (SFI) Tables

- Advanced Configuration and Power Interface (ACPI) Tables

Memory Map

In addition to defining the caching behavior of different regions of memory, for consumption by the OS, it is also firmware's responsibility to provide a map of the system memory to the OS so that it knows what regions are actually available for its consumption.

The most widely used mechanism for a boot loader or an OS to determine the system memory map is to use real mode interrupt service 15h, function E8h, sub-function 20h (INT15/E820), which firmware must implement. One example of this is detailed at http://www.uruk.org/orig-grub/mem64mb.html.

Region Types

There are several general types of memory regions that are described by this interface:

■ *Memory (1)*. General DRAM available for OS consumption.

■ *Reserved (2)*. DRAM address not for OS consumption.

■ *ACPI Reclaim (3)*. Memory that contains all ACPI tables to which firmware does not require runtime access. See the applicable ACPI specification for details.

■ *ACPI NVS (4)*. Memory that contains all ACPI tables to which firmware requires runtime access. See the applicable ACPI specification for details.

■ *ROM (5)*. Memory that decodes to nonvolatile storage (such as flash).

■ *IOAPIC (6)*. Memory that is decoded by IOAPICs in the system (must also be uncached).

■ *LAPIC (7)*. Memory that is decoded by Local APICs in the system (must also be uncached).

Region Locations

The following regions are typically reserved in a system memory map:

■ 00000000-0009FFFF – Memory

■ 000A0000-000FFFFF – Reserved

■ 00100000-???????? – Memory (The ???????? indicates that the top of memory changes based on "reserved" items listed below and any other design-based reserved regions.)

■ TSEG – Reserved

■ Graphics Stolen Memory – Reserved

■ FEC00000-FEC01000* – IOAPIC

■ FEE00000-FEE01000* – LAPIC

See the applicable chipset *BIOS / Firmware Writer's Guide* for details on chipset-specific memory map requirements. See the appropriate ACPI specification for details on ACPI-related memory map requirements.

Nonvolatile Memory Types

Nonvolatile memory does not require power to retain stored information. There are two types of nonvolatile storage in typical Intel architecture systems that are used by BIOS or boot loaders: CMOS and flash.

Complementary Metal-Oxide Semiconductor (CMOS)

CMOS is part of the RTC and consists of two banks of 128 bytes each for a total of 256 bytes. The first 14 bytes are reserved for the RTC data. The rest of the bytes are available for any data that needs retained after the system is powered-off. The typical things that are stored are setup options, such as to allow the user to select the primary boot device. Refer to the chipset datasheet for more details on CMOS and the RTC.

Nonvolatile Flash

Flash can also be used to store nonvolatile data as well. The boot loader must have routines to erase and write the data if flash is to be used. Refer to the specific flash datasheet for more details.

Programmable Interrupt Routing ($PIR) Table

The $PIR table is almost always needed. Details on the $PIR table may be found in the $PIR Specification.

MultiProcessor Specification (_MP_) Table

The _MP_ table is needed if there is more than one Intel processing agent (hardware thread or core) in the system. Details on the _MP_ table may be found in the MultiProcessor Specification.

Simple Firmware Interface (SFI) Tables

The Simple Firmware Interface is defined as minimal requirements needed in order to support an ACPI-aware OS. The SFI tables are only needed if those features are enabled by the boot loader and required by the OS. Refer to the Simple Firmware Interface Specification for more details.

Advanced Configuration and Power Interface (ACPI) Tables

ACPI is used to communicate device configuration and power management capabilities to the OS. The ACPI tables are only needed if those features are enabled by the boot loader and required by the OS. Refer to the Advanced Configuration and Power Interface Specification for more details.

Intel® Atom™ Processor System Simplified Boot Flow Diagram

Figure 5.4 shows a diagram for the system simplified boot flow process discussed in this section. It depicts each step of the process along with decisions that need to be made and the end states. The color code for the process steps is as follows: white is required, blue is optional, red is fault, and green depicts system initialization success.

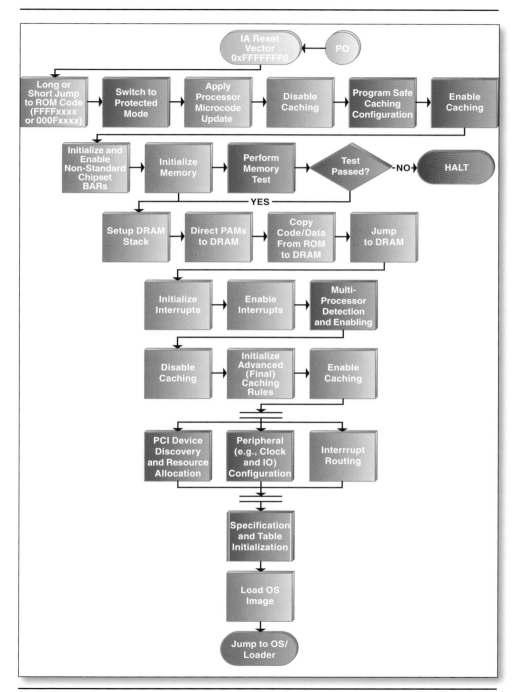

Figure 5.4   Intel® Architecture System Simplified Boot Flow Process

Summary

This chapter discussed the roles and responsibilities of system initialization, and solutions choices for Intel architecture for closed box and open box designs. The choices include custom boot loaders and Basic Input/Output System (BIOS). In addition, the mystery of the system initialization steps required to boot an Intel Atom processor-based system was unveiled. Understanding the system requirements for boot speed, boot loader size, and the amount of configurability will determine which solution is best for a given architecture migration. The list of documents required to implement an Intel Atom processor boot loader is provided in the "References" section.

Chapter **6**

Choosing the Right Operating System

*When one bases his life on principle, 99 percent of his
decisions are already made.*

—Author Unknown

Every architecture migration faces the question of which operating system
will be used. The answer may be as simple as the same operating system
used in the current platform. The answer may be obscure in the case of bare
metal systems where one could claim that no operating system is involved.
Regardless, even in these bare metal systems, there is some software that is
performing functionality associated with an operating system.

For embedded systems targeting the Intel® Atom™ processor, there
are numerous choices of operating systems, each offering a different set of
capabilities. Some operating systems are tuned for the embedded market
segments and offer features typically associated with or required by embedded
devices such as real-time capability and kernel image customization. Some
developers choose to employ mainstream operating systems such as desktop
Linux in their embedded systems and take advantage of the wealth of software
available for the platform. Whatever the operating system choice may be,
developers should understand their options and reasons for choosing.

In choosing an operating system, part of the decision process involves
understanding if a given operating system has the features required by the
embedded application. The potential requirements of the application that

intersect with operating system functionality can be categorized along these five groupings:

■ Power and performance requirements

■ Architecture requirements

■ Embedded specific requirements

■ General operating system requirements

■ Licensing requirements

Once you have narrowed the choices of operating system down to the ones that meet your unique requirements, you now need to finalize the selection. Making this choice involves a measure of which operating system best matches the requirements as well as offering unique features that differentiate one operating system from the next. Knowledge of these unique value-add features is also required.

This chapter details a process for operating system selection for an embedded development project. The chapter first details your options and a thought process to use in making a first pass assessment. Five categories of requirements are then discussed providing criteria to measure each of your operating system options. Five options are then discussed taking note of the specific challenges in porting to each. An overview of commercial and open source operating systems is provided with a mention of features that provide differentiation. The specific operating systems discussed in this chapter do not represent a comprehensive list, but are representative of the different types.

Options in Choosing an Operating System

An embedded development project may be entirely new activity involving creation of a top to bottom hardware and software platform. In many cases, likely the majority of them, the project involves porting and extending an existing hardware and software platform. Meeting a schedule and minimizing risk is often an overriding priority. Therefore, choosing an operating system can be a question of how much change one is willing to bear given the opportunity.

The options in selecting an operating system are listed in Table 6.1. As hinted in the previous paragraph, one method of minimizing risk and time to market is to employ the same operating system used currently if it is available for the Intel Atom processor. This option minimizes risk as it is likely that many of the same features and functionality available for one target platform will be made available for another. The vendor that produces the operating system is typically motivated to keep differences between the operating system on different platforms to a minimum in order to minimize testing, validation, and production complexity.

Table 6.1   Options in Operating System Selection

Option	Description
1. Same operating system	Use the same operating system if it is available for the Intel® Atom™ processor.
2. Port proprietary operating system	Port your proprietary operating system to execute on the Intel Atom processor.
3. Real-time operating system	Adopt a real-time operating system if specifically required by your application.
4. Embedded operating system	Adopt an operating system customized for use in embedded applications.
5. Desktop operating system	Adopt a generally available desktop operating system and its wealth of software.

The second option, porting a proprietary operating system, may be required in cases involving large amounts of legacy software customized to a specific, internally developed operating system. Porting a proprietary operating system is a large undertaking and should only be pursued if a more mainstream operating system cannot meet your needs. It may be possible to port the operating system and obtain basic functionality today, however new Intel technology features requiring operating system support are continually being developed. Taking advantage of these new technologies would require continued implementation and support by the proprietary operating system; this is no small undertaking by any means.

Embedded applications often have requirements for real-time response. Operating systems play a role in helping an embedded system meet its real-time requirements. If your application requires real-time response, choosing an embedded real-time operating system will be likely.

If real-time response is not required, but some level of customization is needed, an embedded operating system may suit your needs. An embedded application may not require every piece of functionality available in the processor. For example, some embedded applications are headless, running with no display. In these cases, operating system customization that enables creation of an embedded image without video support would cut down on the size of the image. Image size can be important in space and memory constrained devices.

The final option is to choose a generally available desktop operating system. The advantage of choosing this type of operating system is the breadth of software available. If your embedded system could take advantage of software that is supported on these desktop operating systems, the choice of a desktop operating system is natural. The disadvantage of employing a desktop operating system is one of generality; the operating system may contain functionality not required in your embedded application. This may add overhead in the operating system and reduce performance.

System Requirements

Your embedded application has a set of requirements which in turn place constraints on the operating system that you end up choosing. These system requirements are intended to be met by features of the operating system. Each operating system offers a unique set of features and capabilities which must be understood before finalizing your selection. These features and capabilities are grouped into five categories which are summarized in Table 6.2.

Table 6.2   Operating System Features

Features	Description
1. Performance and Power	Response time, process architecture, scheduling, and power management capabilities.
2. Architecture	ISA, memory size, Intel technology support.
3. Embedded specific	Customization features, standards support.
4. General OS features	Networking, debugging, security, graphics support.
5. Licensing and Support	Commercial, open source, and technical support models.

Performance and Power Requirements

Performance and power capabilities of an operating system span numerous categories such as boot-up time, shutdown time, context switch time, memory bandwidth, I/O bandwidth, real-time deadlines, and application execution time. No single industry standard benchmark is available to test all of the performance characteristics of an operating system. Instead, an expert opinion on the capabilities of an operating system should be formed based upon the following inputs:

■ Collateral from operating system vendor or provider

■ In house or low level benchmarks

■ Selective industry standard benchmarks

■ Power management capabilities

Operating System Fundamental Capabilities

The first input on operating system performance capabilities is obtained by reviewing basic information on the operating system with respect to the following qualities:

■ Real-time support

■ Multiprocessing

■ Multitasking

■ Scheduling

Real-time support is the ability of the operating system to meet deterministic deadlines imposed by the designer of the system. Real-time deadlines can be classified into two categories, hard deadlines and soft deadlines. *Hard real-time* is where missing a deadline would be catastrophic to the system. *Soft real-time* is where missing a deadline results in lower performance, but is not catastrophic. An example of a hard real-time requirement would be an embedded system running an air-traffic control system where a missed deadline could result in a life-threatening accident. A soft real-time example is maintaining a frame-rate threshold on a video decoder where missing a deadline would result in lower performance, but would typically not be catastrophic.

Multiprocessing is the ability of an operating system to take advantage of multiple processor cores in the system. Chapter 5 discusses the boot process for a multiprocessor system. Chapter 9 discusses different types of multiprocessing.

Multitasking is the ability of an operating system to execute multiple processes concurrently. Many, if not most, modern operating systems enable multitasking; however some operating systems do not. Operating systems may offer several types of multitasking such as preemptive or cooperative. *Preemptive multitasking* is where the operating system kernel manages which process executes and periodically interrupts a running process to enable a different process to execute. *Cooperative multitasking* is where individual processes manage giving up control of the processor and the kernel determines who executes next. The choice of multitasking or not and preemptive or cooperative scheduling has impact in the run time responsiveness of a given operating system.

In a multitasking operating system, the kernel manages scheduling and there are several types of scheduling of which to become aware as they impact the response time. A few of the common scheduling algorithms are described as follows:

- Priority – Enables processing time to be apportioned based on some assessment of process importance.

- Round robin – Enables processing time to be apportioned in equal amounts between processes.

- First in, first out (FIFO) – emphasizes servicing processes in the order spawned.

General purpose operating systems typically use a priority-based scheduling algorithm. Embedded operating systems, particularly real-time operating systems, typically enable a configurable scheduler tuned to the device's unique needs.

In-House or Low Level Benchmarks

The in-house or low level benchmarks should target performance of specific operating system capabilities. For example, the LMBench[1] benchmark measures context switch times across a number of different processes and process sizes. The benchmark measures communication latency using various communications protocols such as UDP, RPC, and TCP. File system latency and memory operation times are also measured. Figure 6.1 shows a portion of the output from LMBench executing on an Intel Atom processor. This sort of benchmark provides an idea of which operating system is efficient and tuned for the platform under consideration. "Measuring Cache and Memory Latency and CPU to Memory Bandwidth" (Ruggiero) shows how to use LMBench for cache and memory evaluation.

If your application has real-time constraints, benchmarking for real-time performance is required. No industry standard benchmark exists for testing real-time performance so you will either need to develop an in house test or rely on benchmarks available online such as the Thread-Metric RTOS Test Suite[2], that test some aspects of real-time performance.

Processor, Processes - times in microseconds - smaller is better

Host	CS	Mhs	null call	null I/O	stat	open clos	slct TCP	sig inst	sig hndl	fork proc	erec proc	sh proc
localhost:	Linux 2.6.30.	1565	0.52	0.66	5.69	6.67	10.5	1.21	5.15	649.	2351	10.K

Context switching - times in microseconds - smaller is better

Host	CS	2p/0K ctrsw	2p/16K ctrsw	2p/64K ctrsw	6p/16K ctrsw	6p/64K ctrsw	16p/16K ctrsw	16p/64K ctrsw
localhost:	Linux 2.6.30.	3.9700	6.4500	6.3600	7.5700	16.2	12.6	17.2

Figure 6.1 LMBench Output

---

[1] For further information on LMBench, see http://www.bitmover.com/lmbench
[2] For further information on Thread-Metric RTOS Test Suite, see ftp://ftp.embedded.com/pub/2007/05Carbone_ThreadMetric/TM_CMP.zip

Industry Standard Benchmarks

Industry standard benchmarks can help assess the performance of an operating system executing on your target platform. A good summary of various industry standard benchmarks pertinent to the embedded market segments is in Chapter 3 of *Software Development for Embedded Multi-core Systems: A Practical Guide Using Embedded Intel Architecture* (Domeika).

The following benchmarks are some commonly employed benchmarks for embedded platform performance evaluation:

■ SPEC CPU2006

■ EEMBC Benchmark Suites

■ BDTI Benchmark Suites

Standard Performance Evaluation Corporation (SPEC) 2006 is a widely used desktop and server benchmark for evaluating platform performance and consists of several C, C++, and Fortran applications. Both integer and floating-point performance is evaluated. SPEC CPU2006 has system requirements that may be out of the range of some embedded devices so may not be a perfect fit for evaluating your options.

The Embedded Microprocessor Benchmark Consortium (EEMBC) creates benchmarks targeting embedded market segments including automotive, consumer, digital entertainment, networking, storage, and telecommunications. The benchmarks tend to be smaller in size than SPEC CPU2006 benchmarks and enable use on very low level embedded systems. The benchmarks also allow modification to the benchmark source code to enable use of accelerators, something common in embedded applications. EEMBC has also created benchmarks to assess multi-core processor performance (Multibench†) and energy performance (EnergyBench†).

The BDTI Benchmark Suites target digital signal processing. The Benchmark Suites themselves are not represented by source code, but by requirements and functionality that an application must meet. This gives the developer the ability to fully customize the hardware and software stack for the application. BDTI would then perform the analysis and certification of the platform and performance results. In this regard, this model of benchmarking is well tuned to the embedded market segments where the application code is developed in conjunction with the hardware and should be evaluated together.

Power Management Capabilities

Operating systems enable control over various power saving modes. These can be as simple as turning off the display after several seconds of idleness. They can be complicated as seen in the variety of demand-based scheduling schemes observed in the latest low power processors including the Intel Atom processor. Chapter 3 summarized the Intel Atom processor power states and ACPI.

Three questions to consider when evaluating the power management capabilities of an operating system are:

- Does the operating system enable configuration of power saving modes by the developer? Examples are control of the display and I/O devices after a specified timeout.

- Does the operating system enable the developer to request sleep state (C-state) levels from the processor?

- Does the operating system enable demand-based scheduling, whereby the processor can go into a lower performance state (P-state) based upon expected and desired application performance?

Architecture Requirements

The next set of requirements in evaluating potential operating systems involves access to Intel architecture capabilities. The various Intel Atom processor models are IA-32 ISA compatible and several versions, but not all, are Intel 64 ISA compatible. However, support and access to these capabilities is enabled through the operating system. Table 6.3 summarizes the architecture requirements.

Table 6.3   Architecture Requirements

Requirement	Description and OS impact
Processor Modes	Support for 32-bit real and protected mode. Support for 64-bit long modes. All IA-32 and Intel 64 ISA processors boot in real mode. Setting of mode is a privileged instruction.
Memory Addressing	Support for 32-bit, 36-bit PAE, and Intel 64 ISA memory addressing. Operating system sets up page tables and memory management mechanisms.

Instruction set	Operating system queries and sets MSRs to enable support. Saves and restores registers on context switches.
Intel® Technology	Intel® Technology features such as Intel® Hyper-Threading Technology require operating system support.
Performance monitoring	Setting and reading counters require privileged access.

Details on several of these requirements were provided in previous chapters. It is important that if you require these capabilities in your embedded application that your operating system support them.

Key questions to answer when evaluating an operating system are:

■ Does the operating system support 36-bit Physical Address Extensions (PAE)?

■ Does the operating system support the 64-bit long modes?

■ Does the operating system support the IA-32 and Intel 64 ISA register sets, including Intel® Streaming SIMD Extensions (Intel SSE)?

■ Does the operating system support various Intel technologies? Which ones?

■ Does the operating system vendor provide a Hypervisor? Does the operating system support being a client OS?

■ What level of support is there for performance monitoring? Are there tools to support reading the performance monitoring counters?

Performance monitoring facilities provide a mechanism of understanding how your application code is executing on a given architecture. The Intel Atom processor supports both the basic time stamp counter and more advanced performance monitoring capability. The time stamp counter enables relative times to be measured, incrementing once per clock cycle. The time stamp counter is accessed by executing the RDTSC instruction, which returns a 64-bit value in registers eax and edx. Note: the time stamp counter increments at the rate of the highest P-state even if the processor is running in a lower P-state. Therefore, the actual number of clock cycles reported by RDTSC may be higher than if the application was executing when the processor was in a higher P-state.

Performance monitoring counters enable the measurement of processor events such as cache misses, branch mispredictions, and instruction decode stalls. Chapter 8 provides details on Intel Atom processor-specific events to assist in performance analysis.

Further details on architecture features are in the *Intel Architecture Software Developer's Manual, Volume 3: System Programming Guide*.

Embedded Specific Requirements

Some operating systems provide features that specifically aid embedded system development and can help you meet your requirements. Examples of these features are summarized as follows:

- Package selection – Enables developers to pick specific software components to include in the embedded image. Enables smaller image size and greater performance.

- Board Support Package – Boot and operating system image tailored to a specific embedded platform.

- Embedded Standards Support – Support for industry standard technology targeted to embedded applications.

- Fast boot support – Enables quick boot times, which is a critical feature in many embedded applications.

- Integrated Development Environment (IDE) – IDEs provide support for all aspects of the embedded development lifecycle.

Package Selection

Many embedded systems have strict form factor and size constraints. The difference between fitting the embedded software into a 128-KB ROM or a 64-KB ROM can have an impact on BOM price and impact profit for a high volume device. The embedded market segments are much more sensitive to this kind of cost. Therefore, many embedded operating systems offer the ability to customize the operating system image that executes on the target device. For example, if the embedded system does not make use of USB or networking, then support for these devices can be removed from the embedded image.

Many embedded operating systems offer profiles specific to the target device, comprised of preconfigured components. For example, Wind River Linux 3.0 offers prebuilt profiles targeting consumer electronics, carrier grade telecommunications, industrial equipment, and mobile devices.

Board Support Package

A board support package is a set of software elements comprising boot and operating system that is specific for a particular embedded development board. The board support package serves two purposes: first, it provides developers preconfigured software to begin development on a target, and second, it improves performance because the board support package includes software components specialized for one target. So for example, if the hardware platform included a SD card slot, the board support package would include an SD card driver.

Embedded Standards Support

Industry standards embody sets of requirements and enable developers' choice in selecting tools or technology that supports a particular standard. Embedded standards available for operating systems cover areas such as language support, reliability, and security. Several of these standards are summarized in Table 6.4.

Table 6.4   Embedded OS Standards

Standard	Description
POSIX	Portable Operating System Interface for Unix defines API, shell, and utilities for operating systems.
ISO/IEC 15408 EAL	International standard for computer security certification, Evaluation Assurance Level (EAL).
FAA/RTCA DO-178B Level A	Software standard in Airborne Systems and Equipment Certification.
IEC 61508	International standard for functional safety of programmable electronic systems.
ARINC 653	Avionics Application Standard Software Interface – for space and time partitioning.
Carrier Grade Linux (CGL)	Telecommunications Linux OS standard around availability, scalability, manageability, and service response.
SELinux	Access control standard.

Fast Boot Support

Intel architecture has its roots in desktop computing and BIOS support that required broad configurability. Fast boot support has been enabled for several systems based on the Intel Atom processor, relying on the fact that in embedded devices, the configuration of the system is specified as part of development. The fast boot support makes assumptions about which features of a traditional BIOS are necessary. Table 6.5 summarizes some of the modifications made to reduce the time it takes to boot using traditional BIOS to a fraction of a second[3] .

Table 6.5   Difference between Fast Boot BIOS and Traditional BIOS

Boot Up Step	Description
Turn off debugging	Compile BIOS code with optimizations.
Decrease flash size	Minimizes access times to Pre-EFI initialization module.
Cache PEI phase	Enable cache to be used as RAM to hold PEI code.
Enable Intel SpeedStep® Technology and fast memory speed.	Enable high processor and memory speed to increase boot performance[4].
Boot Device Selection Optimization	Optimize boot device selection to known device instead of a traditional search.
Delay unnecessary hardware setups	PS/2 Keyboard/Mouse USB, BIOS setup screen, video option ROM.

---

[3] For further information on Fast Boot BIOS, see http://edc.intel.com/Link.aspx?id=1039

[4] Performance results are based on certain tests measured on specific computer systems. Any difference in system hardware, software or configuration will affect actual performance. For more information go to http://www.intel.com/performance.

Embedded Development Tools

Embedded software development tool chains typically comprise a visual and command line interface. The visual interface is in the form of an integrated development environment (IDE) that offers the ability to develop, test, debug, and performance analyze an entire embedded system from one user interface. The integrated tools and activities available in the Wind River Workbench are summarized in Figure 6.2.

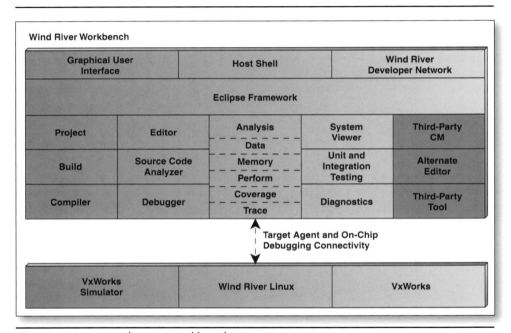

Figure 6.2 Wind River Workbench Components

General Operating System Feature Support

Embedded applications require features common to many operating systems, but not all of them. In addition, the level of feature support can vary between operating systems. For this reason, it is important to first understand if your candidate operating system supports a particular required feature and second to understand what level of support is provided. These qualities are dependent on the particular feature so cannot be precisely defined. Feature categories and example implementations of each are listed in Table 6.6.

Table 6.6   General Operating System Feature

Feature	Description
Networking technology	Communication between devices. Examples: IPv4, IPv6, IPSec, FTP, HTTP, SSH, Telnet
Debugging and tracing support	Technology to help find code problems. Example: JTAG support
Browser support	Web browser. Examples: Internet Explorer[†], Chrome[†], Firefox[†]
User interface support	Library to build custom graphical user interfaces. Examples: GTK+[†], GNOME Qt[†], QNX Photon microGUI[†]
Flash support	Adobe Flash[†] support
Graphics support	Library to support 2D and 3D graphics. Examples: OpenGL, Direct3D
Runtime library support	Underlying development language support. Examples: C & C++ libraries

Licensing and Support Issues

The final category of operating system features for consideration concerns licensing and technical support. Embedded operating systems are licensed under a variety of different means and can impact the cost of the device.

Technical support is a factor in choosing an operating system. Typically, support can be a fee-based service where the higher the fee, the higher touch support is provided. Users of open source software who do not wish to pay for support can obtain some limited assistance from the online community.

Licenses

Most software has some form of a license attached to it that governs how the software can be used. License discussions are in the legal domain, so it is not the intent here to describe all facets of licensing, but merely raise awareness. Licensing has an impact in several areas. First, you may need a license to access the embedded operating system and use the development environment in creating your embedded system. Second, some operating system vendors require royalty payments assessed per shipping device.

A third facet of licensing is relevant when open source software is employed either in the form of the operating system and component libraries or the application itself. In these cases, it is necessary to understand the license under which the open source software is provided and what if any impact applies. Two popular open source licenses are:

■ GNU General Public License (GPL) – license scheme employed in many GNU project software.

■ Berkeley Software Distribution (BSD) – license scheme employed in operating systems such as FreeBSD.

Some key questions to consider regarding licensing:

■ Is royalty payments part of the licensing agreement?

■ Is the source code available and under what kind of license?

■ Does use of the open source code place conditions on my source code?

Support

Support is a factor in selecting an operating system and is primarily dependent on a development group's needs. Obviously, if you port your own operating system, you will typically be responsible for support. On the opposite extreme, if you employ an open source operating system downloaded directly from an open source repository, there is typically no commitment to supporting your use. There may be a community newsgroup to post questions and receive answers.

Alternatively, there are several options for pay support services from operating system vendors and third-party vendors. These vendors typically offer tiered support models with various levels of support from web-based submission to direct support personnel with turn-around time commitments.

Option #1: Use the Same Operating System

The first operating system to consider when migrating to the Intel Atom processor is to employ the same operating system you are currently using. If you are using a proprietary operating system, then you would need to port it to execute on the Intel Atom processor. Considerations in porting a proprietary operating system are discussed in the next section.

If the operating system comes from an external source, then it's a simple matter to see if the operating system is available for the Intel Atom processor.

In general, operating system vendors are motivated to make the same features available on each target platform; however this is not true 100 percent of the time due to unique differences between processor architectures.

Three common differences to consider when employing the same operating system between two different target architectures are:

- Do you use assembly language in your application? If so, you will need to rewrite this code.

- Do you use any unique architecture features like instruction set extensions? If so, you will need to find equivalent functionality.

- Do you use any unique operating system features supported on your original platform? If so, you will need to find equivalent functionality.

Option #2: Porting a Proprietary Operating System

Enabling a proprietary operating system to execute on a new architecture is a large undertaking and should be considered carefully. In some respects, this should be a last option if the alternatives are not possible. It is listed as option #2 because software developers using a proprietary operating system and moving architectures will want to keep the number of project variables to a minimum. In addition, the software may have been developed over many years and have implicit assumptions in the code about the underlying hardware; finding and fixing these issues may require the majority of the development resources.

The high level activities involved in porting a proprietary operating system include:

1. Determine firmware strategy and implement.

2. Implement Intel-specific system initialization, memory management, interrupt structure, and processor mode.

3. Implement SMP support if desired and multiprocessor and multicore initialization sequence.

4. Implement instruction set support including register context switching and function call ABI.

5. Enable any required Intel Technology. For example, Intel® Hyper-Threading Technology (Intel® HT Technology) for IA-32, Intel® 64 requires operating system changes in order to support.

6. Enable your application to execute on Intel architecture.

Typically, the first five activities are not required if an embedded, desktop, or other operating system that specifically targets the Intel Atom processor is employed. These activities can take several months of effort.

One option in porting a proprietary operating system without the effort of the first five steps listed above is to execute the proprietary operating system on top of an operating system that already targets Intel architecture. In other words, your operating system is executing as an application on a different operating system. This is challenging, but not as daunting as it may seem because there are two items working for you. First, you are going to need to rewrite your low level kernel routines that make use of privileged mode functionality. It may be easier to rewrite these to employ more general purpose routines. Second, if this legacy operating system is dated, the speedup in processor technology may mitigate some of the performance loss expected due to the virtualization. More information on this approach is available in "How to Move from Legacy OS to Linux in Easy Stages" (Weinberg and Ready).

An additional alternative is to take advantage of a commercial software tool that aids in porting applications from one operating system to another. OSChanger† from Mapusoft enables use of software developed for one operating system on another operating system, even those requiring real-time performance.

Porting Tips

This section details answers to common questions asked by developers pursuing a migration of low level software to Intel architecture.

CPUID

How do you determine the identity of the processor at startup time? How do you determine the characteristics and capabilities of the processor at startup time?

The CPUID instruction, opcode 0FA2h, takes the value in register EAX as input and returns a variety of information such as vendor identification, processor and stepping information, cache capabilities, processor serial number, advanced power management information, and memory limits. Consult the *Intel Architecture Software Developer's Manual* for details.

Stack Trace

My operating system enables a runtime trace-back capability. How does one perform a runtime function call trace-back with and without debug information?

Typically, the IA-32 and Intel 64 ISA uses the register ebp and rbp respectively as stack frame pointers. The stack frame pointer enables easy access to a function caller and the parameters of a function. A common optimization due to the relative low number of general purpose registers in the instruction set is to use ebp and rbp as a general purpose register. In this case and without debug information, it is difficult for a monitoring program such as a debugger to determine the call chain. If a call chain is required there are three options:

- Compile with debug information. Debug information can be used to determine a call stack.

- Compile with the –fno-omit-frame-pointer (or equivalent) option. Many compilers allow disabling the use of register ebp and rbp as a general purpose register.

- Compile with the trace back option. Some compilers enable an option that provides the equivalent of lightweight debug information specifically suited for function call trace-back. This extra information is placed in a special section in the object file.

No Operation Instructions (NOPs)

How does one insert padding in between various instructions? What NOP instruction sequences should be used?

NOPs are used to add space between different instructions for purposes such as alignment. The standard NOP instruction encoding is 0x90, however other instructions are equivalent to a NOP, but differ in size. In general, it is advantageous to choose as few NOPs as possible to pad a specific number of bytes. A smaller number of NOPs will execute faster. For example, if you needed 5 bytes of NOPs, the recommendation is to use a 1-byte and 4-byte NOP. Table 6.7 lists the recommended NOP sequences for a number of different sizes. The one byte NOP, "xchg %eax, %eax", has special hardware support. Although it still comprises an instruction that flows through the pipeline, its accompanying resources and the dependence upon the old value of register eax is removed. This is the lowest cost NOP possible.

Table 6.7   NOP sequences

NOP Size Requirement	NOP instruction(s)	NOP representation (hexadecimal)
1 byte	xchg %eax, %eax	0x90
2 byte	mov reg, reg (reg = %eax)	0x89, 0xc0
3 byte	lea reg, 0 (reg) (8-bit displacement, reg=%eax)	0x8d, 0x40, 0x00
4 byte	lea esi, 0[esi]	0x8d, 0x74, 0x26, 0x00
6 byte	lea reg, 0 (reg) (32-bit displacement, reg=%eax)	0x8d, 0x80, 0x00, 0x00, 0x00, 0x00

Instruction Decode and Encode

Part of my operating system tool chain performs assembly and disassembly of instructions. Is there a library to help encode and decode IA-32 and Intel 64 architecture instructions?

XED[5] is a software library for encoding and decoding IA-32 and Intel 64 architecture instructions. The decoder takes sequences of 1–15 bytes along with machine mode information and produces a data structure describing the opcode and operands, and flags. The encoder takes a similar data structure and produces a sequence of 1 to 15 bytes. The library is available as part of the Intel Software Development Emulator[6]. Figure 6.3 shows invocations and the output of a command line tool that employs the library to perform an encoding of "addps xmm0, xmm1" and a decoding of the hexadecimal representation of the same instruction.

---

[5] For further information on XED, see http://www.pintool.org/docs/24110/Xed/html/main.html

[6] For further information on the Intel Software Development Emulator, see Intel Software Development Emulator, http://software.intel.com/en-us/articles/intel-software-development-emulator/

```
$ xed -A -e "addps xmm0 xmm1"
Request: ADDPS MODE:1, REG0:XMM0, REG1:XMM1, SMODE:1
OPERAND ORDER: REG0 REG1
Encodable! 0F58C1
.byte 0x0f, 0x58, 0xc1

$ xed -A -d 0f58c1
0F58C1
ICLASS: ADDPS CATEGORY: SSE  EXTENSION: SSE  IFORM: ADDPS_XMMps_XMMps  ISA_SET: SSE
SHORT: addps %xmm1, %xmm0
```

Figure 6.3   XED Commands showing Encode and Decode

Option #3: Real-Time Operating Systems

One key benefit of a real-time operating system is of course, real-time response. Numerous real-time operating systems are available that target the Intel Atom processor. Table 6.8 summarizes the capabilities of several real-time operating systems based upon the criteria discussed in the previous system requirements section. When reviewing, keep in mind the application domain as these operating systems tend to target specific usages where factors such as security and reliability may be more important than support for the latest technology.

Real-time operating systems are commonly employed in mission critical systems where many standards exist and specify operating system requirements. Some of the key standards in this area are as follows:

■ ARINC 653 (Avionics Application Standard Software Interface) – defines a RTOS standard for space and time partitioning of safety critical applications. Operating systems that implement this standard must offer the ability for the developer to partition an operating system's resources to in effect guarantee specified amounts of processor time and memory to specific applications.

■ Evaluation Assurance Level (EAL) – a rating from EAL1 to EAL7 of an operating system conformance to a Common Criteria security evaluation.

■ IEC61508 – international standard focusing on safety in electrical and programmable electronic devices. A certified operating system would need to enact safe failure modes and would have documented use of established software development processes.

■ DO-178B – aviation software standard that certifies aspects of the software development processes.

Table 6.8   Real-Time Operating Systems

Feature	Green Hills INTEGRITY	LynuxWorks LynxOS SE	QNX Neutrino OS	Wind River VxWorks 6.8
Power and Performance				
Multitasking Support (cooperative, preemptive)	Several	Preemptive	Preemptive	Several
SMP, AMP, Hybrid	All	SMP	All	All
Real-Time	Yes	Yes	Yes	Yes
Scheduling	Several	Several	Several	Several
Power Management	Yes	No	Yes	No
Architecture Requirements				
Processor Mode	protected	real, protected	protected	real, protected
Addressing	32 bit, 64 bit	32 bit	32 bit, PAE	32 bit, PAE
LP64 or LLP64	Both	No	No	No
IA-32, Intel 64, SIMD	All	IA-32	IA32, SIMD	IA-32, SIMD
Intel Technology support				
Intel® Hyper-Threading Technology	No	No	Yes	No
Intel® Turbo Boost Technology/Intel® Burst Performance Technology	No	No	No	No

Intel® Virtualization Technology for IA-32, Intel® 64, and Intel Architecture	Yes	Yes	Yes	Yes
Intel Virtualization Technology for Directed I/O	Yes	Yes	Yes	Yes
Intel® Trusted Execution Technology	Yes	No	No	No
Enhanced Intel Speedstep® Technology	No	No	No	No

Embedded Support

Kernel configuration	Microkernel	Embedded	Microkernel	Embedded
Standards	POSIX.1, DO-178B, IEC16508, EN50128, CMMI, FIPS 140-2, IPv4/v6, Common Criteria EAL 6+	POSIX, EAL4+	POSIX PSE52, IEC61508 SIL3, EAL4+	POSIX, TIPC, DO-17B, IEC16508, IPv6, FIPS 140-2, IPSec, IKE
Fast Boot	Yes	No	Yes	No
Development Environment	MULTI	Eclipse-based Luminosity	Eclipse-based Momentics	Eclipse-based Workbench

General Support

Networking technology	Yes	Yes	Yes	Yes
Debugging Support	Green Hills Probe kernel and driver debug, INDRT run-mode debug, in-field-debug, Event Analyzer, Profiler	Debug kernel	Debug kernel	Debug kernel, dynamic printf
Security	Yes, MILS EAL 6+ High Robustness	Yes, SLOSPP	EAL4+	Yes, MILS product

Browser Support	Webkit	Apache web server	Proprietary	3rd party provided
UI Support	GHS high assurance GUI, PEG, Qt	X Windows	Proprietary	Wind River Tilcon GUI
Adobe Flash Support	No	No	Yes	No
Graphics Programming	OpenGL, X, Qt	Xfree86, Mesa3D	OpenGL, Photon	Tilcon GUI, WindML
Licensing and Support				
Licensing	Commercial	Commercial	Commercial	Commercial
Royalties	Optional	Yes	Optional	Optional
Support	Multiple, long life	Priority, long life	Standard, priority, long life	Tiered, long life
Source code	Yes, proprietary	Available for purchase	Open source to licensees	Yes, proprietary

Green Hills INTEGRITY†

INTEGRITY is an RTOS technology from Green Hills, an independent vendor of embedded solutions. INTEGRITY was designed in the late 1990s for high reliability and security while adhering to guaranteed real-time performance. INTEGRITY is used in every major vertical market, including networking, avionics, medical devices, industrial control and automation, automotive, and even desktop PCs. INTEGRITY provides an open standards interface, certified conformance to the latest POSIX.1 standard. The INTEGRITY technology's pedigree in high reliability systems is evident in its certification to numerous safety and security standards, including IEC-61508 (SIL3), EN-50128 (SWSIL4), RTCA/DO-178B (Level A), and Common Criteria (EAL 6+ / High Robustness).

LynuxWorks LynxOS† RTOS

LynuxWorks LynxOS RTOS is offered in three different configurations:

■ LynxOS Embedded RTOS 5.0 – base level RTOS offering Linux ABI compatibility and POSIX conformance.

■ LynxOS-SE – additional features include ARINC 653 conformance enabling time and space partitioning for high availability and secure systems.

■ LynxOS-178 – additional features include conformance to DO-178B level A.

In comparing real-time operating systems, it is clear that LynxOS does not support as many of the Intel Atom processor capabilities as some of the other operating systems. Features such as Intel SSE and Intel Hyper-Threading Technology are not supported. Instead, this operating system stresses conformance to the security and reliability standards necessary in mission critical applications. One novel feature of the operating system is Linux 2.6 ABI compatibility, which enables unmodified Linux applications to execute on LynxOS. LynuxWorks produces LynxSecure, which is an embedded hypervisor targeting Intel architecture.

QNX Neutrino† RTOS

QNX Neutrino RTOS 6.4 features a microkernel architecture that places only critical functionality running inside the kernel. Drivers, applications, the file system, and protocols execute outside the kernel which enables a high level of fault tolerance. Failures in these components do not bring down the entire system.

Some other noteworthy features of the operating system include:

■ Fast Boot – BIOS-free optimization of the boot process, which enables operating system boot up in milliseconds.

■ Bound Multiprocessing (BMP) – A hybrid processing model that enables a given process to have affinity to a selected processor core.

■ Adaptive Partitioning – Provides minimum time guarantees to specified processes while enabling excess cycles to be shared.

■ Aviage multimedia suite – middleware for building consumer media and infotainment applications.

- Foundry 27 – Free access to the QNX source code with online community support forums.

- EAL 4+ certification.

- Support for Intel Hyper-Threading Technology and Intel SSE, two features critical to Intel Atom processor performance.

Several board support packages targeting IA-32 ISA based platforms and Intel Atom processor platforms are available on the QNX community website. Example board support packages targeting the Intel Atom processor are the Intel Crown Beach CRB board support package and an Advantech SOM-6760, which features an Intel Atom z5xx series processor. A third party hypervisor is available from Real-Time Systems.

For further information on QNX support for the Intel Atom processor, please consult "QNX Technology and the Intel Atom Processor."

Wind River VxWorks

Wind River VxWorks 6.8 offers a number of different platforms specialized for different embedded market segments. These offerings include:

- Wind River General Purpose Platform

- Wind River Platform for Automotive Devices

- Wind River Platform for Consumer Devices

- Wind River Platform for Industrial Devices

- Wind River Platform for Network Equipment

- Wind River VxWorks 653 Platform

- Wind River VxWorks DO-178B Platform

- Wind River VxWorks 61508 Platform

- Wind River VxWorks MILS Platform

These platforms include groupings of technology suited for a particular market segment. For example, the Wind River Platform for Automotive Devices includes software for protocols such as Controller Area Network (CAN) and systems including digital dashboard displays, navigation systems, telematics and entertainment. There are also operating system versions certified to ARINC 653, DO-178B, IEC 61508, and EAL6+ respectively.

The operating system includes support for several multiprocessing modes, AMP, SMP with CPU affinity and SMP with CPU reservation. Wind River produces a hypervisor capable of hosting VxWorks as well as other operating systems. The operating system scheduler is modular enabling a variety of different algorithms depending on your RTOS requirements. The next version, Wind River VxWorks 6.9, will introduce support for the Intel 64 ISA and fast boot technology.

Option #4: Embedded Operating Systems

If real-time operation is not necessary for your application, you may consider a traditional embedded operating system. Two broad types of embedded operating systems in wide use today are Windows based and Linux based operating systems.

Embedded Windows operating systems include Windows Embedded Standard 7 and Windows Embedded CE. The discussion in this section focuses on Windows Embedded Standard 7 only.

Embedded Linux operating system vendors include companies such as Wind River, MontaVista, and LynuxWorks. Typically, these companies offer several versions of Linux targeting different usages.

MeeGo[7] is an open source, Linux project which integrates the Moblin project, headed up by Intel, and Maemo, by Nokia, into a single open source activity. MeeGo combines the experience and skills of two significant development ecosystems, with strengths in communications and computing technologies. A special section detailing MeeGo is included at the end of this chapter.

Table 6.9 summarizes feature support for desktop operating systems, however applies to the embedded versions summarized here. Specifically, the power and performance, architecture requirements, Intel technology support,

---

[7] For further information on MeeGo, please consult http://meego.com/

and general support features are similar between Windows Embedded Standard 7 and Windows 7. The features are similar between typical embedded Linux and Linux. Given the right support model, an Embedded Linux OSVs would pull down and implement support for a generally available feature that did not exist in the current version of the embedded Linux. These embedded operating systems do differ from the desktop versions in the categories of embedded specific feature support, licensing and customer support. The following sections on the embedded operating systems attempts to detail these differences.

Windows Embedded Standard 7

Windows Embedded Standard 7 targets IA-32 and Intel 64 ISA based devices with a componentized Windows operating system. The operating system provides the benefit of being compatible with standard Windows 7 applications and enables the creation of customized Windows based operating systems. Features include application-specific component selection, dependency checking, and footprint estimates. A target analyzer is used to query the hardware platform for its capabilities and enables developers to easily determine which drivers need to be included to support required components. A dependency checker is integrated which ensures components have the necessary underlying dependencies met. Windows Embedded Standard 7 includes all of the capabilities of Windows 7 including Internet Explorer, Microsoft Silverlight, Windows Media Player and low level capabilities including power management, Plug and Play support, networking and USB support. Design templates bundle software components into prepackaged devices and include templates for set top boxes, home gateways, retail point of sale, and network attached storage devices. Long life support is available.

Since the operating system is based upon Windows 7, all of the features of the Intel Atom processor, such as Intel Hyper-Threading Technology and Intel SSE are supported. Real-time performance is available from third party products such as Venturcom RTX[†] and TenAsys INtime[†].

Wind River Linux

Wind River Linux solutions aim to help developers focus on creating software that sets their projects apart from the competition, instead of spending the majority of their time on system-integration tasks. All Wind River solutions are backed by 24/7 global technical support, customer education, and specialized professional services.

Wind River's Linux based products include:

- Wind River Linux

- Wind River Platform for Android

- Wind River Linux Platform for Infotainment (automotive industry)

Wind River Linux products are pre-integrated, customizable, and cohesive development and deployment solutions for a wide range of devices and vertical markets, offering embedded specific features beyond the base Linux operating system. Wind River Linux makes available Linux-based software stacks including middleware, application packages, and other components needed to address particular device types, such as network switches, mobile phones, or in-vehicle infotainment systems.

Wind River Linux follows a "pristine-source" approach, providing visibility into the patches and modifications applied to any open source component of the distribution. This enables developers to update specific patches easily, saving time and effort spent deconstructing binary and partially binary distribution solutions, and enables easier interaction with open source developer communities. Additional packages above the base Wind River Linux include integrated open-source networking, security, and real-time technologies.

Wind River offers a specialized Linux Services Practice, essentially a team of engineers capable of delivering Linux-based designs, board support packages, and integration and optimization of open-source technologies. Platform customers can leverage Wind River's engineers as a resource to extend the capabilities of their engineering teams.

Wind River Linux packages a simulation environment with its host development tools enabling a development host to execute code as if it were executing the operating system on a target.

Embedded Operating System Configuration

Embedded operating system configuration is a common activity in embedded system development. Microsoft Windows Embedded features a multistep process with automation tools. The high level steps to create an embedded image using Microsoft Windows Embedded are:

1. Execute Target Analyzer on target platform. Target Analyzer probes the embedded platform, determines the platform components on the target system, and produces a devices.pmq file.

2. Import the devices.pmq in Target Designer. Target Designer automates the process of including the appropriate software drivers for the detected hardware.

3. Select a design template as the basis for your embedded device and add your application components. The design template bundles the required components necessary to build different types of devices.

4. Check Dependencies. This step checks the configuration to ensure all software dependencies are resolved.

5. Build image. Collects the required components to create a ready-to-boot image.

Figure 6.4 displays the Microsoft Target Designer interface after the import of a devices.pmq from an Intel Atom N270 processor based netbook and the selection of the Advanced Set Top Box design template. This picture hints at the relative ease that a developer can graphically configure the components that comprise an embedded image.

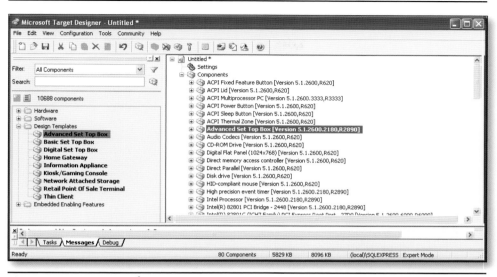

Figure 6.4   Microsoft Target Designer

Option #5: Desktop Operating Systems

One definition of *embedded* is a computing device that is fixed function. Therefore, a desktop computer system running a desktop operating system, but used for one function and one function only, could be considered an embedded device. Ease of development and familiarity with the environment is one reason to use a desktop operating system for your embedded application. Developers could possibly execute and test their application on the same machine they used for development. A second reason is because of the breadth of software available on these mainstream operating systems. The lack of easy customization to an embedded purpose is a negative. Support for specific Intel Atom processor-based systems may be lacking so you may be on your own to develop the equivalent of a board support package. Three operating systems in this category are BSD, desktop Linux, and Microsoft Windows 7. This class of operating system also targets laptops and servers, but are classified here as desktop for the sake of discussion. BSD based operating systems include FreeBSD[†], OpenBSD[†], and NetBSD[†]. Table 6.9 summarizes feature support for the desktop operating systems.

Table 6.9   Desktop Operating Systems

Feature	FreeBSD 8.0	Windows 7	Linux 2.6
Power and Performance			
Multitasking Support (cooperative, preemptive)	Preemptive	Preemptive	Preemptive
SMP, AMP, Hybrid	SMP	SMP	SMP
Real-Time	No	Add-on	Add-on
Scheduling	Priority	Priority	Priority
Power Management	Limited	Yes	Yes
Architecture Requirements			
Processor Mode	protected, long	protected, long	protected, long
Addressing	All	All	All
LP64 or LLP64	LP64	LLP64	LP64
IA-32, Intel 64, SIMD	All	All	All
Intel Technology support			
Intel® Hyper-Threading Technology	Yes	Yes	Yes
Intel® Turbo Boost Technology/Intel® Burst Performance Technology	No	Yes	Yes
Intel® Virtualization Technology for IA-32, Intel® 64, and Intel Architecture	Client	Yes	Yes
Intel Virtualization Technology for Directed I/O	Client	Yes	Yes
Intel® Trusted Execution Technology	No	Yes	Yes
Enhanced Intel Speedstep® Technology	No	Yes	Yes

Embedded Support

Kernel configuration	Yes	No	Yes
Standards	POSIX		SELinux
Fast Boot	No	No	No
Development Environment	No	Visual Studio	3rd party

General Support

Networking technology	Yes	Yes	Yes
Debugging Support	Debug kernel, Dtrace	Debug kernel	Debug kernel
Security	Jails, GBDE	Windows	SELinux
Browser Support	Firefox, Opera, WebKit	IE, Firefox, Chrome	IE, Firefox, Chrome
UI Support	GNOME, KDE, XFCE	Windows	GNOME, Xwin
Adobe Flash Support	Yes	Yes	Yes
Graphics Programming	OpenGL	DirectX	OpenGL

Licensing and Support

Licensing	Open Source	Commercial	Open Source
Royalties	No	No	No
Support	Community	Community	No
Source code	BSD	No	GPL

FreeBSD[†]

FreeBSD[†] is an operating system for modern server, desktop, and embedded computer platforms and targets a variety of processor architectures including IA-32 architectures. It is developed and maintained by a large team of individuals in the development community as opposed to being a commercial offering.

FreeBSD features a large number of ported applications, upwards of 20,000 ported libraries and applications. FreeBSD also has a Linux compatibility layer which enables native Linux applications to execute on the operating system. FreeBSD is available free of charge and includes source code.

One of the recent improvements in FreeBSD is its multicore support. Earlier version of FreeBSD effectively had a lock around the entire kernel which serialized kernel operations. This situation was resolved in FreeBSD 7. FreeBSD features Trusted BSD MAC Framework extensible kernel security, a security model customization feature. The operating system features TrustedBSD Audit, a security event logging service.

Linux

Linux can be obtained from a number of sources: 1) kernel.org, 2) a community-based distribution, and 3) a commercial Linux operating system vendor. Examples of community-based distributions include Fedora and Ubuntu. Commercial Linux distributions include those from Suse and Red Hat.

Windows 7

Windows 7 is a popular operating system with known qualities that will not be detailed here. Microsoft is fulfilling one of the needs for deploying Windows 7 in embedded applications by offering long-life support options. These options and special licensing terms are available in the following Windows 7 offerings:

■ Windows 7 Professional for Embedded Systems

■ Windows 7 Ultimate for Embedded Systems

Unlike Windows Embedded Standard 7, these two versions of Windows 7 are not customizable; the operating system is essentially bit-for-bit the same as Windows 7. These Windows 7 packages also enable the developer to customize the start screen to meet their needs.

Desktop Operating System Tip

Even if you do not plan to use a desktop operating system in your product, a desktop operating system provides a mechanism to quickly evaluate the Intel Atom processor and could also be employed as a quick prototyping system.

An Intel Atom processor based netbook system that commonly ships with Windows 7 can serve as a low-cost and relatively easy means of evaluation. If your operating environment is more similar to Linux, you may want to quickly evaluate on a Linux operating system.

Ubuntu Netbook Remix is a customized version of Linux that targets the Intel Atom processor. It is relatively easy to install Ubuntu Linux and other packages on top of it to perform a quick evaluation. The following summarizes the steps to download and boot Ubuntu Netbook Remix.

1. Download the .iso image of Ubuntu Netbook Remix.

2. Write the ISO to a USB flash drive (at least 2 GB) using usb-creator or Unetbootin.

3. Boot the netbook from the USB flash drive.

4. Run GParted, Ubuntu's partition manager and resize hard disk to create an unallocated partition of at least 4 GB in size.

5. Install Ubuntu Netbook Remix on hard drive.

Once completed the netbook can be used to easily evaluate performance. Figure 6.5 shows the output from the Sysinfo tool executing on an Intel Atom N450 processor based netbook. The number of CPUs output is two because Intel Hyper-Threading Technology is enabled by the operating system. Also, notice processor support mentioned in the Flags section including Intel SSE2, Intel SSE3, and the movbe instruction.

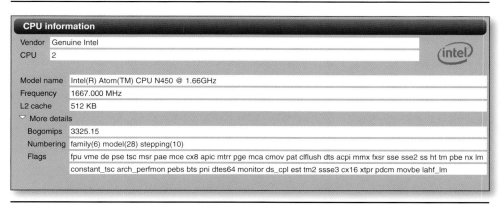

Figure 6.5 Intel® Atom™ N450 processor CPUID information

MeeGo

MeeGo is an open source software platform targeting a broad range of device segments from handsets to connected TV. It supports Intel architecture and ARM[†] hardware architectures. MeeGo is an independent project under the auspices of the Linux Foundation that targets a six-month release cadence. MeeGo was created by the merging of open source Linux distributions Moblin and Maemo.

All of the MeeGo components are fully open source from core OS up through UI libraries, applications, and tools. The platform includes reference user experiences and core applications. Proprietary add-ons can be provided by vendors to support hardware, services, or customized user experiences. For developers, MeeGo provides a common set of APIs across client devices (such as handsets, netbooks, in-vehicle infotainment, connected TVs, and IP media phones).

MeeGo offers a complete set of tools for developers to easily and rapidly create a variety of innovative applications. MeeGo enhances the developer experience through:

- Common development environments.

    - Qt[†] for native C++ and Web runtime for web applications (HTML, JS, CSS, and so on).

    - Qt and Web runtime bring cross-platform development so applications can span multiple platforms including MeeGo and Symbian[†].

- Common tools.

    - Native Qt Creator.

    - Plug-ins for standard Web development tools: Aptana[†], Adobe Dreamweaver[†], Microsoft Visual Studio[†].

- Maximizes accessible installed base through strong, stack-based compatibility.

- Open source tools.

    - MeeGo Image Creator: create custom target images for various boot formats such as USB stick and internal NAND.

    - GNU development tools such as gcc and gdb.

    - PowerTOP: Platform level power analysis and optimization tool.

- Commercial development tools.

    - Intel® C++ compiler: optimized for Intel processor microarchitectures including Intel Atom processor.

    - Intel® JTAG Debugger and Intel® Debugger: Linux OS aware debugging and register level view of Intel processors and chipsets.

    - Intel® IPP: Highly optimized libraries for DSP, image processing, multimedia.

    - Intel VTune™ Performance Analyzer: discover performance bottlenecks in code.

- MeeGo Reference UX.

    - A reference user experience for selected target devices, intended to both illustrate the capabilities of the MeeGo platform and be the starting point for product development.

MeeGo Software Stack Architecture

The MeeGo software stack is subdivided into three layers: OS Base, Middleware and UX. Figure 6.6 illustrates the software stack.

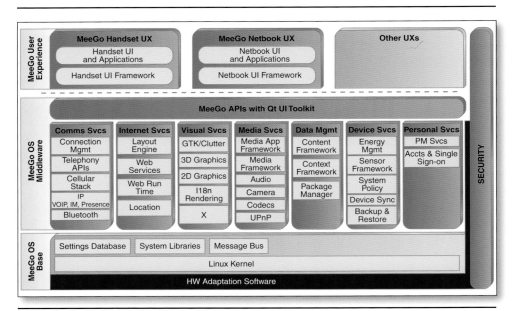

Figure 6.6 MeeGo Software Stack Architecture

MeeGo OS Base

MeeGo OS Base includes a hardware adaptation software, a Linux kernel, configurations, and system libraries. Components of the hardware adaptation software include:

- Device drivers: drivers for wireless, camera, USB, 3G, Bluetooth, and touchscreen.

- Kernel core architecture patches or configuration: additional packages to be added to the kernel to enable additional architecture features.

- X Software.

  - X core architecture patches enable specific graphics hardware features for graphics controller or acceleration.

  - X configuration and runtime parameters for X.

■ Hardware Accelerated Codecs: media codecs with hardware assist or offload.

MeeGo employs a Linux kernel from kernel.org, with architecture-specific configuration and patches. A settings database is used for storing application preferences and configuration information. System libraries include the common LSB libraries such as glibc. D-Bus provides the message bus for application-to-application communication.

MeeGo Middleware

MeeGo middleware consists of services and packages needed for user applications. It includes communication services, Internet services, visual services, media services, data management services, device services, and personal services.

Communication services include ConnMan to manage data connections (Wi-Fi, WiMAX, 3G) and telephony APIs. The oFono product provides the internal APIs for GSM/UMTS telephony applications. Telepathy provides the API framework for IP-based communication. Applications will use Qt APIs to access these services. The cellular stack provides oFono plug-ins to support the IP of specific modems, such as voice-over-IP (VoIP), IM, Presence. IP communications include Telepathy plug-ins for specific instant messaging, VoIP, and video-over-IP protocols. BlueZ provides Bluetooth support including DUN, A2DP, and headset.

Internet services consist of a layout engine, web services, web runtime and location services. The layout engine renders web content (HTML, XML, images) for on-screen display. The Web Services framework (libsocialweb) provides an extensible framework for exchanging data with social networking and social media sites. It also includes libraries to make it easier to interact with RESTful web services (librest). The WebKit-based web runtime provides an environment for building applications using web technologies such as Javascript, HTML, and CSS. GeoClue provides a framework for providing location information. Applications are able to access the location services through Qt APIs layered on GeoClue.

Visual services include 2D/3D Graphics, i18n, and X windows. Three-dimensional graphics rendering including support for hardware acceleration is implemented through OpenGL/OpenGL ES specifications. The 2D graphics includes 2D drawing capabilities. The i18n rendering component supports layout and rendering of text with support for internationalization. X.org provides an implementation of the X Windows system, with architecture-specific drivers, patches, and configuration as needed.

Media services include media application framework, media framework, audio, camera, codecs, and Universal Plug and Play (UPnP) devices. The media application framework provides a set of abstracted services that can be used to build a media player. The Gstreamer media framework supports a wide range of media operations including audio and video playback, recording, streaming, and editing. The audio subsystem includes audio routing and PulseAudio. The camera subsystem supports both still and video cameras. GStreamer-compatible codecs are supported for encoding and decoding of audio and video. Codecs with hardware acceleration are also supported. Only those codecs that do not require commercial licenses such as Ogg Vorbis and Theora will be included with MeeGo. Codecs for other audio and video formats such as MP3, AAC, MPEG-4, and H.264 need to be licensed from the appropriate owners. GUPnP provides a framework for creating devices and control points that adhere to the Universal Plug-and-Play specifications.

Data management services include content framework, context framework, and package manager. Tracker content framework provides indexing, metadata extraction, and search capabilities for a variety of data types. The ContextKit context framework provides a subscribe and publish mechanism for information about device context such as cable status, phone position, and battery level. The RPM package manager is used to install and remove packages.

Device services include energy management, sensor framework, system policy and profile, device synchronization and backup. Energy management controls energy-related device functions such as battery charging. The sensor framework exposes a common, consistent interface for sensors with pluggable support for multiple sensor types including accelerometers and ambient light sensors. System policy provides the central place for managing device-wide policy information such as audio routing, profiles, and device behavior during emergency calls. The system profiles component manages the system-wide device profiles such as ring and vibrate alert levels. SyncEvolution provides data synchronization with both servers and directly with other devices using SyncML. Backup and restore provides services for saving and restoring both user data and device images to an external backup device.

Personal services include PIM Services and account management. Evolution Data Server (EDS) PIM Services provides a common interface for accessing and storing PIM information such as address book, calendar, tasks, and notes. Accounts and single sign-on stores user account information, including information required to implement single sign-on for both local and remote services.

MeeGo Security

The MeeGo security framework is a policy-based access control framework built on top of standard Linux security mechanisms. The set of protected resources and the authority to access the services is defined by an updatable security policy. When available, the platform security framework relies on hardware to provide a trusted execution environment to bootstrap the chain of trust and to provide secure key management and usage services for applications to keep their data encrypted and integrity protected.

MeeGo User Interface and Application Toolkits

The MeeGo User Interface (UI) and Application toolkits supports native (C/C++) and web (HTML, Javascript, CSS) development. The MeeGo UI toolkit is the primary toolkit for developing applications and is based on Qt with specific enhancements and additions such as the Qt Mobility APIs. GTK and Clutter are provided as well for application compatibility for existing Maemo and Moblin applications.

Summary

Choosing the right operating system for your migration to the Intel Atom processor is a significant decision influenced by many constraints. This chapter proposed a process for selecting an operating system based upon realistic concerns regarding a port and feature support of several classes of operating systems.

In the interest of minimizing change and risk associated with a move to Intel architecture, the first option is to consider employing the same operating system used on your current platform. This may be as simple as checking to see if your current operating system is available on Intel architecture. Alternatively, porting a proprietary operating system may be considered, and this requires a significant investment. In addition to porting the software for basic functionality, enabling complete Intel architecture support, which includes supporting a variety of advanced Intel technology features, is no small undertaking.

Considering commercial and open source operating systems that already target Intel architecture is a viable approach and one that mitigates the previously mentioned support for Intel technology features. Many of the operating systems already offer support for these technology features; an example of this is Intel HT Technology. Feature support in the categories of power and performance, architecture, Intel technology, features specific to embedded systems, general operating system, and licensing must be considered for RTOS, embedded operating systems, and desktop operating systems. It is only once these considerations have been thoroughly researched that one truly knows which operating system to employ.

Chapter **7**

Performance Libraries for Embedded Systems

Don't reinvent the wheel.

—Unknown

Employing performance library functions in your embedded application is motivated by several observations about software development:

- In general, it is possible to group a set of common computationally-intensive functions that developers need on Intel® processors.

- Without a performance library, developers must optimize these functions carefully to obtain adequate performance.

- This optimization process is complicated, time-consuming, and required for every processor generation.

With each successive generation of processors, the number of developers who want to program in assembly language is diminishing. Further, every generation has required a new round of assemblers, compilers, and a new set of developer expertise. Tools vendors recognized a need to provide developers with software tools to support every processor release with a variety of functionality, a storehouse of optimized code for developers to draw upon.

Thus performance libraries targeting several application domains have been developed. Intel® Integrated Performance Primitives (Intel® IPP) is one such library and is the focus for this chapter.

The Intel® Atom™ processor microarchitecture is considerably different from previous desktop-targeted Intel processors. Performance libraries that were originally developed for these other processors may not perform well when executed on the Intel Atom processor. Performance libraries tuned for the specific processor of execution are essential for high performance.

The key to low-level performance optimization is processor-specific code. With each successive generation, Intel processors have added new technologies and capabilities. Many of the new capabilities cannot be easily or uniformly accessed from high-level languages. Most prominent among these features are the SIMD instruction set enhancements like MMX™ technology, Intel® Streaming SIMD Extensions (Intel® SSE), Intel SSE2, Intel SSE3, Supplemental Streaming SIMD Extensions 3 (SSSE3), and Intel SSE4. Higher-level languages do not usually have standard constructs for the fine-grained data parallelism enabled via SIMD instruction sets; they require use of specialized tools or programming in assembly language.

However, some computational routines have multiple applications and recur in innumerable programs. These routines are good candidates for inclusion in a library, so that they can be optimized in assembly language once per processor type and that optimized code reused many times. This is exactly what low level libraries such as Intel IPP target, the product of careful processor-specific optimization. This type of library raises the processor capabilities up to the level of C and C++ for use by the embedded developer in their application.

Applications targeted at desktop processors have remained largely processor-neutral. Most applications are compiled into a single version for all Intel architecture processors. Intel IPP is intended to allow such code to take advantage of processor-specific features. Code using Intel IPP can continue to be processor-agnostic while still obtaining the performance benefits of using processor-specific code. The use is hidden inside of Intel IPP.

The dispatching mechanism is the key to maintaining ease of use while providing multiple versions of the code. Intel IPP supplies multiple implementations of each function. The dispatching technology determines the processor type at startup and, using a jump table or processor-specific dynamic library, ensures that the most appropriate version of each function is executed. This library also enables the use of processor-specific tuned library functions directly as many embedded developers constrain the range of processors employed in their application. In many cases, the specific processor is locked in early during development.

This chapter details Intel IPP and its use for embedded applications. The first section details categories of library functions summarizing common operations in each functional category. The second section discusses basics on employing Intel IPP in embedded applications. The third section surveys the broader library ecosystem detailing both industry and other Intel libraries important to Intel Atom processor software development. The last sections discuss optimizing 3D applications and some tips when employing hardware-accelerated video decode.

Performance Library Basics

Performance libraries are constructed by first identifying common functions used in different application areas and then producing optimized routines to perform the required functionality. These optimized routines are built from lower level primitive operations ordered in such a way as to maximize performance on a given hardware platform.

These routines can be classified into domain specific groupings. These groupings pertinent to discussing Intel IPP are as follows:

- Matrix and vector mathematics

- Signal processing and digital filtering

- Cryptography

- Image compression and decompression

- Video encode and decode

- Image processing and object recognition

- String processing

The next sections summarize each of these application groupings.

Matrix and Vector Mathematics

Matrix and vector mathematics are the building blocks for higher level library functionality and are also employed in all manner of scientific and engineering computation. Thus, many performance libraries provide basic linear algebra capabilities offering optimized functions such as those for dot products, matrix multiplication, inverse, and normalization. BLAS[1] is the prototypical matrix and vector mathematics library.

Signal Processing and Digital Filtering

Signal processing is the analysis of, typically, time series data measurements of some physical events. These events can be sound, images, or other sampled representation of a physical occurrence. The types of processing on these signals include filtering, analysis, and transformations. Applications for signal processing include audio content creation and speech recognition.

Digital filters take a series of inputs, manipulate them in some way without destroying all of the original information, and produce a series of outputs. This "some way" generally preserves most characteristics of the original data but removes others. Often it involves noise removal or information extraction. The inputs are often samples from some sensor or medium, such as audio from a microphone or CD player, or samples of a carrier wave from an antenna; however, regardless of the source and meaning, the time at which the samples are filtered is expressed as numerical entries in an array.

Filters are classified based upon a number of different properties:

- *Linear versus nonlinear.* A linear filter is one that meets the following criteria:

    - Adding two inputs then filtering produces the same result as filtering and then adding the two outputs:

        $F(x_1 + x_2) = F(x_1) + F(x_2)$.

    - Multiplying the input by a constant then filtering produces the same result as filtering then multiplying the output by a constant:

        $F(ax_1) = aF(x_1)$.

---

[1] For further information on BLAS, consult http://www.netlib.org/blas/

- *Time-invariant versus time-varying.* Time-invariant filters are defined as systems for which shifting the input in time shifts the output by the same amount without otherwise affecting the output. Linearity and time-invariance simplifies both study and implementation of filters. The core Intel IPP filter operations are time-invariant and linear, because linear filters can be expressed as an array, and time-invariant filters are those for which that array doesn't change in the life of the filter. Frequency-based filters are inherently time-invariant.

- *Causal versus noncausal.* A causal function is one for which the output at time *n* only refers to inputs from time *n* or earlier.

- *Real-time versus batch mode.* If the software system is taking input signals and producing outputs for immediate consumption, it might be thought of as a real-time system. By contrast, systems that have the entire signal available at once and filter it are termed batch-mode.

Fourier Transforms

The *Fourier transform* converts a signal indexed by time into a signal indexed by frequency. The inverse Fourier transform converts this signal back into the original time-based signal. The same information is contained in both the time-based and frequency-based versions of the signal, but the information is arranged differently.

The Fourier transform calculates the set of sinusoids that best represent the original signal. For this reason the sinusoid is called the *basis function* of the Fourier transform. A related transform, the *Discrete Cosine Transform* (DCT), also uses sinusoids, but transforms can and do use square waves, triangle waves, and so on as their basis functions. The use of the sinusoid by the Fourier transform matches a typical physical or electrical oscillation and is therefore appropriate to break down frequency in audio and other physical systems.

The version of this transform that is relevant to software-based filtering is the *Discrete Fourier Transform* (DFT). The DFT is very similar to the Fourier series, in that it breaks a signal into a series of frequencies.

Appealing characteristics of the Fourier transform with respect to digital filtering include:

■ *Linearity.* The Fourier transform is a linear function. One effect of this function is that the time-domain signal can be interpreted as the sum of several independent frequency components. If each single spike transforms to a sine wave, then several spikes transform to the sum of the corresponding sine waves.

■ *Reciprocity.* The Fourier transform is reversible. It is possible to reconstruct the original signal from the information in the Fourier coefficients. If it weren't possible, the DFT wouldn't be useful for filtering, only for analysis.

Classifying Filters

Filters are often classified as "pass" or "stop," meaning that they either attenuate a frequency range or attenuate all but that range. This is generally modified with "low," "high," or "band," indicating that the range is the low end of the frequency spectrum, the high end, or a contiguous range of frequencies in the middle. For example, a *high-pass* filter tries to remove all but a specified range of high frequencies, while a *band-stop* filter tries to eliminate a range of frequencies. A band-stop filter is often referred to as a "notch" filter, particularly when the band in question is narrow.

Time-Domain and Two-Dimensional Filters

Frequency-domain filtering is conceptually simple and intuitive. Time-domain filtering, on the other hand, can be mathematically simple but generally has less-than-intuitive results. Frequency domain filtering typically consists of simple multiplications to enhance or attenuate certain frequencies. In the time domain, that simple element-by-element multiplication with a frequency spectrum becomes a convolution with a signal. The filter that was designed to modify the frequencies becomes an almost random sequence of filter coefficients.

The same mathematical operations that produce filters in one-dimensional signals can be applied to two-dimensional images, generally by a simple expansion of the formula. Image filters can be designed and analyzed using the Fourier transform, and filters can be executed in the frequency domain or using convolution.

Cryptography

Cryptography is the processing of data to conceal any of the information it contains. Algorithms for encoding data are usually complicated and almost always time-consuming. While the cryptographic domain includes some primitive components, the domain has about a dozen popular algorithms implemented completely. The functions can be divided into four groups: symmetric encryption algorithms, public key encryption algorithms, hashing functions, and primitives.

The security of cryptography schemes are generally based on the expense of attempting randomly to decrypt balanced with the practicality of the time to correctly encrypt and decrypt. For this reason, large integers are the core of many cryptographic schemes. Big numbers in this case are generally more than 64 bits long and less than 4,096.

Public-key cryptography allows an entity that wishes to receive secure transmissions to create a system for encrypting data that can only be read by that entity. Such an entity creates a pair of keys based on large primes. The public key is published or provided to any other entity that wishes to send a secure transmission. The private key and primes are kept secret and are used to decode any transmissions encoded with the public key.

The result is an easy and secure transmission method that anyone with the public key can use. Further, if some authority certifies the identity of the owner of the public key, then this method doubles as part of an identity certification scheme, since only the person certified can read the encrypted messages.

Categories of cryptographic algorithms and specific algorithms are listed as follows:

- Symmetric cryptography:

  - Data Encryption Standard (DES) and Triple Data Encryption Standard (TDES)

  - Rijndael, Blowfish, and Twofish block ciphers

- Hash and data authentication algorithm (DAA) functions:

  - MD5, HMAC-MD5

- ■ SHA1, SHA256/384/512, HMAC-SHA1, HMAC-SHA256/384/512

- ■ DAADES, DAATDES

- ■ DAARijdael, DAABlowfish, DAATwofish

■ Public key cryptography:

- ■ Infrastructure functions such as pseudorandom number generation (PNRG) and prime number generation

- ■ Digital Signature Algorithm (DSA)

Image Compression and Decompression

Image and video encoders and decoders, in software called *codecs*, are intended to compress their media for storage or transmission. Raw images are quite large and raw digital video is unreasonably large, absorbing disk or network capacity very quickly. Moreover, processor speed is sufficient that working with these media uncompressed, except for capture and display, is completely unnecessary and inefficient. It is faster to read compressed video from disk and decompress it than it would be to read uncompressed video.

Most compression is based on taking advantage of redundancy and predictability in data to reduce the number of bytes necessary to represent it. Two common techniques are run-length coding, which converts runs of data into run-lengths and values, and variable-length coding, which converts data of fixed bit lengths into variable bit lengths according to popularity. Huffman coding and arithmetic coding are examples of variable-length coding.

Another source of compression is perceptibility. For some kinds of data, such as text and binary executables, compression must be lossless. A compression method that sometimes changed an "a" to an "A" would not be acceptable. Standalone Huffman coding is exactly reversible. However, it is possible to compress media information in a way that is not exactly reversible but is virtually undetectable. Such methods are called *lossy*, meaning that the output is not guaranteed to be exactly the same as the input. However, in many cases the loss can be imperceptible or have acceptable visual effect. Just as with audio coding, the compression algorithm transforms the data into spaces in which information can be removed while minimizing the perceptible impact to the media.

Most media compression is done using transform-based coding methods. Such methods convert the position-based information into frequency-based or position/frequency-based information. The compression benefit is that important information becomes concentrated in fewer values. Then the coder can represent the more-important information with more bits and the less-important information with fewer bits. The perception model dictates the importance of information, but generally higher-frequency information is considered less important.

Figure 7.1 shows the framework of a transform-based encoding and decoding scheme.

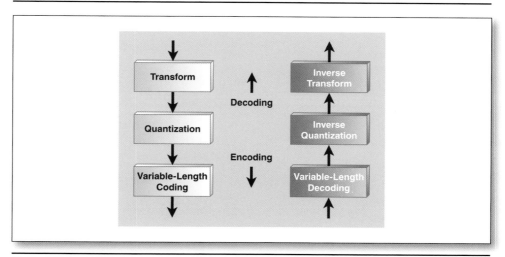

Figure 7.1   Simple Diagram of Transform-Based Image Coding

JPEG

JPEG is a widely used standard for image compression. The term is an acronym that stands for the Joint Photographic Experts Group, the body that designed the specification. JPEG is a powerful and effective compression technique that has been around for over a decade. It has gained popularity because of its effectiveness, because it is an international standard, and because a baseline JPEG codec can be built without using proprietary algorithms.

The Independent JPEG Group (IJG) is a small association that wrote a reference implementation of the JPEG standard. This implementation, often called the IJG library or merely IJG, is widely used as a JPEG codec.

Data Compression Principles

This section summarizes key data compression algorithms. The descriptions are brief and many details are neglected, so these descriptions should be treated as a simple illustration of main ideas of the algorithms. Key descriptions of data compression techniques are as follows:

- *Huffman coding*. Huffman coding is a common example of a variable-length code. Whereas most (uncompressed) schemes encode characters using a fixed number of bits, often 8 or 16, the idea of Huffman coding is to use variable-length bit codes to represent symbols. The algorithm uses the shortest codes for the most frequently-used characters and often much longer codes for the rare symbols. This conversion from fixed-length codes to variable-length can reduce the length of the whole input string significantly.

- *Burrows-Wheeler Transform (BWT)*. Variable-length coding is limited by the statistics of the data. The more uneven the frequencies of the symbols, the better the compression. It is possible to change the statistics of data by performing some kind of transform to make the data further compressible. The Burrows-Wheeler transform and other block-sorting transforms are designed to change the statistics or statistical homogeneity of the input data with this goal in mind.

    BWT rearranges the symbols of the input data in order to obtain an output data block containing long series of equal symbols, creating likely statistical inhomogeneity in the block.

- *Move-to-Front (MTF) Transform*. The goal of the MTF is to turn a series of equal symbols into a series of zeros. To achieve this, the MTF transform changes the statistics of the input string to contain series of equal symbols. This makes the string more compressible.

    The principal idea of the MTF transform is very simple. On every step the transform writes to the output stream a value that's equal to the index of the current symbol of string in the alphabet, then reorders the alphabet so that that symbol is first. It does this by shifting the symbols between the first symbol and the current symbol's original position.

■ *Run-Length Encoding (RLE).* RLE reduces the length of input data vectors that contain runs of zeros, or more generally runs of any number. RLE replaces a series of values with a pair of values: the value of the members of the series and the number of values in the series minus one. When encoding a run of five zeros, for example, the pair of values would be [0, 4].

■ *Lempel-Ziv-77 (LZ77).* The LZ77 algorithm belongs to the family of dictionary-based algorithms. Such algorithms assume the existence of the dictionary filled with indexed strings. They achieve compression by replacing input substrings with the index of a matching string in the dictionary. The LZ77 algorithm uses a sliding dictionary that is a window of perhaps 32 KB into the input stream itself. The encoding algorithm searches the window for substrings also in the look-ahead buffer, which is much smaller, then advances the window and look-ahead buffer across the input stream. If it finds a match, the algorithm encodes the second occurrence of the string using the offset from the beginning of the first occurrence of the string and the length of the string that matches.

■ *Interval Transform.* The Interval transform changes the statistics of input data by replacing the input string with sequences of intervals between matching symbols. The encoder produces a sequence of such intervals for each symbol in the alphabet. In producing these sequences, the algorithm iterates through the alphabet, marking the distances between each pair of symbols and then removing every occurrence of that symbol.

Video Encode and Decode

Video encoding and decoding is similar to image encoding and decoding except that video requires compression and decompression of successive frames. Video typically requires more storage than an image, but the amount typically does not scale linearly with the number of frames encoded and decoded. Video compression and decompression takes advantage of the relatively low entropy between successive frames. Two widely used standards are MPEG-2 and H.264.

MPEG-2

MPEG-2 is intended for high-quality, high-bandwidth video. It is most prominent because it is used for DVD and HDTV video compression. Computationally, good encoding is expensive but can be done in real-time by current processors. Decoding an MPEG-2 stream is relatively easy and can be done by almost any current processor or, obviously, by commercial DVD players.

MPEG-2 is a complicated format with many options. It includes seven profiles dictating aspect ratios and feature sets, four levels specifying resolution, bit rate, and frame rate, and three frame types. The bit stream code is complex and requires several tables. However, at its core are computationally complex but conceptually clear compression and decompression elements.

MPEG-2 components are very similar to those in JPEG. MPEG-2 is DCT based, and uses Huffman coding on the quantized DCT coefficients. However, the bit stream format is completely different, as are all the tables. Unlike JPEG, MPEG-2 also has a restricted, though very large, set of frame rates and sizes. But the biggest difference is the exploitation of redundancy between frames.

There are three types of frames in MPEG: I (intra) frames, P (predicted) frames, and B (bidirectional) frames. There are several consequences of frame type, but the defining characteristic is how prediction is done. Intra frames do not refer to other frames, making them suitable as key frames. They are, essentially, self-contained compressed images. By contrast, P frames are predicted by using the previous P or I frame, and B frames are predicted using the previous and next P or I frame. Individual blocks in these frames may be intra or non-intra, however.

MPEG is organized around a hierarchy of blocks, macroblocks, slices, and frames. Blocks are 8 pixels high by 8 pixels wide in a single channel. *Macroblocks* are a collection of blocks 16 pixels high by 16 pixels wide and contain all three channels. Depending on subsampling, a macroblock contains 6, 8, or 12 blocks. For example, a YCbCr 4:2:0 macroblock has four Y blocks, one Cb and one Cr.

The key to the effectiveness of video coding is using earlier and sometimes later frames to predict a value for each pixel. Image compression can only use a block elsewhere in the image as a base value for each pixel, but video compression can aspire to use an image of the same object. Instead of compressing pixels, which have high entropy, the video compression can compress the differences between similar pixels, which have much lower entropy.

Objects and even backgrounds in video are not reliably stationary, however. In order to make these references to other video frames truly effective, the codec needs to account for motion between the frames. This is accomplished with motion estimation and compensation. Along with the video data, each block also has motion vectors that indicate how much that frame has moved relative to a reference image. Before taking the difference between current and reference frame, the codec shifts the reference frame by that amount. Calculating the motion vectors is called *motion estimation* and accommodating this motion is called *motion compensation*.

H.264

The two series of video codec nomenclature H.26x and MPEG-x overlap. MPEG-2 is named H.262 in the H.26x scheme. Likewise, another popular codec, H.264, is a subset of MPEG-4 also known as MPEG-4 Advanced Video Coding (AVC). Its intent, like that of all of MPEG-4, was to produce video compression of acceptable quality and very low bit-rate—around half of its predecessors MPEG-2 and H.263.

Image Processing and Object Recognition

Geometric transformations constitute a large and important segment of image processing operations. Any function that changes the size, shape, or orientation of the image or order of the pixels can be grouped under this broad classification. The math employed by these transform operations uses two coordinate systems, the source image coordinate system and the destination. Both systems have an origin (0,0) that is defined by the data pointer. The two coordinate systems are related by the geometric transform.

In most cases, the location in the source from which the data is to be drawn, indicated as (x', y'), does not lie exactly on a source pixel. Some form of *interpolation* would then be used to calculate the value. The nearest neighbor method chooses the pixel that is closest to (x', y'). Linear interpolation takes a weighted average of the four surrounding pixels. Cubic interpolation fits a second-order curve to the data to calculate the (x', y') value. Super-sampling interpolation averages over a wider range of pixels and is suitable for resizing images to a much smaller size, such as when creating a thumbnail image.

Other common transformations are summarized as follows:

■ *Resize*. Resizing functions change an image from one size to another. The pixels in the first image are either stretched by duplication or interpolation, or they are compressed by dropping or interpolation. A single resize operation can stretch the image in one direction and compress it in the other.

■ *Rotation*. Turn an image around the origin, around a designated point, or around the center.

■ *Affine Transform*. The affine transform is a general two-dimensional transform that preserves parallel lines and is general enough to shear, resize, or shift an image.

■ *Perspective Transform*. The perspective transform is a general three-dimensional transform. Properly applied, this transform can represent a projection of an image onto a plane of arbitrary orientation.

■ *Remap*. The remap function is a completely general geometric transform. It takes a destination-to-source map the same size as the destination image. Each pixel has a corresponding floating-point (x,y) coordinate pair. The operation calculates the value at that location according to the interpolation mode and sets the destination pixel to that value. The remap function is most useful in morphing or exciting video effects, for which the other geometric transforms are not flexible enough.

Image processing functions are grouped into the following categories:

■ Statistics: norm, mean, median, standard deviation, histograms

■ Analysis functions and filters: erode and dilate, blur, Laplace, Sobel, distance transform, pyramid

■ Feature detection: edge, corner, template matching

■ Motion detection and understanding: motion templates

Many of these functions are closely associated with the Open Source Computer

Vision Library (OSCVL), currently available online (Intel 2003b). The histories of this library and the Intel IPP computer vision domain are intertwined, and the OSCVL uses Intel IPP as its optimization layer.

The next subsections summarize key image processing functionality.

Edge Detection

Perhaps the most important low-level vision task is detection of edges in the image. Edges are visual discontinuities of brightness, color, or both. They are usually detected by an automated operation on a small region of pixels. Interpreted correctly, they convey higher-level scene information, particularly the boundaries of objects in the scene.

Multi-Resolution Analysis

When trying to find an object in a scene, size is as important a characteristic as shape or color. Even if you know exactly what shape or color an object is, you need to know how many pixels wide and tall it is. One easy way of performing an analysis without knowing this size is to perform the search on multiple resolutions of an image. Such a set of resolutions of an image is often called an image pyramid.

Template Matching

In computer vision, a template is a canonical representation of an object used for finding the object in a scene. There are many ways to match the template, such as taking the pixel-by-pixel normalized sum of the squared difference between template and image.

String Processing

Processing of character strings is common to many applications and is embodied by several standard library functions across a number of operating systems. Accelerated versions of these functions exist for various platforms taking advantage of specialized hardware capabilities such as SIMD instruction sets. Typical optimized string functions include functions to perform string copy, search, string length, insertion, removal, compare, uppercase, lowercase, and concatenation.

Performance Library Ecosystem

Numerous performance libraries target both similar and different application areas as Intel IPP and are revelant to performance on Intel architecture. These libraries are listed below and then summarized in subsequent sections:

- Intel® QuickAssist Technology

- VSIPL

- OpenMax

- OpenCV

- OpenSSL

- Framewave

- X264

- Multicore Association Standards

- OpenCL

Intel® QuickAssist Technology

Intel QuickAssist Technology is not strictly a performance library per se, but has a similar goal of enabling a set of code that is compatible and optimized across a range of possible processor and coprocessor accelerators. The specific goals of Intel QuickAssist Technology are as follows:

- Enable programming of accelerators to be similar to programming for the IA-32 ISA and Intel® 64 ISA.

- Accelerator component appears as a functional unit through runtime and OS support.

■ Accelerator component shares memory with general purpose processor cores.

■ Runtime distributes work between cores and accelerators.

Intel QuickAssist Technology employs dispatch functions that automatically take advantage of the accelerators, if present in the embedded system. If the accelerators are not available, the function calls dispatch to a version that executes on the general purpose processor. Suppose your application code contains a call to a video processing algorithm such as MPEG2 decode. If the application was executing on an Intel Atom processor the function call would dispatch to an optimized MPEG2 decode function such as one built from Intel IPP components. If the application were executing on a processor with MPEG2 hardware acceleration, the function call would dispatch to a version that makes use of the hardware accelerator. From an application viewpoint, there is no discernable difference other than the potential performance improvement.

Intel QuickAssist Technology is employed in a set of signal processing and security acceleration applications.

VSIPL

Vector Signal Image Processing Library[2] (VSIPL) is an open standard API for signal and image processing libraries. The library specifies hundreds of functions comprising different "builds" termed Core Lite, Core, and Core Plus. Library functionality includes matrix and vector arithmetic, signal processing functions such as FFTs, correlations, and vector averaging, and image processing functionality including histogram operations, convolution, edge detection, and resizing. In addition, the VSIPL forum hosts a reference test suite so library implementors can test conformance. It is compatible with multiple languages including C, C++, and Fortran. It is possible to employ Intel IPP to provide the low level routines that implement the functionality of VSIPL.

---

[2] For further information on VSIPL, please consult www.vsipl.org

OpenMax

OpenMAX is a media library developed by the Khronos Group, an open standards organization. The library targets media acceleration specifically at three abstraction levels and defines three sets of standards that correspond to those levels. The three standards are summarized as:

- *OpenMAX AL (Application Layer).* Standard interface between applications and multimedia middleware.

- *OpenMAX IL (Integration Layer).* Interface for codes used in embedded applications.

- *OpenMAX DL (Development Layer).* API for low level functions such as signal processing functions optimized for particular hardware.

OpenCV

Open Source Computer Vision (OpenCV[3]) targets computer vision applications and features over 500 optimized algorithms such as basic matrix math, image processing algorithms, motion tracking, fitting, and machine learning algorithms. Binary versions of the library are available for Windows[†] and Linux[†]. OpenCV also includes sample applications showing how to employ the library for face recognition, gesture recognition, motion tracking, and mobile robotics. OpenCV is capable of employing Intel IPP functions to implement the lower level routines in the library.

OpenSSL

Open Source SSL (OpenSSL) is an open source project providing core cryptographic functionality and implementations of the SSL and TLS protocols. Secure Socket Layer (SSL) and Transport Layer Security (TLS) are network protocols providing secure communications over the internet. The library is available for Linux, Mac OS[†], BSD, and Windows operating systems. OpenSSL supports cryptographics algorithms such as AES, Blowfish, MD5, RSA, and DSA. Intel IPP has been employed to boost the performance of sample codes (Nagpal) in OpenSSL.

---

[3] For further information on OpenCV, please consult http://opencv.willowgarage.com/wiki/Welcome

Framewave

Framewave[4] is an open source library consisting of image and signal processing routines targeting 32-bit and 64-bit x86 processor-based systems. Binary versions of the library are available targeting Linux, Mac OS, Windows, and Solaris[†] operating systems.

x264

The x264[5] library is licensed under GNU GPL, targets video encoding, and supports H.264, MPEG-4 AVC formats. The library is employed in several video converters with frontends available for FFmpeg, Avidemux, and HandBrake. The library also provides the video services for YouTube[†], Facebook[†], and Hulu[†].

Multicore Association Standards

Multicore Association[6], an industry standards group, is defining a set of multicore processor focused standards. These are termed Multicore Communication API (MCAPI), Multicore Resource Management API (MRAPI), and Multicore Task Management API (MTAPI). The goal is to create a set of OS-agnostic multicore software building blocks. The first standard, MCAPI, was released in 2008. MRAPI and MTAPI are currently under discussion and development.

MCAPI defines three fundamental communication types and operations. The communication types are summarized as:

- *Messages.* Connectionless data transfers

- *Packet channels.* Connected, unidirectional, arbitrary sized data transfers

- *Scalar channels.* Connected, unidirectional, fixed sized data transfers

MCAPI defines an endpoint, which is a communication termination point. MCAPI messages include a send endpoint and a receive endpoint in addition to the data that specifies the source, destination, and transfer. Packet and

---

[4] For further information on Framewave, please consult http://sourceforge.net/projects/framewave/
[5] For further information on x264, please consult http://www.videolan.org/developers/x264.html
[6] For further information on MCA, please consult http://www.multicore-association.org/home.php

scalar channels require the send and receive endpoint to be defined at channel initialization so that subsequent send calls require only the data to be sent and thus limit the data transfer overhead. Packet channels allow arbitrarily sized data items while scalar channels limit the transfers to fixed sized elements. Scalar channels have the advantage of even lower overhead since the size of the data transfer is implicitly defined.

MRAPI will define routines to handle memory management, basic synchronization, resource registration, and resource partitioning in a multicore processor context.

MTAPI will define task lifecycle, placement, priority, and scheduling in a multicore processor context.

OpenCL

Open Computing Language (OpenCL[7]) targets heterogeneous multicore processor systems with a API to specify and control processing on architectures with different ISAs. The programmer specifies compute kernels written in a C99-like language supplemented with vector datatypes. These compute kernels are then compiled and executed by the OpenCL runtime. As the number of heterogeneous compute platforms grows, the expectation is that OpenCL will be used for accelerated computation on systems based on the Intel Atom processor.

Intel® Integrated Performance Primitives Library

The Intel® Integrated Performance Primitives (Intel® IPP) library can provide your application with a significant performance boost by giving you easy access to the single instruction, multiple data (SIMD) instructions available on your processor. The primitives, or low-level functions, in the Intel IPP library are designed to meet the needs of numeric-intensive vector algorithms like image, video and audio processing, digital filtering, string operations and data compression. These areas of performance enhancement are referred to as *domains* within the library.

The Intel Atom processor supports the Supplemental Streaming SIMD Extensions 3 (SSSE3) level of instructions. When using the Intel IPP library with an Intel Atom processor, the library automatically selects those

---

[7] For further information on OpenCL, please consult http://www.khronos.org/opencl/

primitives that are optimized for the SSSE3 instructions. This is referred to as *dispatching*, and is a useful method by which the library automatically adapts your application to the specific processor being used on your platform. Figure 7.2 provides a visual representation of library dispatch. Alternatively, if your application will only ever run on an Intel Atom processor, for example, you can link with a *non-dispatched* variant of the library that contains support for only your specific processor.

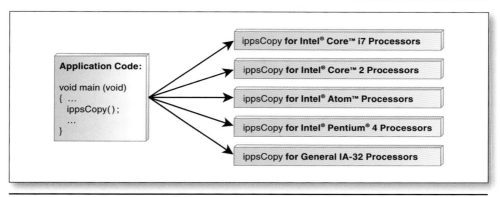

Figure 7.2   Library Dispatch for Processor Targets

Building applications for an Intel Atom processor with the Intel IPP library lets you combine the computational features of a digital signal processor (DSP) with the convenience of a general-purpose processor. Elimination of DSP hardware can substantially lower the cost of your design, and the Intel IPP library provides DSP functionality without significant software complexity.

SIMD Instructions

A DSP is poorly suited to general-purpose tasks; it is designed to quickly execute basic mathematical operations (add, subtract, multiply, and divide) on multiple operands. The DSP repertoire includes a set of very fast multiply and accumulate (MAC) instructions to address matrix math evaluations that appear frequently in convolution, dot product, and other multi-operand math operations. The MAC instructions that comprise much of the code in a DSP application are the equivalent of the SSSE3 instructions. Like the MAC instructions on a DSP, these SSSE3 instructions perform mathematical operations very efficiently on vectors and arrays of data. Unlike a DSP, the

SIMD instructions on an Intel Atom processor are easier to integrate into your application algorithms alongside your complex vector and array mathematical algorithms, because both execute on the same processor and are part of a unified logical execution stream.

For example, an algorithm that changes image brightness by adding (or subtracting) a constant value to each pixel of that image must read the RGB values from memory, add (or subtract) the offset, and write the new pixel values back to memory. When using a DSP coprocessor that image data must be *packaged for the DSP* (placed in a memory area that is accessible by the DSP), the DSP must then be *signaled to execute* the transformation algorithm, and finally the data must be *returned to the general-purpose processor*. Using a general-purpose processor with SIMD instructions simplifies this process of packaging, signaling, and returning the data set.

Intel® IPP Performance Improvement

Figure 7.3 summarizes the level of performance improvements possible using the Intel IPP primitives in a *single-threaded* application. This chart compares the relative performance improvement of the various Intel IPP product domains against the same functions when implemented without the aid of Intel SSE instructions.

The data in the chart in Figure 7.3 was generated using an Intel IPP utility provided with the library called `perfsys`. This utility measures the time to execute each function, within each domain, over a selection of representative inputs. In this case, the `perfsys` measurements were done on a single test machine where the library was configured to use Intel SSE and then again with the library configured to ignore Intel SSE (executed as though the processor was generic and does not support Intel SSE).

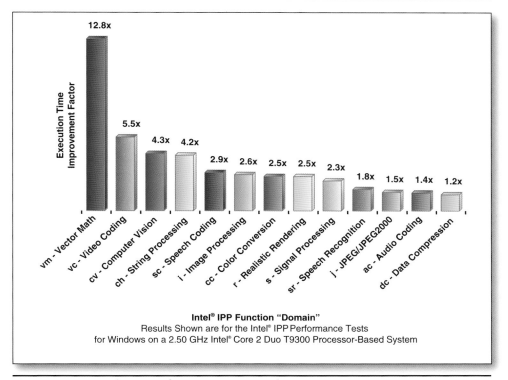

Figure 7.3   Intel® IPP Performance Gains with SIMD Instructions

Real-World Performance Improvement

Figure 7.3 is a somewhat artificial measurement of performance gains. It clearly shows that using SIMD instructions results in faster execution; however, it does not measure the real-world gains you might expect to see from utilizing Intel IPP in your application. The performance gains shown by the chart in Figure 7.3 should not be interpreted as an upper limit of what is possible when using the library—in fact your gains may be better than those shown on the chart!

Your actual performance gains depend heavily on the mix of primitives you use, and how often they are called by your application. For example, if you review the details of the JPEG/JPEG2000 primitive results from the test in the chart in Figure 7.3, which shows an aggregate gain of up to 1.5x over the baseline level (a fifty percent gain), you would see that more than two-thirds of the individual primitives achieve performance gains that are greater than the up to 1.5x shown by the chart. In fact, more than half of the JPEG primitives see an up to 3x improvement over the baseline, with the highest gaining primitive measuring an impressive 45x improvement in execution speed!

To measure real-world performance improvement it is necessary to use a real-world application. The Intel IPP library includes some very useful real-world application code in the form of samples. One of these samples is a version of the popular open source IJG (Independent JPEG Group) library[8]; this library is used by a large number of applications to compress and decompress image files using the JPEG image format.

The version of the IJG library distributed as part of the Intel IPP library samples has been adapted to utilize the low-level library functions. Modifications have been made to the IJG library so it can be compiled and linked to run with or without the Intel IPP primitives. This accommodates very easy testing of the effect of the primitives on real-world applications.

Figure 7.4 represents the time required to perform a set of JPEG encode and decode operations on a collection of images containing random pixels (taller bars correspond to longer execution times). Test images 1 through 7 are compression results and test images 8 through 14 are decompression results. These tests were performed on the same hardware as that used to create the previous `perfsys` chart in Figure 7.3 and were run as single-threaded applications. Blue bars represent the execution time using the original IJG library without the support of the Intel IPP library and orange bars are the execution of the same application on the same test image with a version of the IJG library that employs the Intel IPP library. The numbers at the bottom of each pair of bars (for example, up to 3.2x for image test 1) quantify the real-world performance increase resulting from the use of the Intel IPP library to enhance the performance of the IJG library.

---

[8] For further information on IJG, please consult http://www.ijg.org/

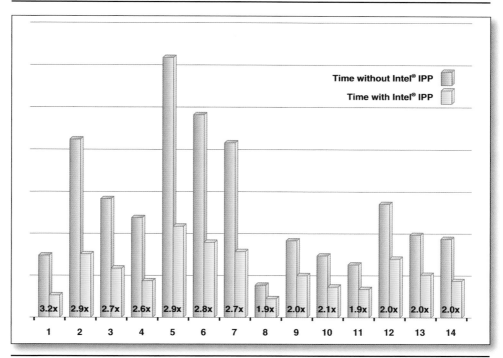

Figure 7.4   JPEG Compress/Decompress Performance without Intel® IPP versus with Intel IPP

Clearly the simpler `perfsys` chart, which averages the performance of all the primitives within an Intel IPP domain, does not tell the whole performance story. Depending on what your application does, how frequently it does it, and which Intel IPP primitives it uses, the savings can be far greater than those measured by the `perfsys` utility. If performance results were predicted based solely on `perfsys` average results we might expect only a 1.5x increase in the application of the Intel IPP library to the IJG library. However, as the real-world performance chart in Figure 7.4 shows, the increase for application of the Intel IPP library to the IJG library varies between up to 1.9x and up to 3.2x.

Other High-level APIs and the Intel® IPP Library

The IJG library is not the only *high-level library* or application that has been performance-enhanced with the Intel IPP library. The library includes a collection of high-level applications and libraries, most supplied in full source format, for easy incorporation into your application. Of particular note are:

■ ZLIB data compression library (ipp_zlib at www.zlib.net)

■ BZIP2 data compression library (ipp_bzip2 at www.bzip.org)

■ GZIP data compression library (ipp_gzip at www.gzip.org)

■ LZO data compression library (ipp_lzopack at www.lzop.org)

■ OpenSSL encryption library (patch for OpenSSL at www.openssl.org)

■ IJG JPEG library (www.ijg.org)

■ UIC image codec (Intel® C++ class library for popular image codecs)

■ UMC media codec (Intel C++ class library for audio/video processing)

■ USC audio and telephony codec (Intel C library for audio processing)

■ ipp_grep regular expression search engine

The applications and libraries listed above are part of a larger collection of samples and supported high-level libraries that are distributed with the Intel IPP library. Additional samples include the implementation of a face detection algorithm, 3D image rendering examples, and a variety of image and multimedia (video plus audio) sample applications.

Threading in the Intel® IPP Library

There is no universal threading solution that is best for all applications. Fortunately the Intel IPP library was designed to be thread-safe (the primitives within the library can be called simultaneously from multiple threads within your application). Applications that use the library can take advantage of threading at the low-level primitive level (that is, within the library via OpenMP†), at the operating system level (for example, native threads), or somewhere in between (for example, Threading Building Blocks).

As of this writing, six variants of the Intel IPP library are delivered: three for IA-32 and three for the Intel® 64 architecture. The three variants within each processor architecture consist of two libraries with multithreading built in (using OpenMP) and one that is single-threaded. All three variants are thread-safe. Note that the OpenMP library represents an indirect dependency on the underlying operating system, since the multithreaded variants of the library can only be used on those platforms for which an Intel-compatible OpenMP library is available (see the following sections for additional information regarding OpenMP and the Intel IPP library).

Threading Choices for Your Intel® IPP Application

In most cases the performance gains due to combining the Intel IPP library with multiple threads of execution that take advantage of the multiple hardware threads common in today's hardware is substantial. Examples of multithreaded Intel IPP applications are part of the sample code that is included with the library. Some of these examples implement threading at the application level, others use the OpenMP threading built into the library primitives.

The quickest way to multithread an Intel IPP application is to use the built-in OpenMP threading of the library. No significant code rework is required on your part and, depending on the functions you use, it can provide additional performance improvements. Note that only about 15–20 percent of the Intel IPP primitives are threaded functions. The remaining 80–85 percent operate only single-threaded functions, regardless of the library variant you link against. Figure 7.5 visually depicts this approach.

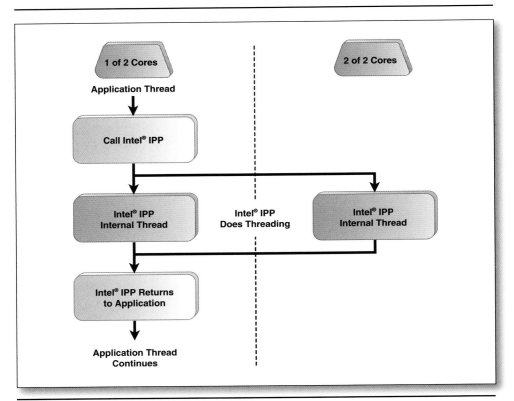

Figure 7.5 Intel® IPP Threading

While linking against the multithreaded variant of the library may be the simplest way to take advantage of multiple hardware threads within your Intel IPP application, this quick approach may not always provide you with optimum results. Since the library primitives are thread-safe, you can implement threads within your application directly and call the primitives simultaneously from your application threads. This gives you more control over threading, and allows you to tune the threading model to meet the precise needs of your application. Figure 7.6 visually depicts this approach.

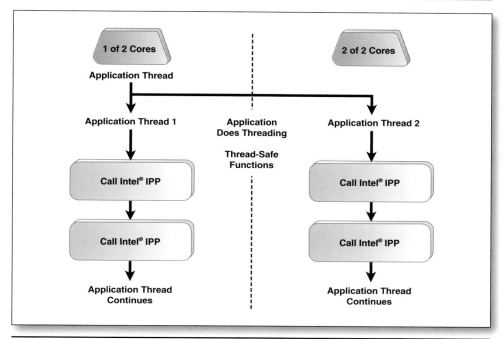

Figure 7.6   Intel® IPP Application Threading

When writing a multithreaded Intel IPP application it is generally recommended that you disable the library's built-in threading. Doing so eliminates competition for hardware thread resources between the OpenMP threading engine and your application's threading mechanism, avoiding an oversubscription of software threads for the available hardware threads.

Disabling internal library threading in a multithreaded application is not a hard and fast rule. For example, if your application has just two threads (such as a GUI thread and a background thread) and the Intel IPP library is only being used by the background thread, then using the internal threading probably makes sense.

Table 7.1 highlights some of the performance improvements that have been achieved by the use of multiple threads of execution in applications employing Intel IPP. Threading was implemented in these examples at the application level and the single-threaded Intel IPP library was used.

Table 7.1   Intel® IPP Application Performance Improvements

Application	Threading Technology	Performance Gain
H.264 decoding	Native threads	~2x on dual-core ~3.2–3.7x on quad-core
Image codec	OpenMP	~1.9x on dual-core
Data compression	Native threads	~10x on quad-core

Memory and Cache Alignment

If you work with large blocks of data, you might expect throughput to be impacted by improper alignment of data with the cache. The Intel IPP library includes memory allocation and alignment functions to address this issue. Additionally, most compilers can pad your data structures for bus-efficient alignment within memory.

What may not be obvious is the importance of cache alignment and spacing of data elements relative to cache lines when implementing parallel threads. If the operations of parallel threads frequently use coincident or shared data structures, the write operations of one thread could potentially invalidate the cache lines associated with the data structures of a parallel thread.

When you use data decomposition to build parallel threads of identical Intel IPP operations, be sure to consider the relative spacing of the decomposed data blocks being operated on by the parallel threads and the spacing of any control data structures used by the primitives within those threads. This is particularly important when the control data structures hold state information that is updated with each iteration of the parallel Intel IPP functions. If these data structures are "too close" (because they share a cache line) an update to one data structure will invalidate the neighboring data structure that is being operated on in parallel.

A simple way to avoid this problem is to allocate your data structures so they occupy cache line multiples (typically 64 bytes). Any wasted bytes used to pad your data structures will more than make up for the lost bus cycles required to refresh a cache line with each iteration of your parallel loop.

OpenMP Threading and the Intel® IPP Library

The low-level primitives within the IPP library represent mostly elemental algorithmic operations (such as small atomic operations). This limits meaningful threading within the library to approximately 15–20 percent of the primitives. As of this writing, the Intel OpenMP library is used within those primitives that are threaded, and is required when you use one of the multithreaded variants of the library.

Multithreaded variants of the library are only supported on the Linux, Windows, and Mac OS X operating systems because the Intel OpenMP library is only available for these platforms. A complete list of the threaded primitives is provided in the `ThreadedFunctionsList.txt` file located in the Intel IPP library's `doc` directory.

Note	The fact that the Intel IPP library is built with the Intel C compiler and the OpenMP library is not a requirement that your application must also be built using these tools. The Intel IPP library is compatible with the C/C++ compiler for your OS platform and is provided ready to link with your application. You can build an Intel IPP application with either your preferred development tools or the Intel tools for your target operating system.

Controlling OpenMP Threading in the Intel® IPP Library

The default maximum number of OpenMP threads used by the multithreaded Intel IPP primitives is equal to the number of hardware threads in your system, which is determined by the number and type of CPUs. That means a quad-core processor with Intel® Hyper-Threading Technology (Intel HT Technology) has eight hardware threads (four cores, each core having two threads), and a dual-core processor without Intel HT Technology has two hardware threads.

There are two Intel IPP primitives available for control and status of OpenMP threading: `ippSetNumThreads()` and `ippGetNumThreads()`. You call `ippGetNumThreads()` to determine the current thread cap and `ippSetNumThreads()` to change the thread cap. The `ippSetNumThreads()` primitive will not allow you to set the thread cap beyond the number of available hardware threads. This thread cap is an upper bound on the number of threads that can be used within a multithreaded primitive. Some Intel IPP functions may use fewer threads than specified by the thread cap, but they will never use more than the thread cap.

To disable OpenMP threading within the library you need to call `ippSetNumThreads(1)` near the beginning of your application. Another method is by linking your application with the single-threaded variant of the library. (Note that disabling OpenMP threading via the `ippSetNumThreads(1)` call does not remove or disable the OpenMP library—it sets the number of OpenMP threads to one.)

The OpenMP library references several configuration environment variables. In particular, `OMP_NUM_THREADS` sets the default number of threads (the thread cap) to be used by the OpenMP library at runtime. However, the Intel IPP library will override this setting, as described above. Other OpenMP applications running on your system that do not use the Intel IPP library might still be affected by the `OMP_NUM_THREADS` environment variable; likewise, other OpenMP applications may be affected by a call to the `ippSetNumThreads()` function within your Intel IPP application.

Nested OpenMP

If your Intel IPP application implements multithreading by using OpenMP, at the application level, the threaded Intel IPP primitives your application calls may execute as single-threaded primitives. This happens when an Intel IPP function is called from within an OpenMP parallelized section of code and if nested parallelization has been disabled, which is the default case for the OpenMP library.

By nesting parallel OpenMP regions you risk creating a large number of threads that oversubscribe the number of hardware threads available. Creating parallel regions always incurs overhead, and the overhead associated with nesting parallel OpenMP regions may outweigh the benefit.

In general, OpenMP threaded applications that use the Intel IPP library should disable multithreading within the library, either by calling `ippSetNumThreads(1)` or by linking against the single-threaded IPP library.

Core Affinity

Some of the Intel IPP functions in the signal processing domain execute multiple parallel threads that are designed to exploit a merged L2 cache. These functions (such as single and double precision FFT, Div, and Sqrt) need a multi-core shared cache processor to achieve their maximum multithreaded performance. In other words, the threads within these primitives should execute on independent CPU cores located on a single die with a shared cache.

To aid in the configuration of the OpenMP library an Intel IPP function is available to automatically determine what sort of CPU your code is running on (Intel HT Technology enabled or not, shared-cache or not, and so on) and effectively configures the `KMP_AFFINITY` environment variable to the optimum value for the processor in use. Calling `ippSetAffinity()` from within your Intel IPP application has precedence over the `KMP_AFFINITY` environment variable.

The main effect of calling `ippSetAffinity()` is to restrict OpenMP thread execution to an optimal hardware thread subset that reduces communication overhead and cache line invalidation cycles, and to ensure that highly optimized Intel IPP functions run on independent cores, especially when using processors with Intel HT Technology. In some instances, running two Intel IPP threads in parallel on a pair of logical processors can cause degradation in the multithreaded function's performance. Intel HT Technology takes advantage of unused CPU resources, or "spare" cycles. The Intel IPP functions are optimized to be CPU-intensive and frequently do not leave many "spare" cycles for sharing with a second thread. Thus, optimum Intel IPP function performance is generally best achieved by ensuring that parallel threads do not run under Intel HT Technology.

Operating System Requirements

In general, the operating system requirements of the Intel IPP primitives are minimal. Access to only a few functions within the standard C library is required, and access to an OpenMP multithreading library for the multithreaded variants of the library (see the previous section). The library primitives make no direct calls for operating system services and make no assumptions about the type of services that may be available within the underlying operating system. Requests for memory allocation and multithreading services are handled by an optionally replaceable intermediate interface.

The primitives do not use locks, semaphores, or static memory; they rely only on the calling application's stack and the standard C library memory allocation routines (malloc/realloc/calloc/free) for occasional temporary and static memory storage. To eliminate the Intel IPP library's dependency on these C library functions you can use the `i_malloc` interface to substitute your own memory allocation routines for the standard C library routines (see the Intel IPP `i_malloc` sample for details).

Standard C ABI

While the Intel IPP library binaries are built using the Intel C++ compiler, it is not necessary to use the Intel compiler for your code in order to utilize the library in your application. Since the library uses a C interface there are no name mangling complexities to contend with (only standard C name mangling rules apply) and the Application Binary Interface (ABI), or application binary interface, is compatible with the popular compilers and linkers used on the validated binary platforms. It is quite common that developers use the Microsoft Visual Studio† compiler for developing Intel IPP applications for the Microsoft Windows operating system and the popular gcc compiler for the Linux operating system.

Application to Non-Supported Operating Systems

As of this writing, the Intel IPP library is delivered on five different operating systems: Microsoft Windows, Linux, Mac OS X, QNX† and VxWorks†. Because the multithreaded variants of the library require access to an Intel-compatible version of the OpenMP library, only the Windows, Linux, and Mac OS X versions of the IPP library are available in a multithreaded format (dynamic and static linkage options). The remaining two operating systems, QNX and VxWorks, are limited to single-threaded static variants of the Intel IPP library.

Application of the Intel IPP library to a "non-supported" operating system requires that two essential conditions be satisfied: compatibility with one of the ABIs defined by the target operating systems listed above and access to a standard C library to satisfy the memory allocation routines (malloc/realloc/calloc/free) used by the library primitives, or replacement of those routines using the `i_malloc` interface. If these conditions are met it is possible to apply the single-threaded static Intel IPP library to applications built for a *non-supported* operating system. Reiterating, only the single-threaded variant of the Intel IPP library can be used on a *non-supported* operating system because the OpenMP library is required for operation of the multithreaded variants of the library.

In essence, applications that run in an environment that follows the ABI rules used by the Linux operating system and the gcc compiler are candidates for application of the Intel IPP library. Likewise, applications built for runtime environments compatible with the Windows calling conventions and the Microsoft Visual C/C++ compiler are also targets for use of the Intel IPP library.

Using the Intel® IPP Library with an RTOS

Use of the Intel IPP library does not require that you limit your applications to general-purpose operating systems like Windows or Linux. The library can be successfully applied to a real-time operating system (RTOS) as well, either one of the explicitly supported real-time operating systems (QNX and VxWorks) or a compatible but *non-supported* RTOS (as defined above). The decision to avoid the use of locks and semaphores within the Intel IPP library, and the atomic nature of the functions within the library, means the primitives are safe to use in a deterministic application. The primitives in the library have not been "characterized" for deterministic applications; that is, they have not been defined to meet specific execution time requirements, so you should measure an individual primitive's execution time before deciding if it is suitable for use inside the time-critical sections of your code. The `perfsys` tool mentioned earlier in this chapter can be used to make such measurements.

An example of the value of applying the Intel IPP library to an RTOS can be illustrated with the TenAsys INtime RTOS[†] for Windows (www.tenasys. com). The INtime RTOS is a special-purpose operating system designed to run alongside Windows, allowing two operating systems to run side-by-side on a single hardware platform (for example, Windows and the INtime RTOS).

One can build Intel IPP applications for the INtime RTOS because it implements an ABI that is compatible with Microsoft Windows (note that the INtime RTOS has a unique API, but uses Windows-compatible function calling and return rules) and uses the Microsoft Visual Studio integrated development environment as its build and debug platform. Likewise, the Windows CE operating system can also support Intel IPP applications (on the IA-32 platform only), for similar reasons (see the Intel IPP Windows CE sample for more information).

Combining the Intel IPP library with an RTOS gives you a means to easily add the raw performance gains of SIMD instructions to the real-time determinism of an RTOS. In some applications displacing a DSP requires both performance *and* determinism.

Busy versus Idle

The JPEG performance charts presented previously were based on data collected from an otherwise idle system. That is, only the JPEG test application was running when the measurements were made, and there were no other significant activities consuming processor cycles on the test machine. An idle machine represents ideal conditions but does not necessarily reflect real-world, real-time performance.

To measure real-world variations in execution time of the JPEG test application the test machine was "loaded down" by multiple simultaneous but noncritical system-intensive activities. Figure 7.7 shows the relative determinism when executing these tests.

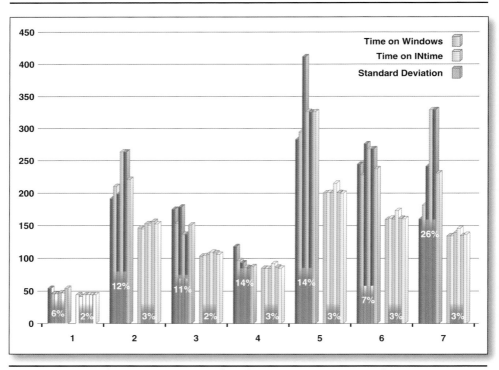

Figure 7.7 Relative Determinism of Intel® IPP Functions on Windows versus INtime

The measurements in the chart in Figure 7.7 include the same seven encoding variants (1–7) used for the chart in Figure 7.4; the seven decoding variants (8–14) were omitted to keep the chart readable. Each blue and orange cluster contains six bars, one for each of six successive test runs. The gray bars overlaying each cluster show the standard deviation of the bars in each cluster expressed as a percent of the mean execution time of that cluster.

Controlling the precedence, or priority, of critical and noncritical processes on a general-purpose operating system is always difficult. The interference of noncritical processes with the execution time of the critical JPEG test application is illustrated by the difference between blue bars and the orange bars in the chart in Figure 7.7, as well as the variability of the bars. On an RTOS your control over the priority of processes is much more refined, and the critical JPEG encode application consistently executes at its optimum rate (green bars).

In this example, the real-time Intel IPP application's runtime on a busy system shows variations of 3 percent or less of the mean time to execute. The same application executing on a busy general-purpose OS exhibits runtime variations between 6 percent and 26 percent. On an idle machine the blue and orange bars are nearly identical; the key difference between the two operating systems is their level of guaranteed determinism, not performance.

Linkage Options

On the Windows, Linux and Mac OS X platforms the Intel IPP library is available as either a dynamic (shared) library or a static library. There are no functional differences between these two library types; both contain the same set of functions. Deciding which of these two linkage models to use depends on how you choose to build and deploy your application. The tradeoff between dynamic and static linkage models is one of complexity versus size versus flexibility. Dynamic linkage allows multiple applications to share code and includes the potential to reduce the overall size of the deployment, but only if enough applications share the library. Static linkage is simpler to deploy and generates a smaller code footprint if the library is used sparsely or by only a few applications.

Since each application has its own unique set of constraints, you should consider the installation and runtime constraints and requirements of your application, as well as the development resources available and the release, update, and distribution needs of your application. Answering the following questions can help guide that decision process:

■ Executable and installation package size. Are there limits to the size of the application executable? Are there limits to the size of the installation package?

■ *File locations at installation time.* During installation, are there restrictions on where deployed files can be placed?

■ *Number of coexisting Intel IPP–based applications.* Does the application include multiple executables based on the Intel IPP library? Are there other Intel IPP applications that may coexist on the end-user's system?

■ *Memory available at runtime.* What memory constraints exist on the end-users' system?

■ *Kernel-mode versus user-mode.* Is the Intel IPP application a device driver or other "ring 0" application that executes in kernel-mode?

■ *Number of processor types supported by the Intel IPP application.* Will the application be installed on systems with a range of SIMD instruction sets, or is the application intended for use on processors that support only one SIMD instruction set?

■ *Development resources.* What resources are available for maintaining and updating custom Intel IPP components? What level of effort is acceptable for incorporating new processor optimizations into the application?

■ *Release, distribution, and update.* How often will the application be updated? Can application components be distributed independently or are they always packaged together?

Table 7.2 compares the four most common linkage models used to build Intel IPP applications. The two rows that compare executable and total binary size are relative measurements, not absolute measurements.

Table 7.2   Intel® IPP Linkage Model Comparison

	Standard Dynamic	**Custom Dynamic**	**Dispatched Static**	**Non-dispatched Static**
Optimizations	All SIMD sets	All SIMD sets	All SIMD sets	Single SIMD set
Distribution	Executable(s) and standard Intel IPP DLLs	Executable(s) and custom DLLs	Executable(s) only	Executable(s) only
Library Updates	Redistribute as-is	Rebuild and redistribute	Recompile application and redistribute	Rebuild custom library, recompile application, and redistribute
Executable Only Size	Small	Small	Large	Medium
Total Binary Size	Large	Medium	Medium	Small
Kernel Mode	No	No	Yes	Yes

Standard Dynamic

The standard dynamic and dispatched static models are the simplest options to use in building Intel IPP applications. The standard dynamic library is ready to use for both development and deployment. The library includes the full set of processor optimizations and provides the benefit of runtime code sharing between multiple Intel IPP-based applications. Detection of the runtime processor, and dispatching to the appropriate optimization layer is automatic.

Benefits of this model include:

■ Automatic runtime dispatch of processor-specific optimizations.

■ Ability to redistribute minor updates without a recompile or relink.

■ Ability to share a single library distribution among multiple Intel IPP executables.

■ More efficient use of memory at runtime for multiple Intel IPP applications.

Considerations when using this model include:

- Potentially large deployment (install) package size.

- Application executable requires access to Intel IPP runtime DLLs (Shared Objects).

- Not appropriate for kernel-mode (ring-0) and/or device-drivers.

- Potential performance penalty when the DLLs (SOs) are first loaded.

Custom Dynamic

If your application needs dictate the use of a dynamic library but the standard DLL (SO) files are too large, you may benefit from building a custom dynamic library, especially if the number of Intel IPP functions used in your application is small (which is common).

Benefits of this model include:

- Automatic runtime dispatch of processor-specific optimizations.

- Ability to redistribute minor updates without a recompile or relink.

- Ability to share a single library distribution among multiple Intel IPP executables.

- More efficient use of memory at runtime for multiple Intel IPP applications.

- Reduced hard-drive footprint compared to standard DLLs (SOs).

Considerations when using this model include:

- Application executable requires access to custom DLLs (SOs).

- Not appropriate for kernel-mode (ring-0) and/or device-drivers.

- Potential performance penalty when the DLLs (SOs) are first loaded.

- Additional resources required to create and maintain your custom DLL (SO).

Dispatched Static

Like the standard dynamic library, the dispatched static library is one of the simplest options to use for building Intel IPP applications. It is also the simplest to deploy, since no separate DLL (SO) files are required to be distributed. The standard static library is ready to link and includes the full set of processor optimizations. Detection of the runtime processor and dispatching to the appropriate optimization layer within the library is automatic (be sure you call the `ippInit()` function before using the library).

Linking against a static library has the advantage of avoiding shared library version conflicts (also known as "DLL hell") and automatically including only those functions that your application requires. Your application includes all the optimization layers required to support all processors, but only for those functions called by your application, providing an excellent tradeoff between size, performance, and deployment complexity. The distribution of applications built with a static link library is very simple because the application executable is complete and self-contained.

Benefits of this model include:

■ Automatic runtime dispatch of processor-specific optimizations.

■ Simple recompile/relink/redistribute executable for updates.

■ Single self-contained application executable.

■ Smaller footprint than most DLL (SO) distributions.

Considerations when using this model include:

■ Intel IPP code may be duplicated across multiple Intel IPP executables.

■ Appropriate for real-time and non-supported operating systems.

Non-Dispatched Static

If you need to minimize the footprint of your Intel IPP application, you should link against a non-dispatched static version of the library. The development process is slightly more complex than that required of the standard dispatched static library but yields an executable containing only the optimization layer required for your target processor. This model achieves the smallest footprint at the expense of restricting your optimization to one specific processor type (one SIMD instruction set).

This linkage model is most appropriate when a self-contained application is needed and only one processor type (or SIMD instruction set) is required. It is also the recommended linkage model for use in kernel-mode (ring-0) and/or device-driver applications. A common use is embedded applications where the application is guaranteed to be bundled with only one processor type.

Benefits of this model include:

■ Small executable size with support for only one processor type.

■ An executable suitable for kernel-mode (ring-0) and/or device-driver applications.

■ Self-contained application executable that does not require Intel IPP runtime DLLs or SOs to run.

■ Single self-contained application executable.

■ Smaller footprint than most DLL (SO) distributions.

Considerations when using this model include:

■ Intel IPP code may be duplicated across multiple Intel IPP executables.

■ Appropriate for real-time and non-supported operating systems.

■ Executable will run on only the optimized processor type (or greater).

Optimizing 3D Applications for Intel® Atom™ Platforms

Platforms based on the Intel Atom processor and the POWERVR† SGX† graphics core, such as those intended for the in-vehicle infotainment (IVI) market, can deliver a tremendous 3D graphics experience in a very low power envelope. This, however, requires that the application be written so that the platform can operate in its most efficient manner. This involves optimizing communication between the CPU and the graphics core, as well as appropriately distributing tasks between both components.

The graphics core supports 3D acceleration features that allow off-loading tasks from the CPU that the graphics processing unit (GPU) can execute faster. However, the graphics core is also constrained by the power envelope and does not pretend to compete with high-end video cards found in the desktop environment. For this reason it may not be appropriate to offload to the GPU tasks not directly related to 3D scene rendering—especially if a fluent 3D experience is expected. Take, for example, scene geometry creation processing. Even though it is possible to defer a large part of this processing to vertex shader code executed on the GPU, if the geometry or significant portions of it remain static over a large number of frames, pre-computing the geometry on the CPU and sending ready-to-render data to the GPU will probably yield a better balanced load on the platform components than letting the GPU redo this same operation on the same data at each frame.

From an API perspective, OpenGL† allows multiple ways of interacting with the GPU: immediate mode, vertex arrays, display list, and vertex buffer objects (VBOs). These, however, exhibit very different performance patterns. On desktop systems, all modes may provide adequate performance for many situations, but on low-power platforms, it is often of utmost importance to select the most efficient API mode.

This section summarizes a set of techniques that can be used to optimize the communication between the CPU and the graphics subsystem and to achieve a good balance of the tasks between both components. The techniques covered are not specific to embedded or low-power platforms. However, they are critical in achieving optimal performance on low-power platforms based on Intel Atom processors and POWERVR SGX graphics cores.

Although the discussion uses the OpenGL API, the guidelines given can also be applied to applications using the Direct3D† API.

Scene Content and Data Organization

The first aspect to consider is the content of the scene being submitted to the GPU for rendering. The application should use a scene data organization (scene graph) that allows it to effectively reduce the scene content according to the current viewpoint. As an extreme example, a 3D navigation application should not request the GPU to draw an entire city when the current view only shows a few streets away from the current position. Furthermore, the screen resolution of the target system should be taken into account when selecting the size of the textures to be applied to the 3D surfaces. For example, there is no point in using a 1024 × 1024 pixel resolution texture for items that, under normal conditions, will not be wider than a hundred pixels on the screen. Reducing the size of the textures improves performance of the graphics pipeline and also allows the application to fit more textures into the video memory.

OpenGL API Implementation

The OpenGL API offers multiple choices to transfer the scene data to the GPU, although they exhibit very different levels of efficiency. The immediate mode OpenGL API functions such as `glVertex3f()` used between `glBegin()` and `glEnd()` function pairs, should be avoided. This is because this approach requires far too many interactions with the graphics subsystem to render a complete scene. It also transfers the scene data in several tiny chunks, which is highly inefficient. Even worse, the data transferred contains redundancy in terms of vertex coordinates, since adjacent triangles often include common vertices.

Vertex Buffer Objects

Contrary to the immediate mode API, the vertex buffer objects (VBOs) technique offers a much more efficient approach. VBOs are buffers that can be allocated in video memory, loaded with data pertaining to large sets of vertices, and be referenced from any subsequent operation for the next frame or any subsequent one, without the need to repeatedly transfer the data. This technique drastically reduces the number of OpenGL API function invocations and corresponding data transfers. Additionally, through the use of a combination of vertex arrays and associated index arrays, VBOs also provide the means to avoid redundant vertex data for shared vertices. This not only reduces the size of the data set, but also allows the render pipeline to avoid repeating the same processing for duplicate vertices.

Pre-Compute Static Scene Elements

To leverage the full benefits of VBOs it is very important to pre-compute as many geometry elements as possible. Elements that are purely static or that remain fixed for many consecutive frames will then require no per-frame processing on the CPU and almost no data transfer. When the scene geometry needs to be updated, the `glBufferSubData()` function allows updating only the affected portions of the VBO.

Vertex data consists typically in more than just vertex coordinates. Texture coordinates are usually present as well. The way the data is laid out in the buffer may also influence performance of the rendering process. One approach to organize vertex data consists in interleaving of the various data types for each consecutive vertex. For example, vertex coordinates of first vertex followed by texture coordinates of first vertex, then vertex coordinates of second vertex, texture coordinates of second vertex, and so on. This interleaved vertex data scheme often proves beneficial, since all data pertaining to a same vertex has a much higher chance of being available from the GPU cache during processing.

Avoid Unnecessary State Changes

Reducing the number of OpenGL state changes is one of the most important ways to improve the performance of a 3D application. One cause of state changes is the changes to the model-view matrix, which can be performed, for example, to position or scale an object in the scene. Typical code using this would include a pair of `glPushMatrix()` and `glPopMatrix()` calls surrounding calls to `glScale()` and `glTranslate()`, followed themselves by the code doing the actual drawing of the object in its default size and position, typically the origin. This change in the model-view matrix represents a state change in the GL state machine for every object that is constructed this way and a state change often implies a possibly far-reaching flush of the GL pipeline with potentially big impact on performance. This is particularly true for the graphics cores that implement tile-based deferred rendering (TBDR) as is the case on platforms such as those featuring the Intel Atom processor Z5xx Series and Intel® System Controller Hub US15W (Intel SCH US15W), and will be the case on similar future platforms. To avoid this performance impact, the geometry of the objects should be fully pre-computed in the VBO data so that no final positioning or scaling needs be done and the only changes to the model-view matrix are then due to viewpoint changes.

Front-to-Back Sorting Is Not Beneficial; Favor Render State Sorting

There are other causes for state changes and not all of them can be removed. For that reason, when rendering complex scenes, it is particularly important to architect the rendering code so that geometry is sorted based on rendering state. This allows drawing the largest possible collection of elements for each state, thereby reducing the number of state changes for the overall scene. One way to achieve this is to maintain a separate scene graph, sometimes referred to as a *render graph*, which reflects the render state of the scene elements instead of their logical relationships or spatial repartition.

Worth noting is that TBDR will not benefit from front-to-back sorting of scene elements as is typical on desktop systems. It is therefore very important to adapt the geometry sorting scheme to the platform.

An application often uses many different textures and changing the current texture also represents a state change in the GL pipeline. Assuming these are the only state changes the application actually requires, it could then sort the geometry based on the textures. The drawing code would then iterate through the various textures and issue a `glDrawElements()` call for each, using an appropriate offset in the array of vertices that was previously loaded into the VBO. Each invocation of `glDrawElements()` would draw all the triangles that use a same texture.

With such an implementation the CPU will usually be dispatching enough work for the GPU to operate independently for some time, thereby allowing the CPU to remain idle part of the time or to perform other tasks.

Texture Atlases

If the number of textures is very large and only a low number of triangles can be drawn by each `glDrawElements()` invocation, the approach described above may fail to yield the expected performance. This can usually be addressed by grouping multiple textures together in what is often referred to as a *texture atlas*. A texture atlas is a large texture which contains several smaller textures that are often used together in rendering. The texture coordinates can then be adapted to use the appropriate part of the atlas for each surface, corresponding to the original single texture. As a consequence, many more surfaces can be rendered by a single `glDrawElements()` and the corresponding `glBindTexture()` calls are eliminated.

Performance Results

The techniques discussed in this section, along with others discussed in the original white paper (Verbeiren and Lecluse, 2010[9]), helped double the performance[10] of the sample application in terms of achieved frame rate while dividing the CPU usage by four.

Additional recommendations are detailed for implementations that use OpenGL ES API on POWERVR SGX enabled devices in the document titled *POWERVR SGX OpenGL ES 2.0 Application Development Recommendations* (Imagination Technologies Ltd., 2009[11]). The following list shows a few of the key elements covered in the document:

- Use depth culling and always clear depth buffer at the beginning of each frame.

- Use mipmaps. On the POWERVR SGX, bilinear filtering comes at almost no performance cost, but you should limit the mipmapping mode to GL_LINEAR_MIPMAP_NEAREST for best performance. Mipmaps increase texture memory footprint by 33 percent but allows the graphics core to use a lower-resolution mipmap when possible.

- Consider using compressed textures. The decompression can be done in hardware and the smaller size in memory may actually speed up texture data reading.

- Smaller texture formats (bits per pixel) may bring immediate performance boosts.

- The GPU uses a 32-bit floating point depth buffer, and as a result, higher precision in z-buffering can be obtained by using an inverted depth range.

For complete details and more information, refer to the referenced Imagination Technologies document.

---

[9] Optimizing 3D Applications for Platforms Based on Intel® Atom™ Processors. 2010.
http://edc.intel.com/Download.aspx?id=3422&returnurl=/Software/Downloads/IEGD/default.aspx

[10] Performance results are based on certain tests measured on specific computer systems. Any difference in system hardware, software or configuration will affect actual performance. For more information go to http://www.intel.com/performance.

[11] POWERVR SGX OpenGL ES 2.0 Application Development Recommendations, Imagination Technologies. 2009
http://www.imgtec.com/factsheets/SDK/POWERVR%20SGX.OpenGL%20ES%202.0%20Application%20
Development%20Recommendations.1.1f.External.pdf

Hardware-Accelerated Video Decode

Platforms based on the Intel Atom processor provide a dedicated graphics and video engine to enhance the media experience on small-footprint/low-power consumption/low-cost designs. The Intel SCH US15W chipset featuring hardware video acceleration relieves the decode burden from the Intel Atom processor and reduces power consumption of the system.

Full hardware acceleration of H.264[12], MPEG2[13], VC1[14], MPEG4[15], and WMV9[16] is supported, which eliminates the need for software decode and off-loads the host processor (Girotra, 2009[17]). Using a video engine to decode video reduces the CPU workload by more than 50 percent (Verma, 2010[18]). It requires the application, such as a media player, to use VA API to communicate with Intel Embedded Media and Graphics Driver (EMGD) to maximize utilization of the video engine. By default, if the media player or codecs are not able to use the video engine the media playback will be handled by the CPU, which in turn affects the media experience, as well the overall system performance. Platforms based on the Intel Atom processor, such as the Intel® Atom™ processor E6xx series, also provide a video encode engine, which can be used for accelerating the process of encoding video. Video encoding is necessary to compress a video bit stream into a format that can be stored and transmitted easily with limited overhead.

Simultaneous encode and decode of HD streams is possible by using the video encode/decode engine. An example of this use case is the Media Phone market segment, which is covered in detail in Chapter 2. The media phone's camera continuously captures video, encodes the video stream, and transmits the encoded stream to another system (or to the same system), where the video is decoded. The media phone uses the video encode/decode engines while maintaining very low levels of CPU utilization.

---

[12] ITU-T Rec. H.264 / ISO/IEC 11496-10, "Advanced Video Coding", Final Committee Draft, Document JVTE022, September 2002

[13] ISO/IEC 13818-2, "Information Technology – Generic coding of moving pictures and associated audio information: video", 1995

[14] SMPTE 421M, "VC-1 Compressed Video Bitstream Format and Decoding Process", Final Draft SMPTE Standard, 2006

[15] ISO/IEC 14496-2, "Information Technology – Coding of audio-visual objects – Part2: Visual", 3rd Edition, 2004

[16] Srinivasan et. al, "Windows Media Video 9: overview and applications", pp. 851-875, Signal Processing: Image Communication, vol. 19, October 2004

[17] A. Girotra, "Hardware- Accelerated Video Decode on the Intel® Atom™ Processor with the Intel® System Controller Hub US15W Chipset Platform," 2009
http://download.intel.com/design/intarch/papers/322503.pdf

[18] I. Verma., "Enabling Hardware Accelerated Playback for Intel® Atom™/Intel® US15W Platform and IEGD Case Study Using MPlayer on Moblin", 2010 http://edc.intel.com/Download.aspx?id=3476&returnurl=/Software/Technical-Documents/default.aspx

For the complete details about enabling hardware accelerated decode for platforms based on the Intel Atom processor refer to the white paper "Enabling Hardware Accelerated Playback for Intel® Atom™/Intel® US15W Platform and IEGD Case Study Using MPlayer on Moblin" (Verma). For a deeper understanding of the technical details in the hardware accelerated video decode refer to the white paper "Hardware-Accelerated Video Decode on the Intel® Atom™ Processor with the Intel® System Controller Hub US15W Chipset Platform" (Girotra).

Summary

Performance libraries enable developers to use prepackaged highly optimized routines and help eliminate the need to "reinvent the wheel" for functionality that already exists or when moving to a new processor. The Intel Integrated Performance Primitives is one such library that offers optimized routines in a number of embedded application domains including digital signal processing, cryptography, and image processing.

Intel IPP enables a variety of uses in multi-core processing and flexibility in linkage models which enable the embedded developer to harness processor specific functionality.

A number of industry standard libaries exist that can be deployed on systems based on the Intel Atom processor and help application porting from one architecture to another. Examples of these industry standard libraries include Multicore Assocation's Multicore Communication API and VSIPL.

Since many Intel Atom processors integrate graphics acceleration and some integrate hardware media acceleration, some tips for optimizing 3D graphics and hardware acceleration were also discussed.

Chapter 8

Performance Optimization

We should forget about small efficiencies, say about 97 percent of the time: premature optimization is the root of all evil.

—Donald Knuth

Practioners of performance tuning must deal with increasing levels of complexity in both the targeted applications and the underlying embedded systems executing the applications. This is in part due to the level of integration and faster speeds of current and future embedded systems. Software developers now need to concern themselves with the performance of a complex system comprised of potentially several processor cores. In addition, focusing on one aspect of performance such as execution time of the application is not enough anymore. Now, performance as measured by power utilization must also be considered. To further complicate the issue, it is possible for an optimization focused on a single processor core, multiple processor cores, or power to adversely affect performance in another area. Embedded developers targeting an Intel® Atom™ processor migration require knowledge of a performance optimization process employing the right tools and analysis techniques. This optimization process must integrate tuning steps for single core performance, multi-core performance, and power performance. Each of these tuning steps builds upon each other and is equally important; it can mean the difference between a successful and an unsuccessful migration.

The quality of tools support has a direct impact on the effectiveness of your optimization efforts. Performance tools that target single processor core performance provide insight into the application and how the application is behaving at the level of the microarchitecture. Multi-core performance tools provide insight into how the application is executing in the context of Intel® Hyper-Threading Technology (Intel HT Technology) and multi-core processing. Finally, performance tools focused on power optimization provide insight into application behavior that impacts power utilization. Understanding the capabilities of tools and how to use them is critical to your Intel Atom processor migration.

This chapter instructs on the performance optimization process for systems based on the Intel Atom processor. First, an overview of the optimization process is discussed followed by a description of the tools employed in this process. The steps of single processor core performance analysis and tuning are detailed. Next, multi-core performance analysis and tuning techniques are discussed. Finally, power analysis and tuning techniques are shared. After reading this chapter, you will understand the tools and process required to optimize the performance of your application executing on the Intel Atom processor.

Optimization Process

Good software design seeks a balance between simplicity and efficiency. Performance of the application is an aspect of software design; however correctness and stability are typically prerequisite to extensive performance tuning efforts. A typical development cycle is depicted in Figure 8.1 and consists of four phases: design, implementation, debugging, and tuning. The development cycle is iterative and concludes when performance and stability requirements are met. Figure 8.1 further depicts a more detailed look inside of the tuning phase, which consists of single processor core optimization, multi-core processor optimization, and power optimization.

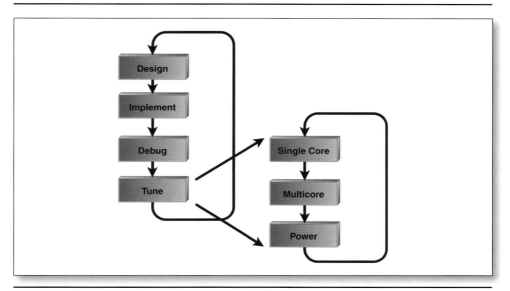

Figure 8.1   Development and Optimization Process

One key fact to highlight about the optimization process is that changes made during this phase can require another round of design, implementation, and debug. It is hoped that a candidate optimization would require minimal changes, but there are no guarantees. Each proposed change required as a result of a possible optimization should be evaluated in terms of stability risk, implementation effort, and performance benefit.

Similarly, the tune step is also iterative with the goal of reaching a satisfactory equilibrium between single core, multi-core, and power performance. The components of the tune step are summarized as follows:

■ *Single processor core tuning*. Optimization of the application assuming execution on one Intel Atom processor core. This step focuses on increasing performance, which is typically the reduction of execution time.

■ *Multi-core tuning*. Optimization of the application taking advantage of parallel technology including Intel Hyper-Threading Technology and multiple processor cores. This step focuses on increasing performance, which is typically the reduction of execution time.

■ *Power tuning*. Optimization of the application focusing on power utilization. This step focuses on reducing the amount of power used in accomplishing the same amount of work.

Single Processor Core Tuning

Single processor core tuning focuses on improving the behavior of the application executing on one physical Intel Atom processor core. Intel Hyper-Threading Technology is not considered during this phase; it enables one physical processor core to appear as two cores and introduces issues more related to multi-core processing. This tuning step isolates the behavior of the application from more complicated interactions with other threads or processes on the system. This step is not entirely focused on what traditionally is called serial tuning because parallelism in the form of vector processing or acceleration technology can be considered.

The foundation of performance tuning is built upon complementary assertions that of the Pareto principle and Amdahl's law. The Pareto principle, colloquially known as the 80/20 rule, states that 80 percent of the time spent in an application is in 20 percent of the code. This observation helps prioritize optimization efforts to the areas of highest impact, namely the most frequently executed portions of the code. Amdahl's law provides guidance on the limits of optimization. For example, if your optimization can only be applied to 75 percent of the application, the maximum theoretical speedup is 4 times.

Single processor core tuning is itself comprised of multiple steps, which are characterized as first gaining an understanding of the application and then tuning based upon general performance analysis and tuning and then analysis and tuning specific to the Intel Atom processor. The single processor core tuning process is summarized by the following steps, which are detailed later in the chapter:

1. *Benchmark*. Develop a benchmark that represents typical application usage.

2. *Profile*. Analyze and understand the architecture of the application.

3. *Compiler optimization*. Use aggressive optimizations if possible.

4. *General microarchitecture tuning*. Tune based upon insight from general performance analysis statistics. These statistics, such as clock

cycles per instruction retired, are generally accepted performance analysis statistics that can be employed regardless of the underlying architecture.

5. *Intel® Atom™ processor tuning.* Tune based on insight about known processor "glass jaws." These include statistics and techniques to isolate performance issues specific to the Intel Atom processor.

Multi-Core Processor Tuning

The focus of multi-core processor tuning is on the effective use of parallelism that takes advantage of more than one processor core. This step pertains to both Intel Hyper-Threading Technology and true multi-core processing. There are some issues specific to each; where appropriate these differences are highlighted. Second, at the application level, two techniques allow you to take advantage of multiple processor cores, multitasking and multithreading. *Multitasking* is the execution of multiple operating system processes on a system. In the context of one application, multitasking requires the division of work between distinct processes and special effort is required to share data between processes. *Multithreading* is the execution of multiple threads and by default assumes memory is shared, which introduces its own set of concerns. This chapter limits itself to discussion of multithreading because multitasking is a more mature technology and one where the operating system governs much of the policy of execution. Multithreading in the context of the Intel Atom processor is much more under the control of the software developer.

Developing software for multi-core processors requires good analysis and design techniques. A wealth of information on these techniques is available in literature by Mattson et al., Breshears, and many others.

Tuning of multithreaded applications on the Intel Atom processor requires ensuring good performance when the application is executing on both, logical processor cores available via Intel Hyper-Threading Technology, and multiple physical processor cores. General multithreading issues that affect performance regardless of the architecture must be addressed. These issues include for example lock contention and workload balance. One of the performance concerns when executing under Intel Hyper-Threading Technology is on the shared resources of the processor core. For example, the caches are effectively shared between two concurrently executing threads. In a worst case scenario, it is possible for one thread to cause the other to miss in the cache on every access.

Tuning for multi-core processors adds another level of complication as the possible thread interactions and cache behavior can be even more complicated. It is possible for two threads to cause false sharing, which limits performance but can be easily addressed. Understanding techniques to analyze performance and how to mitigate these performance issues are essential.

Converting a serial application to take advantage of multithreading requires an approach that uses the generic development cycle, consisting of these five phases: Analysis, Design, Implementation, Debug, and Tune. There are threading tools that help with code analysis, debugging, and performance tuning. Refer back to Chapter 4 for more information about software development tools and choices that are used throughout the tuning cycle.

1. *Analysis*. Develop a benchmark that represents typical system usage and comprised by concurrent execution of processes and threads. In many cases, the benchmark from the single core tuning phase and the initial parallel implementation may be an appropriate starting point. Use a system performance profiler such as the Intel® VTune™ Performance Analyzer to identify the performance hotspots in the critical path. Determine if the identified computations can be executed independently. If so, proceed to the next phase; otherwise look for other opportunities with independent computations.

2. *Design*. Determine changes required to accommodate a threading paradigm (data restructuring, code restructuring) by characterizing the application threading model (data-level or task-level parallelization). Identify which variables must be shared and if the current design structure is a good candidate for sharing.

3. *Implementation*. Convert the design into code based on the selected threading model. Consider coding guidelines based on the processor architecture, such as the use of the PAUSE instruction within spin-wait loops. Make use of the multithreading software development methodologies and tools.

4. *Debug*. Use runtime debugging and thread analysis tools such as Intel® Thread Checker.

5. *Tune.* Tune for concurrent execution on multiple processor cores executing without Intel Hyper-Threading Technology. Tune for concurrent execution on multiple processor cores executing with Intel Hyper-Threading Technology.

Chapter 9 provides further information on multi-core technology solutions.

Power Tuning

Tuning that is focused on power utilization is a relatively new addition to the optimization process for Intel architecture processors. The goal of this phase is to reduce the power utilized by the application when executing on the embedded system. One of the key methods of doing so is by helping the processor enter and stay in one of its idle states.

Basics on Power

In an embedded system, power at its fundamental level is a measure of the number of watts consumed in driving the system.

Power can be consumed by several components in a system. Typically, the display and the processor are the two largest consumers of power in an embedded computing system. Other consumers of system power include the memory, hard drives, solid state drives, and communications. Power management features already exist in many operating systems and enable implementation of power policy where various components are powered down when idle for long periods. A simple example is turning off the display after a few minutes of idle activity. Power policy can also govern behavior based upon available power sources. For example, the embedded system may default to a low level of display brightness when powered by battery as opposed to being plugged into an outlet.

Several statistics exist for characterizing the power used by a system including:

■ *Thermal design power (TDP).* The maximum amount of heat that a thermal solution must be able to dissipate from the processor so that the processor operates under normal operating conditions. TDP is typically measured in watts.

■ *"Plug load" power.* A measure of power drawn from an outlet as the embedded system executes. Plug load power is typically measured in watts.

■ *Battery power draw.* A estimate of power drawn from a battery as the embedded system executes. Typically, battery power draw is stated in watts and is based upon estimates from ACPI.

Your project requirements will guide which of these power measurements to employ and what goals will be set with regard to them.

The Intel Atom processor enables a number of power states, which are classified into C-states and P-states. C-states are different levels of processor activity and range from C0, where the processor is fully active down to C6[1] where the processor is completely idle and many portions of the processor are powered down. P-states, known as performance states, are different levels of processor frequency and voltage. Chapter 3 provides detailed information on software and hardware power support for the Intel Atom processor.

Power Measurement Tools

In order to determine if optimizations improve power utilization, a tool is required to measure power utilization. There are two categories of tools to measure power on an embedded system. The first category provides a direct measurement and employs physical probes to measure the amount of power used. These probes could be as simple as a plug load power probe between the device and the electrical outlet. They could require more extensive probes placed on the system board monitoring various power rails such as those required to execute the EEMBC Energybench[2] benchmark.

The second category, power state profiling tools, employs an indirect method of measuring power utilization. Instead of directly measuring power, this class of tool measures and reports on the amount of time spent in different power states. The objective when using these tools is to understand what activities are causing the processor to enter C0 and to minimize them.

---

[1] Not all Intel Atom processors support the C6 deep sleep state.
[2] For further information on EEMBC Energybench, consult http://www.eembc.org/benchmark/power_sl.php

Tuning Overview

The goal of power tuning is two-fold:

■ Minimize time in active state.

■ Maximize time in inactive state.

On the surface it may seem like these goals are redundant; however in practice both are required. Power is expended in transitioning into and out of idle modes. A processor that is repeatedly waking up and then going back to sleep may consume more power than a processor that has longer periods in an active state. In general, the end result is for the system to be in idle mode 90 percent of the time. Of course, this end result depends on the specific workload and application. Techniques to meet this goal follow one of two tuning strategies, which are summarized as follows:

■ *Race to idle.* The tasks are executed as quickly as possible to enable the system to idle. This approach typically entails aggressive performance optimization using similar techniques as single core and multi-core performance tuning.

■ *Idle mode optimization.* Iteratively add software components executing on the system and analyze power state transitions to ensure these components are as nondisruptive to power utilization as possible.

High power utilization has several causes, including:

■ Poor computational efficiency

■ Poor memory management

■ Bad timer and interrupt behavior

■ Poor power awareness

■ Bad multithreading behavior

The power tuning section later in the chapter details techniques to analyze power performance and offers tips on tuning.

The Performance Tuning Cycle

It is important to note that the tuning process is not sequential, but iterative. It is typically not sufficient to step through the three phases only once. Changes made during the power optimization phase may require a new pass at single-core and multi-core optimization to meet performance targets. A subsequent multi-core focused optimization may place inappropriate demand on power and require further power optimization. The hope is that the changes made have less and less of an impact until an equilibrium is reached and the performance targets are met. This is when one can consider performance tuning to be complete. That said, performance regression tests should be run to ensure subsequent bug fixes and changes do not impact performance negatively.

Power and Performance Analysis Tools Overview

Software tools for performance and power optimization aid in your analysis and tuning efforts. The specific tools detailed in this section are arranged according to the performance tuning phase. The breadth of tools available for Intel Atom software development is detailed in Chapter 4. The information here provides further details on the capabilities and usages of the tools specific to performance optimization.

Single Core Performance Tools

Tools for analyzing single core processor performance provide insight into how an application is behaving as it executes on one processor core. These tools provide different views on the application ranging from how the application interacts with other processes on the system down to how the application affects the processor microarchitecture. Many tools are available that provide profiling capability in different ways. Typically, they fall into one of the following categories:

- *System profilers*. Provide a summary of execution times across processes on the system.

- *Application profilers*. Provide a summary of execution times at the function level of the application.

- *Microarchitecture profilers*. Provide a summary of processor events across applications and functions executing on the system.

Two definitions relevant to profiling concern how the data is viewed. A *flat profile* is a correlation of processes and functions with the amount of time the profiler recorded in each. A flat profile does not show relationships between the processes and functions listed with any other processes or functions executing on the system. A *call graph profile* shows these relationships and contributions to the measured times between the caller functions and called functions.

Profilers obtain information by sampling or tracing the system while the application is executing. Three techniques for sampling the system are summarized as follows:

- *Operating system provided API.* Operating system provides capability to periodically sample and record information on executing processes.

- *Software instrumentation.* Application has code added to trace and record statistics.

- *Hardware performance monitoring counters.* Employed by microarchitecture profilers. Provides information on microarchitecture events such as branch mispredictions and cache misses.

Table 8.1 describes several tools used in single core performance analysis. These tools are not all equal. Some of the tools provide functionality that is a superset of others. For example, sysprof[†] is capable of providing a call graph profile across all applications executing on a system; GNU[†] gprof[†] is not. However, gprof is available across a wide range of operating systems; sysprof is a Linux[†] tool. An exhaustive list of profiling tools is outside the scope of this chapter; we merely list a few tools representative of the profiler categories above.

Table 8.1   Single Core Performance Tools Examples

Tool	Type	Description
Sysprof	System profiler	Easy to use, start and stop profiler. Provides system-wide flat profile and call graph information if debug information is present.
GNU gprof	Application profiler	Ubiquitous, widely available single application profiler. Requires recompilation to add instrumentation. Provides flat profile and call graph profile.
Oprofile	Microarchitecture profiler	Linux-targeted microarchitecture profiler. Enables event-based sampling using hardware performance monitoring counters.
Intel® VTune™ Performance Analyzer	Microarchitecture profiler	Windows† and Linux-targeted microarchitecture profiler. Enables event-based sampling using hardware performance monitoring counters. Powerful GUI enables easy visualization.
Intel® Performance Tuning Utility	Microarchitecture profiler	Similar to VTune Performance Analyzer with enhanced event-based profiling features. Basic block view.

System Profiling: Sysprof

Sysprof3 is a Linux hosted and targeted system profiler that provides information across the kernel and user level processes. The tool offers a very simple user interface as depicted in Figure 8.2. To begin profiling, the user presses the Start button. If an application is being profiled it must be started independently of sysprof. The application itself does not require special instrumentation; however if detailed function-level information is desired then debug information should be provided. To stop profiling and show the collected results, the user clicks on the Profile button. Figure 8.2 displays a profile of an application viewed using sysprof. The screen is divided into three sections. The top left section labeled *Functions* is a listing of functions where the greatest amount of time was measured during profiling. Time per individual function includes the time spent in any function called as a result of the function, such as descendents in

---

3 For further information on Sysprof, consult http://www.daimi.au.dk/~sandmann/sysprof/

the call chain. Time is reported in two forms, self time and total time. *Self time* is the execution time inside the function and does not include called functions. *Total time* is the amount of time inside the function and all of its descendents. The bottom left window is labeled *Callers* and is a list of functions that call the highlighted function in the Functions box. Time in the Callers window is relative to the highlighted function. The self time indicates how much time is spent in the caller function while the total time is the component of time spent calling the highlighted function. The sum of the total time column in the Callers box equals the total time of the highlighted function in the Functions box. The Descendents window shows a portion of the call graph of the highlighted function. To follow a path through the call graph further, click the right-facing triangle, which will show another level of the call graph. At each node of the call graph that represents a function, time is reported for it in both, self time and cumulative time. Self time has been previously described. *Cumulative time* is the time in the function and all of its descendents and is a fraction of the time spent by a caller higher in the call graph.

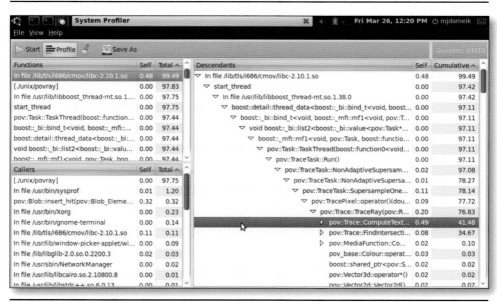

Figure 8.2   Sysprof Display

A command line version of the tool is also supported. It is also possible to dump the profile results to a file for offline processing.

Application Profiling: GNU gprof

GNU gprof[4] is an application-level profiling tool that serves as the output and reporting tool for applications that have been compiled and instrumented using the –pg option. This option is supported by GNU gcc and other compilers and results in instrumentation being added to the application to collect profile information. The instrumented application generates a profile data file (gmon.out is the default profile file name) when executed. Gprof is then employed to process the profile data and generate reports such as an ordered listing of the functions that consume the largest amount of execution time.

Figure 8.3 shows sample gprof profile output obtained by profiling the SPEC CPU2000 benchmark, 179.art[5]. The first report is a flat profile and shows a rank ordering of the various functions in the application based upon the amount of time recorded during the execution. Based upon this report, the function, *match*, had the longest amount of time spent in it, 183.25 seconds, which was 80.64 percent of the total execution time. The profile reports that the function, *match* was called 500 times. The self s/call column represents the average amount of time spent inside the function per call. The total s/call column represents the average amount of time spent inside the function and its descendents per call. For the function, *match*, these times are 0.37 seconds and 0.38 seconds respectively.

```
Flat profile:

Each sample counts as 0.01 seconds.
  %   cumulative   self              self     total
 time   seconds   seconds    calls  s/call   s/call  name
80.64    183.25    183.25      500    0.37     0.38  match
14.79    216.86     33.61      554    0.06     0.07  train_match
 1.93    221.25      4.39     4922    0.00     0.00  simtest2
 1.32    224.26      3.01     4922    0.00     0.00  reset_nodes2
 0.47    225.33      1.07      554    0.00     0.00  weightadj
 0.32    226.05      0.72     1054    0.00     0.00  reset_nodes
 0.32    226.77      0.72      554    0.00     0.00  simtest
 0.11    227.02      0.25 11080000    0.00     0.00  g
 0.07    227.17      0.15        1    0.15   191.15  scan_recognize
 0.01    227.19      0.02        3    0.01     0.01  init_bu
```

Figure 8.3   Gprof Flat Profile Output

---

4 For further information on GNU gprof, consult http://sourceware.org/binutils/docs-2.20/gprof/index.html
5 For further information on 179.art, consult http://www.spec.org/cpu2000/CFP2000/179.art/docs/179.art.html

GNU gprof also provides call graph information. Figure 8.4 shows a portion of the call graph from the function, *match*, which shows the primary caller is identified by index [2], *scan_recognize*. For further details on gprof, see the online documentation.

```
index % time    self  children    called     name
-----------------------------------------------------------
               183.25    7.75    500/500       scan_recognize [2]
[3]     84.1   183.25    7.75    500         match [3]
                 4.39    0.00    4922/4922      simtest2 [5]
                 3.01    0.00    4922/4922      reset_nodes2 [6]
                 0.34    0.00    500/1054       reset_nodes [8]
                 0.01    0.00    4422/4422      find_match [13]
                 0.00    0.00    78/78          print_f12 [16]
```

Figure 8.4   Gprof Call Graph Output

Microarchitecture Profiling: Oprofile

Oprofile is a command line-based microarchitecture profiler providing access to the performance monitoring counters. Oprofile targets Linux systems and requires a kernel driver that acts as a daemon to collect the profile information. One of the positive aspects of the tool is that no instrumentation or recompilation of applications is required. In addition, Oprofile can profile optimized versions of applications.

The use model for Oprofile consists of configuring the daemon for profiling and instructing the daemon to begin collecting profile data. The utility, *opcontrol*, is used to issue commands to the collection daemon. The activity to monitor is then started, which typically implies user invocation of the application on a relevant benchmark. After the activity or application execution is complete, the user shuts down collection. A separate command line tool, *opreport*, is called with an option specifying the type of report desired. Other utilities are available that round out the functionality. The command line utilities that comprise oprofile and a description of each follows:

■   *opcontrol*. Configures the collector, initiates and terminates collection.

■   *opreport*. Displays profile in human readable form, merging available symbolic information where possible.

- *opannotate.* Displays profile information correlated with source and assembly code.

- *oparchive.* Saves profile for offline viewing and analysis.

- *opgprof.* Translates profile into gprof-compatible file.

Table 8.2 summarizes the steps for employing oprofile to collect and output a profile of an application reporting clock cycle information. Each step is described followed by the command line to perform the action. These commands should be executed with root privileges.

Table 8.2   Oprofile Profile Generation

Step	Command line or Description
1. Initialize the oprofile daemon	opcontrol –init
2. Configure profile collection	opcontrol –setup –event="default"
3. Start profile collection	opcontrol –start
4. Start activity	Begin activity to profile.
5. Stop profile collection	opcontrol –stop
6. Produce report	opreport –g –symbols

Figure 8.5 shows the output of oprofile after collecting a profile of the 179. art application. The application was generated with debug information, which enables function level reporting as evidenced by line number of symbol names provided for the a.out application. The largest percentage of time, 44.2886 percent, was in the kernel (no-vmlinux). Using oprofile, it is possible to turn off collection of events from the kernel. The second through fifth highest ranked functions are inside of the 179.art application.

```
CPU: Intel Atom, speed 1000 MHz (estimated)
Counted CPU_CLK_UNHALTED events (Clock cycles when not halted) with a unit mask of
0x00 (core_p Core cycles when core is not halted) count 100000
samples  %          linenr info                  image name   app name      symbol name
957979   44.2886    (no location information)    no-vmlinux   no-vmlinux    /no-vmlinux
691019   31.9467    scanner.c:388                a.out        a.out         train_match
356627   16.4873    scanner.c:525                a.out        a.out         match
21716    1.0040     scanner.c:168                a.out        a.out         weightadj
15813    0.7311     scanner.c:90                 a.out        a.out         simtest
```

Figure 8.5   Oprofile Sample Output

Profile information can be collected based upon other processor events as well. For a complete list of events supported by oprofile on your particular target, use the –list-events option.

Microarchitecture Profiling: Intel® VTune™ Performance Analyzer

On desktop operating systems, the Intel VTune Performance Analyzer can create flat profiles, application call graph profiles, and microarchitecture profiles. The Intel® Application Software Development Tool Suite for Intel Atom Processor includes the VTune analyzer and the VTune analyzer Sampling Collector (SEP), a targetside profile collector for the Intel Atom processor. For embedded form factors that take advantage of Linux, SEP provides microarchitecture profiling capability. Using SEP requires installation of a kernel daemon that is specific to the particular Linux kernel employed. The source code to the daemon can be built to enable collection on specific Linux kernels. The process of using SEP is similar to oprofile. Facilities for configuring collection, starting, and stopping are provided. Once complete, the profile is then transferred to a host environment for visualization inside of the VTune analyzer GUI.

Table 8.3 describes the steps and command lines employed to configure and collect a profile.

Table 8.3   SEP Profile Generation Steps

Step	Command line or Description
1. Initialize the vtune_drv daemon	/opt/intel/vtune/vdk/insmod-vtune
2. Configure and start profile collection.	sep –start -nb –d 0
3. Start activity	Begin activity to profile.
4. Stop profile collection	sep –stop
5. Produce report	Transfer profile data file to host environment for viewing.

The SEP data collector supports additional options to further configure collection including:

■ *Sampling.* Specify duration, interval between samples, sample buffer size, and maximum samples to count.

■ *Application.* Specify an application to launch and profile.

■ *Events.* Configure events and event masks. Use –event-list for a list of supported options.

■ *Continuous profiling.* Aggregates data by instruction pointer, reducing space and enabling monitoring and output during execution.

■ *Event multiplexing.* Enables collection of multiple events concurrently by modulating the specific event being measured while the application is profiled.

Figure 8.6 shows a flat profile of the 179.art application collected using SEP and transferred to a host system for analysis under the VTune analyzer GUI. The highlighted ratio in the top right shows the measurement for clocks cycles per instruction retired.

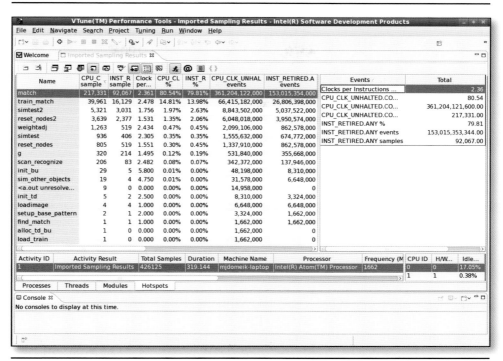

VTune(TM) Performance Tools - Imported Sampling Results - Intel(R) Software Development Products

File Edit Navigate Search Project Tuning Run Window Help

☑ Welcome   Imported Sampling Results ✕

Name	CPU C sample	INST R sample	Clock per...	CPU CL %	INST R %	CPU CLK UNHAL events	INST RETIRED.A events
match	217,331	92,067	2.361	80.54%	79.81%	361,204,122,000	153,015,354,000
train_match	39,961	16,129	2.478	14.81%	13.98%	66,415,182,000	26,806,398,000
simtest2	5,321	3,031	1.756	1.97%	2.63%	8,843,502,000	5,037,522,000
reset_nodes2	3,639	2,377	1.531	1.35%	2.06%	6,048,018,000	3,950,574,000
weightadj	1,263	519	2.434	0.47%	0.45%	2,099,106,000	862,578,000
simtest	936	406	2.305	0.35%	0.35%	1,555,632,000	674,772,000
reset_nodes	805	519	1.551	0.30%	0.45%	1,337,910,000	862,578,000
g	320	214	1.495	0.12%	0.19%	531,840,000	355,668,000
scan_recognize	206	83	2.482	0.08%	0.07%	342,372,000	137,946,000
init_bu	29	5	5.800	0.01%	0.00%	48,198,000	8,310,000
sim_other_objects	19	4	4.750	0.01%	0.00%	31,578,000	6,648,000
<a.out unresolve...	9	0	0.000	0.00%	0.00%	14,958,000	0
init_td	5	2	2.500	0.00%	0.00%	8,310,000	3,324,000
loadimage	4	4	1.000	0.00%	0.00%	6,648,000	6,648,000
setup_base_pattern	2	1	2.000	0.00%	0.00%	3,324,000	1,662,000
find_match	1	1	1.000	0.00%	0.00%	1,662,000	1,662,000
alloc_td_bu	1	0	0.000	0.00%	0.00%	1,662,000	0
load_train	1	0	0.000	0.00%	0.00%	1,662,000	0

Events	Total
Clocks per Instructions ...	2.36
CPU_CLK_UNHALTED.CO...	80.54
CPU_CLK_UNHALTED.CO...	361,204,121,600.00
CPU_CLK_UNHALTED.CO...	217,331.00
INST_RETIRED.ANY %	79.81
INST_RETIRED.ANY events	153,015,353,344.00
INST_RETIRED.ANY samples	92,067.00

Activity ID	Activity Result	Total Samples	Duration	Machine Name	Processor	Frequency (M	CPU ID	H/W...	Idle...
1	Imported Sampling Results	426125	319.144	mjdomeik-laptop	Intel(R) Atom(TM) Processor	1662	0	0	17.05%
							1	1	0.38%

Processes | Threads | Modules | Hotspots

Console ✕

No consoles to display at this time.

Figure 8.6   VTune™ Analyzer Flat Profile View

Microarchitecture Profiling: Event-based Sampling

One issue with performance monitoring collection is that access to the performance counters requires kernel, or ring 0, access. Event-based sampling functions by setting up a performance monitoring counter to overflow periodically and then recording the instruction pointer location with the particular event. During profiling and as these events are recorded, a correlation of the number of events to instruction pointers is created. Implementing event-based sampling requires an interrupt handler to record these performance monitoring counter overflows and a driver that writes the counts to a file after collection is complete. The VTune analyzer includes its driver source code, which can be used as a model for other operating systems. In addition, a TBRW utility is included that enables a performance monitoring driver to read and write the VTune analyzer's data format, tb5. This enables other performance monitoring utilities to take advantage of the GUI provided by VTune analyzer.

Microarchitecture Profiling: Intel® Performance Tuning Utility

For more advanced microarchitecture profiling, the Intel® Performance Tuning Utility (Intel® PTU) leverages the same technology as the Intel VTune analyzer and offers sophisticated views of performance events. This tool is available on the whatif.intel.com site, which means it is an experimental tool. Some of the capabilities of Intel PTU include:

- *Basic block analysis.* Creates and displays a control flow graph and hotspots corresponding to basic blocks in the graph.

- *Events over IP graph.* Generates a histogram of performance events distributed over application code.

- *Loop analysis.* Identifies loops and recursion in the application to aid optimization.

- *Result difference.* Compares the results of multiple runs to measure changes in performance

- *Data access profiling.* Identifies memory hotspots and relates them to code hotspots.

Intel PTU is integrated into Eclipse[†], which places requirements on the system under test to be able to execute the Eclipse environment. Figure 8.7 shows a screenshot of the basic block analysis feature of Intel PTU.

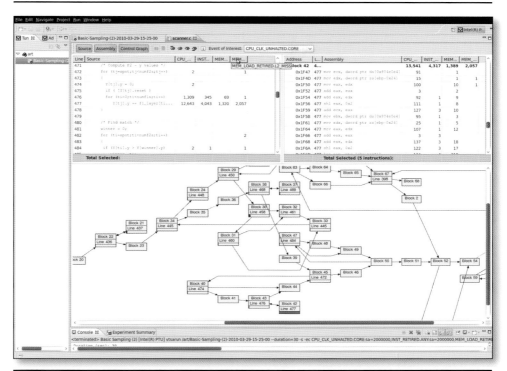

Figure 8.7   Intel® PTU Basic Block View

Multi-Core Performance Tools

Unique tools for analyzing performance related to multi-core processors are still somewhat few in number. System profilers can provide information on processes executing on a system; however interactions in terms of messaging and coordination between processes are not visible. Tools that offer visibility into this coordination typically must be cognizant of the particular API in use. POSIX† Threads is a commonly employed multi-core programming API and therefore has relatively broad tools support.

Intel® Thread Profiler

The Intel® Thread Profiler identifies thread-related performance issues and is capable of analyzing OpenMP†, POSIX, and Windows† multithreaded applications. When used to profile an application, some of the key capabilities include:

- The display of a histogram of aggregate data on time spent in serial or parallel regions.

- The display of a histogram of time spent accessing locks, in critical regions, or with threads waiting at implicit barriers for other threads.

Intel Thread Profiler employs what is termed *critical path analysis* where events are recorded including spawning new threads, joining terminated threads, holding synchronization objects, waiting for synchronization objects to be released, and waiting for external events. An execution flow is created that is the execution through an application by a thread, and each of the listed events above can split or terminate the flow. The critical path is defined as the longest flow through the execution from the start of the application until it terminates. The critical path is important because any improvement in threaded performance along this path would increase overall performance of the application.

Data recorded along the critical path includes the number of threads that are active and thread interactions over synchronization objects. Figure 8.8 depicts the Intel Thread Profiler GUI divided into two sections: Profile View and Timeline View. On top is the Profile View, which gives a histogram representation of data taken from the critical path and can be organized with different filters that include the following:

- Number of active threads on the critical path.

- Object view: identifies the synchronization objects encountered by threads.

- Thread view: shows the contribution of each thread to the critical path.

Benefits of these filters and views include:

■ Knowledge of the amount of parallelism available during the application execution.

■ Helping locate load imbalances between threads.

■ Determining what synchronization objects were responsible for the most contention between threads.

The Timeline View shows the critical path over the time that the application has run. The critical path travels from one thread to another and shows the amount of time threads spend executing or waiting for a synchronization object.

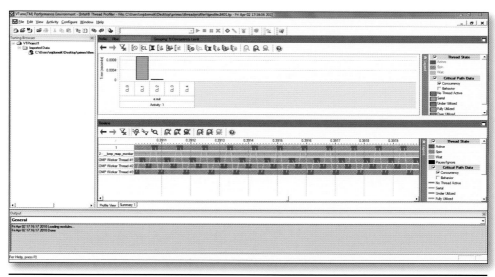

Figure 8.8   Concurrency Level and Timeline View

CriticalBlue Prism†

CriticalBlue Prism† is another example of a toolsuite aimed at optimized software development for multi-core and/or multithreaded architectures. Prism can be used across the full range of activities needed to migrate existing sequential single core software onto a multi-core platform.

CriticalBlue Prism's what-if scheduling can be used to explore the benefit of Intel® Hyper-Threading Technology on multi-core execution performance.

Prism's analyses are based on a dynamic tracing approach. Traces of the user's software application are extracted either from a simulator of the underlying processor core or via an instrumentation approach where the application is dynamically instrumented to produce the required data. Once a trace has been loaded into Prism the user can start to analyze the application behavior in a multi-core context. In addition to standard profiling data showing functions and their relative execution times, Prism provides the user with specific insight relevant in a multi-core processor context. Examples of the views and analyses available in Prism are:

■ Histogram showing activity over time by individual function and memory.

■ Dynamic call graph showing function inter-relationships and frequency.

■ Data dependency analysis between functions on sequential code.

■ What-if scheduling to explore the impact of executing functions in separate threads.

■ What-if scheduling to explore the impact of varying the numbers of processor cores employed.

■ What-if scheduling to explore the impact of removing identified data dependencies.

■ What-if scheduling to explore the impact of cache misses on multi-core execution performance.

■ What-if scheduling to explore the benefit of Intel Hyper-Threading Technology on multi-core execution performance.

■ Data race analysis between functions on multithreaded code.

Figure 8.9 is a screen shot of Prism analyzing sequential code where the user has forced several functions to execute in their own threads and a trial schedule has been generated on 4 cores. This trial schedule was modeled on unchanged sequential code and enables the user to exhaustively test and optimize the parallelization code prior to making code changes. For more information on Prism, see www.criticalblue.com.

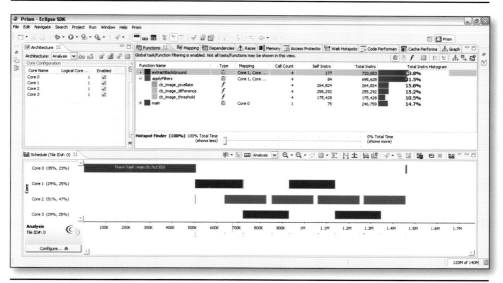

Figure 8.9　CriticalBlue Prism What-if Exploration Running on Sequential Code

Power Performance Tools

As previously mentioned, the "race to idle" power optimization strategy is implemented by employing the single-core and multi-core performance tools mentioned previously. The focus of this section is on tools to assist with idle mode optimization.

Two types of tools assess power performance. The first type of tool measures the actual power used by the device via physical probes, a technique referred to as *probe-based profiling*. The second type of tool employs counters in the platform that measure power state transitions, a technique referred to as *power state-based profiling*. For the sake of completeness a brief description of each type of tool follows; however only power state-based profiling is discussed at length and employed in the case study.

Probe-based profiling employs an external device to measure and record the power utilized by the system as a specific application executes. Typically, there is some mechanism to correlate the power readings with points in the application. An industry example of such a tool is the TMS320C55x[†] Power Optimization DSP Starter Kit, which integrates National Instruments Power Analyzer to provide a graphical view of power utilization over time. The Intel Energy Checker SDK[6] is another probe-based profiling tool that targets desktop and server platforms. This tool measures power from the AC adaptor using a measurement tool such as those available from Watts up?[7] and enables correlation with specific regions of application code. The data transfer assumes a shared file system, which currently limits applicability to desktop and server computing platforms.

Power-state profiling tools rely upon software interfaces into the platform's power states, which, instead of providing a measure of power utilization, provide the number of times transitions occur between the platform power states. The process of idle-mode optimization works by enabling increasing application functionality and inspecting the recorded power data at every stage. In many cases, additional power state transitions will be recorded. Many of these additional transitions are necessary because as more functionality of the application is enabled, more processing is required. However, at each step, power state differences should be measured, understood, and optimized away if truly unneeded.

PowerTOP[8] is a Linux targeted tool that performs power state profiling and targets idle mode optimization techniques. The tool executes on the target device with an operating mode similar to the common Unix[†] tool, *top*, where the tool provides a dashboard-like display. The intent is that the display would provide real-time updates as your applications execute on the target device. Figure 8.10 displays a screenshot of PowerTOP and highlights its functionality. The tool provides six categories of information, which are summarized as follows:

■ *C state residency information.* The average amount of time spent in each C state and the average duration that is spent in each C state.

---

[6] For further details on Intel Energy Checker, see http://software.intel.com/en-us/articles/intel-energy-checker-sdk/

[7] For further information on Watts up?, consult https://www.wattsupmeters.com/secure/index.php

[8] For further information on PowerTOP, consult http://www.lesswatts.org/projects/powertop/powertop.php

■ *P state residency information.* The percentage of time the processor is in a particular P state.

■ *Wakeups per second.* The number of times per second the system moves out of an idle C state.

■ *Power usage.* An estimate of the power currently consumed and the amount of battery life remaining.

■ *Top causes for wakeups.* A rank ordered list of interrupts, processes, and functions causing the system to transition to C0.

■ *Wizard mode.* Suggestions for changes to the operating system that could reduce power utilization.

```
    PowerTOP version 1.11      (C) 2007 Intel Corporation
Cn                 Avg residency      P-states (frequencies)
C0 (cpu running)        (16.5%)          1.67 Ghz    23.3%
polling            0.0ms ( 0.0%)        1334 Mhz     0.3%
C1 mwait           0.0ms ( 0.0%)        1000 Mhz    76.4%
C2 mwait           0.2ms ( 0.1%)
C4 mwait           7.2ms (83.4%)
Wakeups-from-idle per second : 122.0    interval: 10.0s
Power usage (ACPI estimate): 9.4W (4.7 hours) (long term: 12.4W,/3.6h)

Top causes for wakeups:
  40.5% (109.0)      <kernel core> : hrtimer_start_range_ns (tick_sched_timer)
  12.2% ( 33.0)   window-picker-a : hrtimer_start_range_ns (hrtimer_wakeup)
  11.2% ( 30.2)       <interrupt> : acpi
   8.6% ( 23.1)      <kernel IPI> : Rescheduling interrupts
   5.2% ( 14.0)       <interrupt> : uhci_hcd:usb5, HDA Intel, ra0
   4.4% ( 11.9)     <kernel core> : hrtimer_start (tick_sched_timer)
   4.2% ( 11.2)       <interrupt> : PS/2 keyboard/mouse/touchpad
   4.0% ( 10.7)            povray : hrtimer_start_range_ns (hrtimer_wakeup)
   3.7% ( 10.0)     <kernel core> : add_timer (rtmp_timer_MlmePeriodicExec)
   2.0% (  5.5)     <kernel core> : add_timer (rtmp_timer_ScanTimeout)
   1.1% (  3.0)     gnome-terminal : hrtimer_start_range_ns (hrtimer_wakeup)
   0.4% (  1.2)       <interrupt> : ahci
   0.4% (  1.1)    update-manager : hrtimer_start_range_ns (hrtimer_wakeup)
   0.4% (  1.0)              Xorg : queue_delayed_work (delayed_work_timer_fn)

Suggestion: increase the VM dirty writeback time from 5.00 to 15 seconds with:
  echo 1500 > /proc/sys/vm/dirty_writeback_centisecs
This wakes the disk up less frequently for background VM activity
 Q - Quit  R - Refresh  W - Increase Writeback time
```

Figure 8.10 PowerTOP

Single Processor Core Tuning

This section details the single processor core tuning steps summarized previously.

Benchmark

The first step in tuning is to develop a benchmark that represents typical usage of the application. The benchmark is comprised of the application and a set of inputs that exercises the functionality of the application. The benchmark should be abbreviated in execution, but repeatable and should exercise common cases. One would not necessarily employ a regression test suite that exercises the corner cases of execution. Baseline performance of the application executing the benchmark is established and used in subsequent steps to help quantify the benefit of specific optimizations.

Profile

The second step in tuning is to gain an understanding of the application. If you are the author or the designer of the software, then this process occurs naturally. If you are not the author, profiling tools can be employed to gain a basic understanding of the application. Profilers were discussed previously in the chapter.

The key questions to answer in this step are as follows:

■ In order from highest to lowest, which processes, functions, and regions of code comprise 90 percent of the execution time? These are termed *hotspots*.

■ How are these hotspots entered and exited? What steps in terms of application events, function calls, and input is responsible for entry and exit?

Compiler Optimization

Once a benchmark is created and application characteristics are understood, tuning can begin. The third step, which is one of the easier methods of tuning, is to employ an optimizing compiler with aggressive optimization.

Use of aggressive optimization must be balanced against usability. Aggressive optimization can limit the quality of debug information so if the application must ship with debug information, the impact should be assessed. Aggressive optimization typically requires more effort; in some cases a two- or three-step compilation process is employed.

Recommendations for employing aggressive optimizations include:

■ *Use an Intel® Atom™ processor targeting option.* This option enables instruction selection and scheduling specifically tuned for the Intel Atom processor microarchitecture.

■ *Use automatic vectorization.* This option transforms code to use Intel® Streaming SIMD Extensions (Intel® SSE) and later extended instruction sets for vectorized data processing.

■ *Use the -O3 option.* The O3 optimization has become the de facto standard for aggressive general optimization.

■ *Use interprocedural optimization.* This option enables aggressive inlining and optimization across function calls.

■ *Use profile guided optimization.* This option enables use of runtime application behavior to optimize.

See your compiler documentation for option availability.

Automatic vectorization is an advanced optimization that analyzes loops and determines when it is safe and effective to execute several iterations of the loop in parallel by taking advantage of SIMD extensions such as Intel SSE3. Figure 8.11 is a graphical representation of a vectorized loop that shows four iterations computed with one SIMD operation. Use automatic vectorization to optimize your application code and take advantage of these extensions when running on the Intel Atom processor.

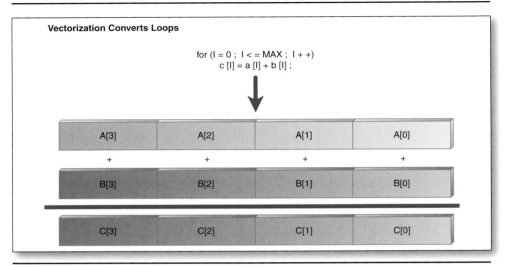

Figure 8.11   Automatic Vectorization

Compiler optimization results vary depending on the code and optimization option, but in general it is a prudent practice. For example, Table 8.4 shows 179.art benchmark execution times when compiled with different options. The first row shows the 179.art benchmark completing execution in 6 minutes and 16 seconds (6:16) when compiled using the GNU gcc compiler at the −O2 optimization level. When the benchmark is compiled by the Intel Compiler, icc, at the −O2 optimization level, it completes in 3:07. The benchmark completes execution in 1:55 when compiled by icc with Intel Atom processor specific scheduling and automatic vectorization(-xSSE3_ATOM). If the −O3 optimization is added, the benchmark executes in 1:39. Finally, if interprocedural and profile-guided optimizations are used in addition, then the benchmark completes execution in 1:37.

Table 8.4   179.art Execution Times under Compiler Optimization[9]

Compiler and options	Time (minutes:seconds)
gcc −O2	6:16
icc −O2	3:07

---

[9] Performance results are based on certain tests measured on specific computer systems. Any difference in system hardware, software or configuration will affect actual performance. For more information go to http://www.intel.com/performance.

icc –O2 –xSSE3_ATOM	1:55
icc –O3 –xSSE3_ATOM	1:39
icc –O3 –xSSE3_ATOM –ipo –profuse	1:37

General Microarchitecture Tuning

This phase of single processor core tuning employs the performance monitoring counters of the Intel Atom processor to conduct event-based statistical sampling of the application. Performance monitoring counters measure microarchitecture events occurring in the processor core such as branch mispredictions, cache misses, and bus requests. Processor event-based statistical sampling enables correlation of processor events to specific regions of code in the application. To employ this class of tuning the developer measures these performance events as the application executes, analyzes the results, and pinpoints performance problems in the code.

The Intel Atom processor performance monitoring counters offer many advanced capabilities. A large number of processor events can be monitored and the counting can be specially configured. Examples of specialized profiling include counting events only when operating in ring 3 or ring 0 and counting only when a multiple of an event occurs. Advanced profiling techniques such as cycle accounting (Levinthal) employ these advanced features. For most performance work, the basic default settings of the particular microarchitecture profiling tool can be employed.

Table 8.5 lists the application statistics to obtain during the general microarchitecture tuning phase. The first event to profile on is clock cycles. On typical tools, the event is CPU_CLK_UNHALTED. A statistical profile based upon clock cycles enables understanding of which regions of code are most frequently executed. The second event is instructions retired (INST_RETIRED), which occurs when an IA-32 or Intel 64 ISA instruction completes the retirement stage in the processor. Using these two event profiles, calculate cycles per instruction (CPI), which is a measure of how efficiently the Intel Atom processor is executing instructions. If the processor pipeline is frequently stalled, the CPI measure will be high. Since the Intel Atom processor is a two-instruction-wide superscalar microarchitecture, the theoretical lower bound for CPI is 1 cycle per 2 instructions, or 0.5. The inverse of CPI is instructions per cycle (IPC) and is also commonly employed, but functionally equivalent. The theoretical limit for IPC is 2 on the Intel Atom processor.

Table 8.5 General Microarchitecture Profiling

Event or Statistic	Description	Calculation
	Computational Efficiency Metrics	
Clock cycles	Processor core cycles while the core is not in a halt state.	CPU_CLK_UNHALTED
Instructions Retired	IA-32 and Intel® 64 ISA instructions that complete the retirement stage.	INST_RETIRED
CPI	Clock cycles per instructions retired.	CPU_CLK_UNHALTED / INST_RETIRED
IPC	Instructions retired per clock cycle.	1 / CPI
	Memory Performance Metrics	
Instruction Cache Events	Instruction cache misses.	ICACHE.MISSES
	Instruction cache accesses.	ICACHE.ACCESSES
L1 Events	Number of cache lines brought into the L1 data cache.	L1D_REPL
L2 Load Events	L2 cache load misses.	MEM_LOAD_RETIRED. L2_MISS
	L2 cache load hits.	MEM_LOAD_RETIRED.L2_HIT
Misaligned memory references	Misaligned data memory references – load splits.	MISALIGN_MEM_REF. LD_SPLIT
	Branch Events	
Branch Prediction Events	Branch mispredictions.	BR_INST_RETIRED.MISPRED
	Branch instructions retired.	BR_INST_RETIRED.ANY

The next set of events to measure relate to cache activity. In many applications, memory access times have a large impact on application performance. Finding regions of code with high cache miss rates are prime targets for optimization. Specifically, cache miss information at the level 1 and level 2 caches should be collected.

Multiple L1 cache events are available to measure and include loads, stores, and reference events. One key event to measure is L1 cache lines replicated (L1D_REPL), which is a measure of how much new data is brought into the cache, which is in turn an indication of L1 cache misses.

In general, different applications place different demands with regard to memory usage and access patterns so no general recommendation can be made for upper bound on cache misses. Instead, one should derive relative information comparing the cache misses observed at different regions of the code. The recorded numbers can be normalized against clock cycles or instructions retired to prevent the case where a frequently executed region with relatively good cache behavior compares poorly against a less executed region with dismal cache performance.

Areas of the application with a relatively high miss rate should be examined for possible improvement. Two functions, `cache_miss_func()` and `cache_access_func()`, were profiled on the events listed in Table 8.6. Each sample represents 2,000,000 events. The function, `cache_miss_func()` was designed to have poor cache behavior and the function `cache_access_func()` was designed to have more regular cache access.

Table 8.6   Event-Based Statistical Profile of Two Functions

Event	cache_miss_func	cache_access_func
CPU_CLK_UNHALTED	11577	258
DECODE_STALL.IQ_FULL	11501	226
MEM_LOAD_RETIRED.L2_HIT	0.2	1.0
MEM_LOAD_RETIRED.L2_MISS	34.52	0.04

Based upon the event profiles, the amount of time recorded in the function `cache_miss_func()` was two orders of magnitude greater than the function `cache_access_func()`. One event that helps pinpoint performance issues is decoder stalls (DECODE_STALL or ILD_STALL) due to the instruction queue being full (IQ_FULL). This event indicates that the front end of the pipeline is stalled because of delays in the back end of the pipeline. The large number of cycles measured for this event indicates such a case. The cache events measured in this example are L2 cache events, memory loads retired that hit in the L2 cache (MEM_LOAD_RETIRED.L2_HIT) and memory loads retired that miss in the L2 cache (MEM_LOAD_RETIRED. L2_MISS). The number of L2 cache load misses for `cache_miss_func()` indicates an opportunity to improve memory access performance. Once the problem is determined using these events, optimizations aimed at improving specific problems can be employed.

Some common optimizations for improving memory performance include the following:

■ *Take advantage of spatial and temporal locality.* Rearrange data layout so that data frequently accessed in terms of space and time are close together.

■ *Prefetch.* Supplement the Intel Atom processor's hardware prefetch in cases of irregular access that can be characterized and embodied by software prefetch instructions. Be careful when employing software prefetches as it is possible to degrade performance when interacting with the hardware prefetcher.

■ *Align data for best performance.* The Intel Atom microarchitecture handles each 64-byte cache line of the first-level data cache in 16 4-byte chunks. Unaligned memory access can incur performance penalties. In general, align data on the data types' natural boundaries. For example, 4-byte data should be aligned to a 4-byte boundary. Additionally, smaller access (less than 4 bytes) within a chunk may experience delay if they touch different bytes.

The last set of events in this category is branch prediction related, branch mispredictions retired, and branch instructions retired. Processors feature hardware to predict the direction of branches. When a branch misprediction occurs, instructions that are partially executed in the processor pipeline are flushed and a new instruction stream enters the pipeline. Frequent mispredictions slow performance. The following software optimizations help improve branch prediction performance but are really intended for developers programming at the assembly language level:

■ Transform indirect branches to if-then statements for common cases.

■ Transform branches that perform a test and set into a conditional move.

Intel® Atom™ Processor Tuning

This phase of tuning employs event-based statistical profiling again, but focuses on events that are known to cause performance issues that have a high impact due to the unique microarchitecture of the Intel Atom processor. These problem areas, known colloquially as glass jaws, are performance issues that should be addressed in areas of the application that are frequently executed. Table 8.7 lists the application statistics to obtain during this phase.

Table 8.7 Intel® Atom™ Processor Profiling Events

Event or Statistic	Description	Calculation
Decode Stall Events	Decoder stalls due to an empty prefetch buffer.	DECODE_STALL.PFB_EMPTY
	Decoder stalls due to a full instruction queue.	DECODE_STALL.IQ_FULL
Decode Events	Number of CISC instructions decoded.	MACRO_INSTS.CISC_DECODED
	Number of all types of instructions decoded.	MACRO_INSTS.ALL_DECODED
Partial register stalls	Number of cycles instruction execution is stalled due to a partial register access.	RAT_STALLS.PARTIAL_CYCLES
Divide busy	Number of cycles the divider is busy executing divide or square root operations.	CYCLES_DIV_BUSY
SIMD and x87 operations	Number of SIMD instructions retired employing packed double.	SIMD_INST_RETIRED.PACKED_DOUBLE
	Number of SIMD instructions retiring employing scalar doubles.	SIMD_INST_RETIRED.SCALAR_DOUBLE
	Number of x87 instructions executed.	X87_COMP_OPS_EXE.ANY.AR
Multiply operations	Number of integer and x87 multiply operations retired.	MUL.AR

The first set of events to measure concerns processor decode efficiency. The reasons for the processor's decoder to be stalled can be split into two categories, front-end related and back-end related. Front end stalls occur when the decoder is not receiving enough instructions to decode and can be caused an excessive number of branch mispredictions or instruction cache misses. The event that indicates this condition is decoder stalls due to the prefetch buffer being empty (DECODE_STALL.PFB_EMPTY). Another reason for the front end to be stalled or limited is if a large number of CISC instructions are decoded. This can be determined by profiling for CISC instruction decodes (MACRO_INSTS.CISC_DECODED) and comparing against a profile measuring all instructions decoded (MACRO_INSTS.ALL_DECODED).

Back-end related stalls occur when the instruction decoder is full of instructions but cannot pass the instructions to the next stage because of bottlenecks later in the pipeline. This can occur for example when the processor is executing an excessive number of serialized instructions like divides. The event that indicates this condition is decoder stalls due to instruction queue being full (DECODE_STALL.IQ_FULL).

Partial register stalls occur when a smaller component of a register is modified by one operation and a subsequent operation attempts to access a second component piece of the register. Figure 8.12 shows an example of a partial register stall where the third instruction is dependent on both the first and second instruction even though semantically the second instruction is unrelated. The issue is that the microarchitecture cannot efficiently track the partial components and merge the values correctly. Instead, the Intel Atom processor treats these partial register updates as a dependency on the entire register. So, even though the read of register al is not really dependent on the modification to ah, the Intel Atom processor tracks them as being dependent. The partial register stall event (RAT_STALLS.PARTIAL_CYCLES) counts this activity.

```
movb    8, %ah
movb    8, %al
movb    %ah, %bh
```

Figure 8.12 *Partial Register Stall*

The Intel Atom processor pipeline has a limited ability to execute divide instructions and an excessive number of divide instructions can cause performance delays. The number of cycles the divider is busy (CYCLES_DIV_BUSY) can be profiled. If the number of cycles correlates to hotspots in the application, optimizations to limit the number of divides should be considered. These optimizations include transforming a division by constant into a multiply by reciprocal.

When possible, floating point operations should be performed using the Intel SSE instructions instead of x87. The use of x87 floating point can be determined by profiling for x87 operations executed (X87_COMP_OPS_EXE_ANY.AR). There is a caveat when employing the SIMD instruction sets for floating point: packed double operations serialize the pipeline and prevent other SIMD operations from entering the pipeline until complete. For example, packed double multiplies have a latency of 9 cycles and a throughput of 9 cycles, whereas scalar double multiplies have a latency of 5 cycles and a throughput of 2 cycles. It is therefore recommended whenever possible to use scalar SIMD instructions on double precision floating point instead of packed SIMD instructions. The use of packed SIMD instructions (SIMD_INST_RETIRED.PACKED_DOUBLE) can be profiled as well as scalar SIMD instructions (SIMD_INST_RETIRED.SCALAR_DOUBLE) to monitor the use of each.

Integer multiplies take several cycles to execute and prevent single cycle integer instructions from issuing until the integer multiply is complete. Integer multiplies can be issued back-to-back with other long latency instructions. In general, group integer multiplies with other long latency instructions where possible. Multiplies (MUL.AR) can be profiled to determine areas of frequent use.

There are some glass jaws of the Intel Atom processor that cannot be measured directly by performance monitoring counters. These events require manual inspection of the assembly code around hotspots. Table 8.8 lists several performance issues and summarizes techniques to diagnose them. The precise characteristics of these performance issues were discussed in Chapter 3.

Table 8.8   Intel® Atom™ Processor Performance Issues

Performance Issue	Analysis Technique
Mix implicit and explicit ESP changes	Inspect hotspots for use of implicit and explicit ESP changes in close proximity. An implicit change is a push or pop instruction. An explicit change is an add or sub instruction with esp as an operand.
Lea to do adds	Inspect hotspots for lea instructions and track register operands. If the register operands of lea are computed by previous add and sub instructions close in proximity, the lea instruction will stall.
Flag update	Inspect hotspots for instructions that set status flags. If the immediately preceding instruction sets the status flag, a delay occurs.

The single-core processor tuning process was applied to the 179.art benchmark and provided insight into the application and how to best optimize. Table 8.9 summarizes the profiles and statistics obtained for two versions of the benchmark. The first version, compiled using gcc with the –O2 optimization, completed execution in 6:16. CPI is measured at a relatively high 6. The decoder is stalled due to the instruction queue being full for a relatively high number of clock cycles. The L2 misses seem to be high and the number of cycles the divider busy is high as well.

Table 8.9   Performance Events Analysis

Statistic	Version 1	Version 2
CPU_CLK_UNHALTED.CORE	332179	82773
INST_RETIRED.ANY	56661	24735
Cycles per instruction	6	3
DECODE_STALL.PFB_EMPTY	5895	3334
DECODE_STALL.IQ_FULL	275318	71361
ICACHE.ACCESSES	17250	12681
ICACHE.MISSES	14	4
L1D_CACHE.REPL	5333	1107
MEM_LOAD_RETIRED.L2_HIT	3321	522
MEM_LOAD_RETIRED.L2_MISS	189	27
L2 Misses / L2 Hits	0.06	0.05
MISALIGN_MEM_REF.LD_SPLIT	250	63
BR_INST_RETIRED.ANY	9924	3880
BR_INST_RETIRED.MISPRED	321	85
Branch mispredictions per branch retired	0.03	0.02
CYCLES_DIV_BUSY	26958	11878
X87_COMP_OPS_EXE_ANY.AR	9999	0
SIMD_INST_RETIRED.PACKED_DOUBLE	0	8
SIMD_INST_RETIRED.SCALAR_DOUBLE	0	5463
Execution Time (mm:ss)	6:16	1:39

The second version, compiled with icc and aggressive optimization, shows better performance completing execution in 1:39. The following observations are made based upon these statistics:

- CPI is much better, 3 versus 6, indicative of improved computational efficiency.

- The number of decode stalls due to the instruction queue being full is an order of magnitude lower. The back end of the processor is not stalled as frequently in the higher performing version (Version 2).

- Memory performance is much higher. The number of L2 references, both hits and misses, are substantially lower in Version 2. This is indicative of a higher L1 cache performance and data optimizations.

- Floating point performance is closer to optimal in Version 2. The number of cycles the divider is busy is down by half. Intel SSE is employed instead of x87 floating point in Version 2 and it is confirmed that operations on doubles are accomplished predominantly using scalar versions.

Table 8.10 shows a portion of the profile results and contains a correlation of the source code, assembly language, and performance events for Version 1. Notice the large counts for the CYCLES_DIV_BUSY event and the use of x87 floating point instructions. Enabling use of faster floating point via Intel SSE is one of the keys to improving performance as observed by the results from Version 2.

Table 8.10   179.art Hotspot

Line Number	Code	CPU_CLK_ UNHALTED.CORE	CYCLES_DIV _BUSY
554	for (tj=0;tj<numf1s;tj++)	5174	3696
555	f1_layer[tj].X = f1_layer[tj].W/tnorm;	15102	11387
	Block 16		
555	fld st0, qword ptr ds[eax+0x4]	249	242
554	add ecx, 0x1	3308	1913
555	fdiv st0, st1	61	10
555	fstp qword ptr ds[eax+0xc], st0	14792	11135
554	add eax, 0x3c	1494	1528
554	cmp ecx, ebx	60	49
554	jnz Block 16	238	206
	Block 17		
554	fstp st0, st0	0	0
554	fld st0, qword ptr ds[0x804d0a8]	0	0
554	xor ecx, ecx	17	0
562	mov ebx, dword ptr ss[ebp-0x20]	0	0
554	fld st0, qword ptr ds[0x804d128]	15	0
554	fldz st0	5	0
554	fld st0, st0	0	0
554	lea esi, ptr [esi]	0	0

Multi-Core Tuning

Tuning an application for improved performance on a multi-core processor assumes an already developed implementation that takes advantage of parallelism. The parallel implementation should have started with an application optimized for single core performance. This application should then have been extended to execute in parallel employing well-known techniques. The design and implementation of an application that takes advantage of parallelism is outside of the scope of this book. Therefore, this tuning section will be modest, summarizing the process for multi-core processor tuning when employing multithreading. The focus of discussion is on analyzing and addressing common multi-core performance issues such as load imbalance and lock overhead. An additional section on memory optimization is included.

Application and Hardware Environment

A sample application serves as illustration for the multi-core tuning process. In this section, not all of the multi-core tuning steps documented earlier in the chapter are detailed; only the key ones pertinent to the example are discussed. The application counts the number of prime numbers from 1 to n, where n is the user supplied end point. It employs a brute force method of finding the prime numbers by individually testing each odd number between 1 and n. The test includes trying to divide the number by every number less than n. A counter records the number of primes and is incremented each time one is found. After the range of numbers has been tested, the total number of primes found is output.

The application is written in the C programming language and employs OpenMP directives to enact parallelism. Figure 8.13 shows pseudocode for the key loop that performs the work. The Intel C++ Compiler, version 11.1, is used to compile the application.

```
#pragma omp parallel for private(prime)
for (index = start; index <= end; index+= ) {
  prime = test_for_prime(index);
  #pragma omp critical
  if (prime) number_of_primes++;
}
```

Figure 8.13 OpenMP Prime Number Counter

The system employed is based upon the Intel Atom 330 processor and its configuration is summarized in Table 8.11. The processor is dual core and supports Intel Hyper-Threading Technology, and therefore the OS sees a total of four logical processor cores with which to execute processes.

Table 8.11   Benchmark System Specifications

Component	Description
Processor	Intel® Atom™ 330 processor Dual Core supports Intel® Hyper-Threading Technology
Motherboard	Intel 945GCLF2
Memory	1 GB RAM
Clockspeed	Processor 1.6 GHz, Bus 533 MHz
Operating System	Ubuntu† 9.10

Analysis: Benchmark

Creating a benchmark for multi-core tuning is similar to the process for creating a benchmark for serial tuning. In many cases, the same benchmark can be employed. One note of caution: since the benchmark is executing on multiple processor cores under the direction of the operation system, there is increased exposure to variability from execution to execution. In an SMP operating system that is executing many concurrent processes the precise order and placement of threads on processor cores is not deterministic. Some ordering and placements may be advantageous or disadvantageous with regard to cache behavior from execution to execution. Therefore, it is necessary to execute the benchmark more times when evaluating performance.

The example application, being fairly simple employs one input into the program for benchmarking. The benchmark consists of counting the number of primes between 1 and 10,000,000, which is known to total 664579. Execution time of the serial version of the benchmark is 37.5 seconds. The serial version of the benchmark is the same as the OpenMP version of the application detailed later on, but with the OpenMP directive disabled.

Profile

In order to understand the characteristics of the application, a profile of the benchmark is obtained using IPTU. The profile correlated to source code is depicted in Figure 8.14. The serial version of the application is executed. Note that this example shows a bit more of the code that implements the step test_for_prime in the pseudocode from Figure 8.13.

Source Code	Clock cycles
`for(index = begin; index <= end; index += 2) {`	0.01%
`  limit = (int) sqrt((float)index) + 1;`	0.71%
`  prime = 1; /* assume number is prime */`	0.00%
`  factor = 3;`	0.00%
`  while (prime && (factor <= limit)) {`	6.11%
`    If (index%factor == 0) prime = 0;`	5.07%
`    factor += 2;`	88.04%
`  }`	0.00%
`  if (prime)`	0.00%
`    number_of_primes++;`	0.05%
`}`	0.00%

Figure 8.14 Hotspots in Prime Counter

Based upon the profile of the benchmark, the majority of execution time occurs inside of the while loop that determines if a number is prime. The percentage of time recorded in the profile for the while loop is 99 percent. The initial parallel implementation detailed in Figure 8.15, termed "Parallel 1" employs an OpenMP parallel for loop to parallelize the iterations of the outer for loop that iterates from 1 to 1000000.

Tuning for Physical Multi-Core Processors

The step of tuning for a physical processor requires turning off Intel Hyper-Threading Technology. This is accomplished by manually disabling it in the BIOS during bootup. Once Intel Hyper-Threading Technology is disabled, the benefits of the physical cores are isolated and focus on them can occur. For a multithreaded application, Intel Thread Profiler can be used to analyze the concurrency between the threads executing on the system. This tuning step looks to see how the work is distributed between the processor cores.

Table 8.12 shows the report of concurrency level obtained using Intel Thread Profiler on the benchmark. These results were obtained on a version of the application employing two threads set using the *omp_set_num_threads* API. The initial version, termed "*Parallel 1*" shows that 59.05 percent of execution time occurs in concurrency level 2. The goal of course is to spend as much time as possible taking advantage of both cores. Increasing the amount of time the application executes in a higher concurrency level should result in faster execution.

Table 8.12   Concurrency Level of Prime Counter, 2 Threads

Concurrency	Parallel 1	Parallel 2
0	0.64%	0.55%
1	40.3%	37.12%
2	59.05%	62.33%

The application exhibits a workload imbalance issue as shown by the profile in Figure 8.15. The application employs two threads to perform the work of computing if a number is prime. These two threads are labeled "1" and "OMP Worker Thread #1". The first thread finishes execution after approximately 33.5 seconds. The second thread completes execution after approximately 39 seconds. Workload balance is an important issue to consider in optimizing for multi-core processors. The goal is to balance the workload and thus employ the processor cores to execute equivalent amounts of work. The performance issue illustrated occurs because the iteration space is divided into two with one thread handling the lower half of the range and the second thread the upper half. The issue is that the second thread has substantially more work because it takes more checks to see if a larger number is prime.

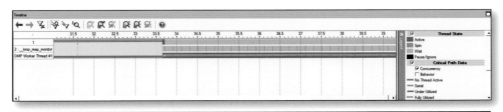

Figure 8.15   Timeline View of Parallel 1

Figure 8.16 shows a modification to the original parallel implementation making use of the OpenMP schedule clause. Instead of dividing the iteration space into half, the iteration space is divided into chunks of 10 numbers each. The assignment of these sets of 10 numbers to check is managed by the OpenMP at runtime and based upon when one thread is available to take on more work. This version is labeled "Parallel 2" and based upon Table 8.12

shows an improvement in reported concurrency level, from 59.05 percent to 62.33 percent.

```
#pragma omp parallel for private(prime)
        schedule(dynamic, 10)
for (index = start; index <= end; index+= ) {
  prime = test_for_prime(index);
  #pragma omp critical
  if (prime) number_of_primes++;
}
```

Figure 8.16   OpenMP Prime Number Counter with Schedule Clause

Tuning for Logical Multi-Core Processors

The step of tuning for logical multi-core processors is started by enabling Intel Hyper-Threading Technology in the BIOS. The application now has more resources to execute the application as the number of processors has increased; one physical processor core now appears as two logical processor cores to the underlying OS.

Executing on two logical processor cores is not the same as executing on two physical processor cores. More processor resources are shared so the performance increase observed may not be as great. For example, if an application is multithreaded and each thread places the same stress on the processor core such as being heavy on memory accesses, the demand on the memory subsystem has effectively doubled; however the processor resources such as cache are split.

Table 8.13 shows the concurrency level when executing Parallel 2 on the configured system with Intel Hyper-Threading Technology enabled. The processor core is capable of executing four threads concurrently; however the concurrency level is still reported as two for over 50 percent of execution. A timeline view of the application appears in Figure 8.17. The timeline view shows the execution of the threads across time. The dark blocks indicate when parallel execution occurs. The lines connecting the different threads with what could be described as a "sine wave" appearance is the transition of lock ownership from one thread to the next as the application executes. This lock transition is preventing greater parallel execution.

Table 8.13   Concurrency Level of Prime Counter, 4T

Concurrency	Parallel 2	Parallel 3
0	0.6%	1.11%
1	47.12%	6.79%
2	50.26%	0.01%
3	2.02%	0.23%
4	0.01%	91.83%

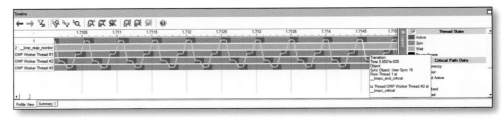

Figure 8.17   Intel® Thread Profiler view

Lock contention is one of the common performance issues in multithreaded software. There are many techniques for improving lock performance; however a detailed explanation is outside of the scope of this book. As shown by the listing in Figure 8.18, the issue is resolved by employing the OpenMP reduction clause and removing the use of the OpenMP critical directive. The reduction clause enables each thread to maintain a private copy of the *number_of_primes* variable and to merge the private copies into the sum total for the whole application after the parallel region is exited. Table 8.13 shows that the concurrency level of this version, termed "Parallel 3", is at four for 91.83 percent of execution.

```
#pragma omp parallel for private(prime)
        schedule(dynamic, 10)
        reduction(+: number_of_primes)
for (index = start; index <= end; index+= ) {
  prime = test_for_prime(index);
  if (prime) number_of_primes++;
}
```

Figure 8.18 OpenMP Prime Number Counter with Reduction Clause

Memory Optimization

Optimizing data structures and data access is important for effective multi-core processor performance and is impacted by the specific memory hierarchy of the Intel Atom processor. One key architecture difference between SMT and multi-core processors is the configuration of caches on the processor cores. With SMT, one physical process appears to be two processor cores; the two processor cores correspondingly share the caches inside the Intel Atom processor. Alternatively a true dual-core processor such as the Intel Atom 330 processor has two separate physical processor cores with their own L1 and L2 caches. These differences impact the types of optimizations to consider.

Multi-Core Processor Cache Guidelines

One of the common optimizations in multithreaded software is eliminating locks through the use of private variables; an example was shown in the previous Parallel 3 version of the primes program. This optimization impacts cache behavior as well as lock overhead performance. Without use of private variables, a variable that is shared in memory would need to be synchronized across the different processor cores that the threads are executing upon. This level of sharing can result in a data value moving from processor core cache to processor core cache. Instead, employ a private variable and a reduction once the local processing work is complete.

Depending on processor resources such as cache architecture and size, the software developer might architect the code to reduce the potential for cache misses so that optimum performance can be achieved.

False sharing results when separate data items that are accessed by separate threads are allocated to the same cache line. Since a data access causes an entire cache line to be read into cache from main memory, if one data item in the cache line is shared, all of the data items in that cache line will be treated as shared by the cache subsystem. Two data items could be updated in unrelated transactions by two threads running on different cores but, if the two items are in the same cache line, the cache subsystem will have to update the system memory in order to maintain cache coherency setting up a condition where pingponging can occur.

These techniques will reduce the number of times the cache data will be evicted and reloaded when another thread executes, and then evicted and reloaded again as the first thread continues to execute.

Here are some tips to consider when optimizing caches on multi-core processor systems:

■ Process a specific size of data, one that fits into the available cache memory or within a cache line.

■ Perform all processing on that data while it's in cache instead of having to read it into cache several times for different steps of the processing to the same data.

■ Pin threads that share data to cores that share cache. This technique benefits from data locality. Thus, it reduces cache misses.

SMT Cache Guidelines

Since Intel HT Technology shares some processor resources between cores, performance depends on the threads limiting contention for the same resources. If the software performance degrades when Intel HT Technology is enabled in the BIOS, the cause could be that threads are contending for cache, which can result in an extraordinarily high number of cache misses. This situation is called *cache thrashing*. The use of a performance analysis tool, such as the Intel® VTune™ Performance Analyzer, will identify and provide information about cache misses. The Intel Press book *Programming with Hyper-Threading Technology* (Binstock and Gerber, 2004) provides many more details to achieving optimum performance with Intel HT Technology.

False sharing is not an issue when two threads are sharing the same data in the same cache line. In the case of SMT, the one cache line is truly shared between the two threads, which has the affect of keeping memory use down.

The previous section on general microarchitecture tuning suggests employing alignment or padding to keep two different data items out of a cache line with the downside of increasing memory use. The article "Avoiding and Identifying False Sharing Among Threads" provides a full discussion on identifying and rectifying issues around false sharing.

The main issue of which to be aware is that two threads are sharing the cache at the same time so if both of them have large demands on the memory subsystem, then an increase in cache misses can be expected. In the worst case, cache thrashing could occur. This is a case where one thread references large amounts of memory causing the cache to be filled with the data it needs and then a second thread executes and performs the same sort of action. The threads alternate execution in a way that the caches are missing a large portion of the time. In these cases, you would want to employ a profile to see how cache misses are increasing and consider changing the algorithm to cut down on the memory referenced. For example, if the application was tuned with knowledge that the data cache is 512 KB, it may be better to tune it for a cache size of 256 KB. Alternatively, you could consider executing these threads on different processor cores by employing affinity instructions in the OS.

Intel HT Technology does not provide any additional memory bandwidth. So, for applications where memory bandwidth is fully consumed without enabling Intel HT Technology the throughput capability is already constrained. Thus, enabling Intel HT Technology to add more threads just exacerbates the condition and could degrade the performance.

Synchronization Optimization Techniques

The nature of synchronization constricts the application to executing serially, because a thread cannot run when it's waiting for access to shared data. Synchronizing access to shared data with controlled access is required for data shared between threads, but should be kept to a minimum to mitigate the negative impact of synchroniza¬tion on performance. These tips are documented in detail within the *Intel Guide for Developing Multithreaded Applications*.

Specific tips are summarized here:

■ Manage lock contention for large and small critical sections. Critical sections execute serially. Threads should spend as little time inside a critical section as possible to reduce the amount of time other threads sit idle waiting to acquire the lock, a state known as lock contention. In other words, it is best to keep critical sections small.

■ Use synchronization routines provided by the threading API rather than hand-coding synchronization.

■ Choose apropriate synchronization primitives to minimize overhead. Understand the available synchronization objects and their tradeoffs. Examples include simple operations on variable, inter-process synchronization and timed waits, and controlled spin counts for critical sections. Spin counts can greatly affect SMP performance on processors employing Intel HT Technology.

■ Use non-blocking locks when possible. Use non-blocking threading calls to avoid context-switch overheads. The non-blocking synchronization calls usually start with the try keyword in C++.

Spin-wait loops are efficient in a multiprocessor system since a thread will have exclusive access to a processing core. However, a thread that executes a spin-wait within an Intel HT Technology environment ties up a core without doing any useful work.

Specific tips include the following:

■ In multithreaded applications the spin-wait loops are normally executed in the thread API functions.

■ When a spin-wait loop is used outside of a thread API and it is suspected that a thread will release a lock within an OS quantum of time, it is recommended that a "PAUSE" instruction be used inside the spin-wait loop. If longer than OS quanta of time, use OS synchronization techniques.

Integrated Multi-Core Development Using Prism

A JPEG encoder example is used to illustrate the development flow of a project that migrates existing sequential single core software onto a multi-core platform. The starting point for the example is an open source JPEG encoder, mb-jpeg[10]. Sampling is fixed at 4:2:0 on macroblock boundaries, and basic sequential Huffman 8-bit mode is supported.

It seems appropriate to adopt a first-do-no-harm mentality within the development flow. The greatest challenge is usually not in finding the parallelism, but in exploiting it in a correct and efficient manner. A sensible and pragmatic approach starts with sequential code and incrementally adds parallelism, testing the changes at each step of the way.

Understanding the original program, the target platform, and best parallel programming practices all influence the refactoring of code from sequential to a proper parallel implementation. Each incremental change that increases parallelism also has the potential to introduce bugs, so take small steps and test frequently.

Considering Amdahl's law; it is crucial to focus first on areas in the code base that account for most of the execution time. Leverage profiling and analysis tools to understand both the critical paths and also the ordering dependencies in the code that restrict how parallelism can be applied.

Prism performs dynamic analysis of application traces to profile the code and determine threading and dependency relationships. The JPEG code uses a small image to JPEG conversion example that exercises all stages of the JPEG encoder.

This case study uses a simplified parallelization flow. Initially, the sequential code is compiled and executed to generate trace files. Prism's initial analysis is employed to profile the execution and identify functions that consume the most execution time and to understand the data dependencies between them. Prism what-if analysis is used to explore different parallelization strategies. Once a strategy is decided upon, the parallel program is incrementally implemented and debugged. Inside Prism, the debug phase involves checking and resolving data races and verifying the performance efficiency of the implementation. Refinements to the parallelization strategy are evaluated at each step.

The first phase of the flow is to analyze the existing sequential code and to experiment with different partitioning approaches and different platform

---

[10] For further information on the Embedded JPEG Codec Library, consult http://sourceforge.net/projects/mb-jpeg/

scenarios. Figure 8.19 shows a typical stage in a Prism what-if analysis. Here execution profile information is visible from which candidate functions can be identified for possible parallel execution on a multi-core platform with a certain number of cores. The number of cores is set by the user. In this case the candidate functions are "forced" to execute in parallel on a quad core platform. A schedule is automatically generated by Prism without requiring source code changes or re-executing the software application. Note that the schedule that is generated honors all data dependencies in the code and it should not be surprising to discover that there is little concurrent activity in the schedule.

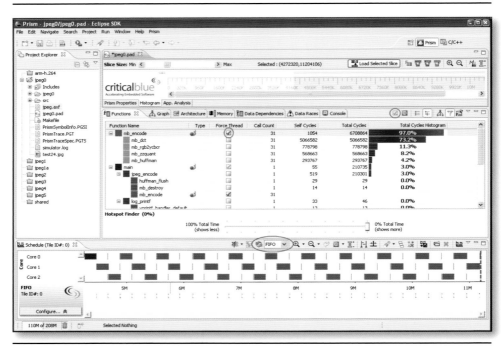

Figure 8.19 Prism What-if Analysis on Sequential Code

To see this effect more clearly, the user can switch from the core view shown in Figure 8.19 to the thread view in Figure 8.20. Although multiple threads have been created, it has not been possible to execute them in parallel due to the data dependencies between them.

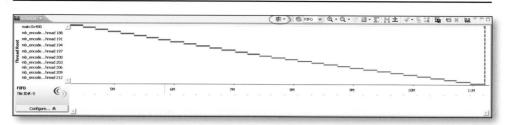

Figure 8.20 Thread View on Sequential Code

Effective parallel programming requires understanding inter-relationships between functions and data flow through the software application. Having established that data dependencies are preventing the unlocking of concurrent behavior in the JPEG encoder case study, Prism helps the user to investigate the nature of the data dependencies and to map them back to the application source code lines that cause them, as shown in Figure 8.21. Prism also supports what-if analysis for data dependency removal such that the user can also establish which data dependencies impact the overall schedule. It is likely that some data dependencies need not be removed since they do not impact the parallel execution of the application.

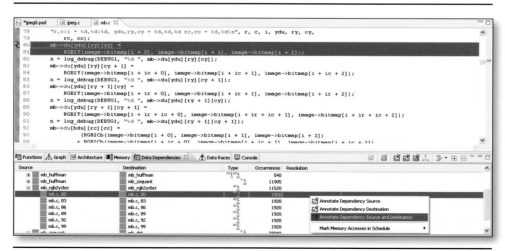

Figure 8.21 Prism Source Code Annotation of Data Dependencies

This iterative process can be executed several times in order to establish the most efficient parallelization strategy and the code changes needed (thread insertion and data dependency removal) to exploit the identified concurrency.

Once the code changes have been made and the application has been checked to ensure it is still functionally correct, the next stage of the process is to validate performance and check for potential data races. Data races may show themselves in causing immediate functional failures in the application code but may also be latent and may only show themselves in subsequent and different scheduling conditions. This uncertainty of failure is what makes data races so dangerous within multi-core software systems.

Prism can analyze the users' multithreaded code and, in addition to showing an execution schedule on multiple cores to validate that the expected levels of parallelism have been achieved, data race analysis can be performed. As shown in Figure 8.22, analysis of the complete trace of the multithreaded version of the JPEG case study shows that data races are present.

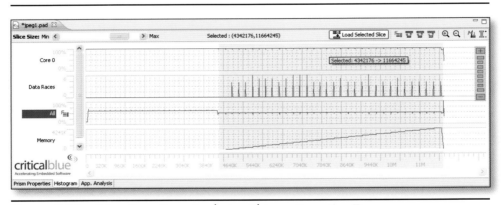

Figure 8.22 Prism Data Race Analysis within an Execution Trace

When multiple threads access the same memory location and at least one thread writes to that location, the resultant data will depend on the interleaved execution order of the threads. This is known as a race condition and leads to unpredictable results that may be masked by external effects such as the thread scheduling policy. Correct execution requires forcing partial execution order either by serializing threads or by using mutual exclusion locks for critical sections. These devices ensure that a thread has exclusive access to a memory location to guarantee the proper ordering of reads and writes. Locks must be explicitly specified by the programmer. Sequential code is often filled with many ordering dependencies, which are implicitly satisfied by the serialized execution of the program. Miss any dependency in the parallel scenario, and a latent bug has been created.

In a very similar process to that described for data dependencies, the user can investigate the data races on a detailed multi-core schedule, link the data races back to their application source code causes, perform what-if analysis to experiment with potential solutions, and eventually map out a set of implementation changes that will render the parallel application safe under all scheduling conditions while at the same time delivering the desired parallel performance levels. Figure 8.23 is a screenshot that illustrates Prism's ability to focus on individual data races in the application code.

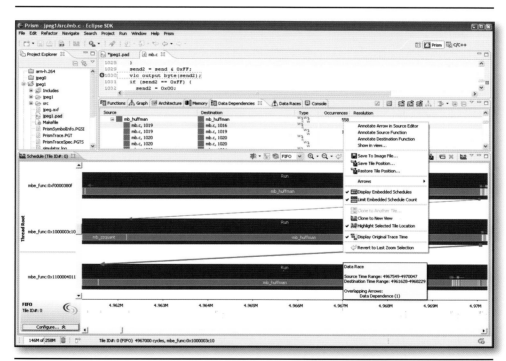

Figure 8.23   Prism Data Race Cause Identification and Resolution

It is never too early to start analyzing your sequential application and planning the process of migrating to a multi-core platform. Using tools like Prism to understand your application in a multi-core context will make the eventual migration to a parallel platform smoother, more predictable, and a little less painful.

Power Optimization

The power performance tuning phase begins after successful optimization for single core and multi-core, but the reality is that many of the steps performed during the previous optimization phases benefits power performance as well.

Table 8.14 summarizes power saving guidelines across several categories: computational efficiency, memory management, timer and interrupts, power awareness, and multi-core processing efficiency. The next several subsections provide further details on each category.

Table 8.14   Power Saving Guidelines

Guideline	Description
Computational Efficiency	
Hurry up and get idle.	Employ optimized code.
Memory Management	
Improve cache locality.	Operate on small data one time to ensure good cache locality. Prefetch.
Manage memory efficiently.	Employ buffering and preallocation to reduce reads from longer latency and higher power utilizing devices.
Timers and Interrupts	
Avoid polling.	Convert polling-based architecture to event-driven.
Avoid busy waits.	Eliminate spin loops that wait for a specific action.
Reduce interrupts.	Avoid waking up the processor.
Use timers effectively.	Optimize periodic timer usage.
Power Awareness	
Be power-aware.	Reduce QoS when executing from battery.
Be power-smart.	Handle CPU sleep transitions effectively.
Employ multi-core effectively	
Multithreading.	Use multiple threads to increase performance. Balance the workload.

Computational Efficiency

Computational efficiency in the context of power optimization is colloquially termed, "hurry up and get idle." The motivation is to execute the processing work of the application as quickly as possible so the system can transition into a low power consumption idle state. The techniques for implementing computational efficiency overlap with single processor core and multi-core processor tuning detailed earlier in the chapter.

Memory Management

Power-efficient memory management also overlaps with memory management for both single-core and multi-core performance. The general goal is to keep the data about to be operated upon as close to the processor core as possible. Use of prefetching and buffering should be scrutinized to reduce access to more remote memory devices. Cache access should be favored over memory access. Memory access should be favored over disk access. Some general recommendations include:

- Consider prefetching and buffering at every level of the memory hierarchy.

  - Prefetch and buffer data from memory employing prefetch instructions and cache-friendly data structures.

  - Prefetch and buffer data from optical, hard drive, and solid state drive enabling the devices to stay idle as frequently as possible.

  - Balance prefetching and buffering against efficiency. Is there data being moved that is never referenced due to proximity to other data? Is the caching of the data causing an increase in cache and buffer misses on other data items?

- Pack and align data structures for efficient memory access. Reduce working set to fit into cache.

- Consider bundling read and write requests to drives.

- Favor algorithms that minimize data movement over high performance.

- Operate on small data all at once so data stays in caches.

  - Repeated streaming through memory is not efficient in terms of power or performance.

- Employ efficient memory allocation and deallocation.

    - Allocate buffers at first use and reuse buffers where possible.

    - Avoid zeroing of buffers during execution time.

Timers and Interrupts

Use of timers and interrupts in an embedded system is required for many functions of the operating system and its interactions with the application and devices connected to the processor cores. These timers and interrupts can cause disruption to the executing and idle states of the processor and increase power utilization. An idle processor core can be made active to process an interrupt several times a second. A currently executing process will have its execution state suspended with the numerous memory and cache operations required to suspend one process and start executing an interrupt handler. Effective use of timers and interrupts therefore can have a bearing on processor performance and power.

Recommendations for effective use of timers and interrupts include:

- Avoid polling. Use an event driven software architecture. Some poor examples of polling include:

    - Checking to see if the mouse has moved.

    - Checking to see if the sound volume has changed.

    - Checking to see if it is time to update the minute hand once per second.

    - Checking to see if a peripheral device was inserted into a slot frequently.

- Avoid busy waits.

    - Minimize use of spinning loops.

    - Convert polling loops to be event driven.

- Reduce interrupts.

    - Delay interrupts to the maximum delay that is tolerable.

    - Coalesce interrupts.

- Reduce usage of high-resolution periodic timers.

    - Do you need a timer every 10 milliseconds?

    - Disable periodic timers when not in use.

Power Awareness

A power-aware embedded system responds to the type and amount of power available. Behavior of the system is modified based upon the type of power available such as AC or DC or if the device is plugged into a wall outlet or executing off of battery power. Second, behavior could be modified based upon the amount of power remaining such as in the case of an almost drained battery.

Some recommendations include the following:

- Create default power policies when executing from wall outlet or battery. For example, when the system is powered by AC, the processor could execute at its fastest and the display could be brightest. When switched to battery, the processor could modulate to a slower P state more aggressively and could dim the display. The system could avoid background tasks.

- Consider powering down unused peripherals. Shutting down networking if in an offline mode.

Employing Multi-Core Technology Effectively

Efficient use of multi-core processors can improve performance and thus help an application idle as quickly as possible. In addition, the type of memory optimizations one performs for multithreading benefit performance first and foremost. These optimizations also benefit power utilization.

Special care is needed when employing multi-core technology to align activity. Synchronize multiple threads to interrupt at the same time. Figure 8.24 shows two sets of runtime behavior of two threads executing a video playback application comprised of decode and rendering steps. The first set corresponds to the top two timelines labeled Thread 1 and Thread 2 and the second set corresponds to the bottom two timelines. Thread 1 is tasked with the decoding portion of application. Thread 2 is tasked with the rendering portion of the application. Processor active time is indicated by the rectangles between Thread 1 and Thread 2 on the timelines.

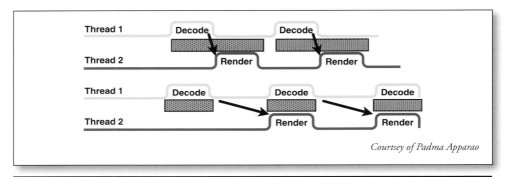

Courtsey of Padma Apparao

Figure 8.24 Thread Optimization for Power

PowerTOP was employed and showed an excessive number of wakeups while the application executed. The first set illustrates that the processor stayed active while Thread 1 executed and continued in the active state to handle the processing of Thread 2. The processor is unable to stay idle for a significant period. Changing the timing of the rendering phase to coincide with the decode phase of the next stream enabled a gap in activity for both threads and enabled the processor to drop into an idle state for a longer period.

Isolating Power Performance Issues

When performing power optimization one key question is: how is a power issue diagnosed and subsequently isolated? PowerTOP indicates whether the system has a power utilization problem. Symptoms may include unexplained time monitored in C0 or an unexplained large number of wakeups per second.

Once the problem is observed, how is it isolated to the specific cause? The answer is that a combination of tools and insight is employed to determine the root cause of the power utilization issue. The process is summarized as follows:

1. Employ idle mode optimization. Record the PowerTOP statistics when the target application is not executing.

2. Record the PowerTOP statistics when the target application is executing in what should be a minimal execution mode. Note any unexplained increases in activity such as an increase in C0 average residency or wakeups per second. Note any application functions listed in the rank ordered Top causes for wakeups listing.

3. Obtain a flat profile and call graph to determine the hotspots and call tree in the target application.

4. Search the hotspots for functionality around processing events, polling, and monitoring activity.

To highlight the technique this process is applied to a graphical application, DreamChess[†11]. DreamChess is an open source chess program that displays a 3D representation of the chess game and includes a chess playing engine called Dreamer. The particular system employed is an Intel Atom N450 processor-based netbook.

The first step is to record statistics when the system is idle. PowerTOP recorded the percentage of time the processor idled in the lowest C state, C4 at 99.2 percent and the number of wakeups-from-idle per second as 69.0. This can be considered the baseline.

The second step is to execute the application and analyze portions where the application should be idle. Figure 8.25 shows the PowerTOP profile when executing DreamChess. A game has been started; however the mouse has not been moved for several seconds. As can be seen, the amount of time in C0 is 44.5 percent and the total number of wakeups-from-idle per second is 343.9. These numbers indicate a potential problem. In addition, the third process listed as a top cause of wakeups is the Dreamer process, part of the application. The next step is to focus inside the application to find the problem.

---

[11] For further information on DreamChess, consult www.dreamchess.org

```
     PowerTOP version 1.11      (C) 2007 Intel Corporation

Cn                    Avg residency      P-states (frequencies)
C0 (cpu running)           (44.5%)          1.67 Ghz    41.0%
polling               0.0ms ( 0.0%)         1334 Mhz     0.3%
C1 mwait              0.0ms ( 0.0%)         1000 Mhz    58.7%
C2 mwait              0.2ms ( 0.1%)
C4 mwait              1.7ms (55.4%)

Wakeups-from-idle per second : 343.9     interval: 10.0s
Power usage (ACPI estimate): 12.1W (2.4 hours) (long term: 11.1W,/2.6h)

Top causes for wakeups:
  44.3% (407.8)       <kernel core> : hrtimer_start_range_ns (tick_sched_timer)
  27.2% (250.7)        <kernel IPI> : Rescheduling interrupts
  10.5% ( 96.2)            dreamer : hrtimer_start_range_ns (hrtimer_wakeup)
   7.9% ( 72.9)        <interrupt> : acpi
   2.4% ( 22.4)        <interrupt> : uhci_hcd:usb5, HDA Intel, ra0
   1.1% ( 10.0)       <kernel core> : add_timer (rtmp_timer_MlmePeriodicExec)
   1.0% (  8.9)        <interrupt> : i915
   0.9% (  8.1)        <interrupt> : ehci_hcd:usb1, uhci_hcd:usb2
   0.9% (  8.1)    USB device  2-1 : USB-PS/2 Optical Mouse (Logitech)
   0.8% (  7.8)               Xorg : schedule_timeout_uninterruptible (process_timeout)
   0.8% (  7.0)               hald : schedule_timeout_uninterruptible (process_timeout)
   0.6% (  5.9)       <kernel core> : hrtimer_start (tick_sched_timer)
   0.4% (  4.0)       <kernel core> : usb_hcd_poll_rh_status (rh_timer_func)
   0.2% (  2.0)     gnome-terminal : hrtimer_start_range_ns (hrtimer_wakeup)

Suggestion: Enable USB autosuspend by pressing the U key or adding
usbcore.autosuspend=1 to the kernel command line in the grub config

 Q - Quit   R - Refresh   U - Enable USB suspend
```

Figure 8.25   PowerTOP Profile of DreamChess

A profile of the application is obtained by executing Sysprof. The application is built with debug information by default so function information is available after the profile is collected. Figure 8.26 shows the profile of DreamChess. The focus in the function listing is dreamchess. The call graph of DreamChess is shown in the descendants window with the function, `poll_move`, highlighted.

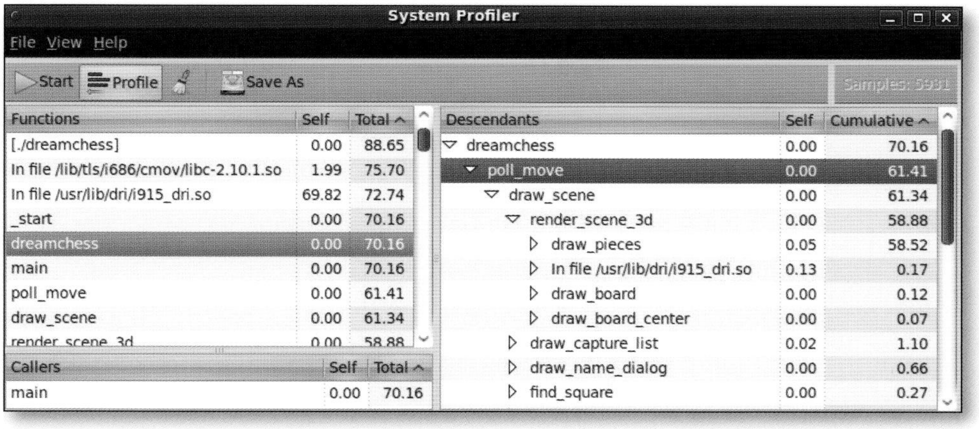

Figure 8.26 Sysprof Profile of DreamChess

The source code of the application shows that the function `poll_move` effectively polls until a chess piece has been moved. If the mouse is not moving, the polling loop still executes. This is the primary cause of the increase in C0 residency. A solution to this issue is to have an event driven software architecture where if no activity was detected, the system would idle until woken up by a mouse move and mouse click. Fixing this issue may require substantial source code change and is outside the scope of this chapter; however what is important is the process used to find the problem.

Summary

Performance optimization is a necessary step in migrating applications to systems based on the Intel Atom processor. This optimization process consists of multiple steps, is iterative, and concludes once the performance requirements are met.

The optimization process itself is broken down into component pieces to lessen the difficulty and to enable focus on these individual pieces. First, optimization targeting single processor core performance is conducted. Single processor core performance consists of creating a benchmark, profiling the benchmark, applying compiler optimization, and conducting architecture tuning. Architecture tuning employs microarchitecture performance tools to understand the performance of the application as it executes on the Intel Atom processor. Both, general microarchitecture analysis and Intel Atom processor–specific analysis is conducted.

The second phase focuses upon multi-core processor tuning and begins with developing a benchmark of a parallel version of the application. This application is tuned for performance on physical processor cores by turning off Intel Hyper-Threading Technology support in the processor. Afterwards, the logical processor cores are enabled and tuning on both physical and logical processor cores commences. Performance issues such as lock overhead, workload balance, and cache efficiency are addressed in a multi-core processor context.

The final step in performance optimization focuses upon power efficiency, which is a more recent addition to the performance tuning cycle. Optimizing for power begins with optimizing for performance. In fact, many of the optimizations performed during the single-core and multi-core phases will have a positive impact on power performance. Other areas for power optimization include scrutiny of timers and interrupts and power context awareness.

At every stage of optimization it is important to employ tools effectively. This chapter reviewed the tools to employ showing examples of how to optimize at all stages to maximize performance of the application on the Intel Atom processor.

Adopting Intel® Atom™ Product Technologies

Stop thinking in terms of limitations and start thinking in terms of possibilities.

—Terry Josephson, 20th/21st-century motivational author

One of of the notable benefits of designing products based on Intel® Atom™ processors is the ability to unleash further capabilities through a variety of Intel product technologies. According to step four of the migration design guide explained in Chapter 4, after the software executes correctly on one Intel Atom processor core the next step is to adopt the Intel Atom processor technologies that apply to the migration plan. The goal of this chapter is not to provide detailed mechanics for implementing these technologies, but rather is intended as a reference to methodologies for adopting the Intel product technologies.

Intel® Atom™ Processor Technologies

The Intel products and their processor family feature support are located at http://ark.intel.com. This Web site provides details about product technologies, also referred to as *Advanced Technologies*, supported by each processor. This is a handy reference since the features can vary between processor products, as well as within a processor product family. This chapter describes the following Intel Atom processor product technologies, as well as software methodologies for adopting and benefiting from the technologies:

■ Intel® Hyper-Threading Technology[1] (Intel® HT Technology). Provides two logical cores per processor.

■ Intel® dual-core technology. Provides two physical cores, or two single core processors within one processor package.

■ Intel® Virtualization Technology[2] (Intel® VT) eases software migration, improves real-time performance, and enhances security. The list of all Intel processors supporting Intel VT is located at http://ark.intel.com/VTList.aspx.

■ Intel® 64[3]. Improves performance by allowing systems to address more than 4 GB of both virtual and physical memory.

---

1 Intel® Hyper-Threading Technology (Intel® HT Technology) requires a computer system with an Intel® processor supporting Intel HT Technology and an Intel HT Technology-enabled chipset, BIOS, and operating system. Performance will vary depending on the specific hardware and software you use. See www.intel.com/products/ht/hyperthreading_more. htm for more information including details on which processors support Intel HT Technology.

2 Intel® Virtualization Technology requires a computer system with an enabled Intel® processor, BIOS, virtual machine monitor (VMM) and, for some uses, certain computer system software enabled for it. Functionality, performance or other benefits will vary depending on hardware and software configurations and may require a BIOS update. Software applications may not be compatible with all operating systems. Please check with your application vendor.

3 64-bit computing on Intel® architecture requires a computer system with a processor, chipset, BIOS, operating system, device drivers and applications enabled for Intel® 64 architecture. Processors will not operate (including 32-bit operation) without an Intel 64 architecture-enabled BIOS. Performance will vary depending on your hardware and software configurations. Consult with your system vendor for more information.

Processor Core and Thread Features

Intel Atom processor features include Intel HT Technology and Intel Dual-Core Technology. In general, applications that are written to run well on symmetric multiprocessing (SMP) architectures will garner the benefits from Intel HT Technology or dual-core. However, there are software techniques that help to extract the greatest performance benefits from these technologies if the software design comprehends their subtle differences, which are explained in this chapter. Note:

■ Although the term *Intel HT Technology* refers to Intel's specific implementation of this technology and *simultaneous multithreading* (SMT) refers to the technological concept, they are used interchangeably in this chapter.

■ The term *multi-core* will be used in this chapter for references to core features and solutions that are generic to Intel HT Technology, dual-core, as well as multi-core technologies.

Intel® Hyper-Threading Technology

Intel Hyper-Threading Technology is Intel's implementation of SMT, which means that the processor allows multiple threads to issue instructions on each clock cycle. On the Intel Atom processor Intel HT Technology provides two hardware threads for high performance-per watt efficiency in an in-order pipeline. Intel HT Technology also provides increased system responsiveness in multitasking environments. One execution resource is seen as two logical processors, and parallel threads are executed on a single core by sharing, partitioning, and replicating certain processor execution resources, which are listed Table 9.1.

Intel HT Technology provides:

■ Simultaneous multitasking on the single core.

■ Appears as two independent processors to the software.

■ Increases utilization of the execution unit of the processor.

■ Accelerates performance of multithreaded applications.

Table 9.1   Intel® Hyper-Threading Technology Processor Resource Policies

Policy	Processor Execution Resources
Shared	Level 2 cache, execution engine, branch predictors, control logic, and system bus.
Partitioned	Registers, Advanced Programmable Interrupt Controller, Timestamp Counter, Instruction reorder buffer, load/store buffer, queues.
Replicated	Architecture states, instruction pointers, renaming logic, ITLB, return stack, level 1 instruction cache, level 1 data cache.

What's the Difference Between Intel® Hyper-Threading Technology and Dual-Core Technology

Intel HT Technology delivers *thread-level parallelism* on each processor resulting in more efficient use of processor resources. The result is higher processing throughput and improved performance[4] running multithreaded software. The performance benefit of Intel HT Technology will vary between different implementations.

■ The Intel Atom processor is an in-order processor, capable of a throughput of up to two instructions per clock cycle. The execution resources of in-order processors are typically not fully utilized due to the latency between instructions. To that end, Intel HT Technology takes advantage of unused processor execution resources to provide a significant performance[4] benefit with very little additional hardware.

■ Processors based on the Intel® Core™ microarchitecture can hide some latency through its out-of-order implementation. The Intel Core microarchitecture is capable of a throughput of up to four instructions per clock cycle, a throughput level not attained by most applications. So, in the case of Intel Core microarchitecture, Intel HT Technology allows the processor to achieve a throughput level closer to the theoretical limit.

It should be noted that several improvements have been made in Intel's current processor microarchitectures since the original Intel HT Technology

---

[4] Performance results are based on certain tests measured on specific computer systems. Any difference in system hardware, software or configuration will affect actual performance. For more information go to http://www.intel.com/performance.

that debuted in the Intel® Pentium® 4 processors based on Intel® Netburst™ microarchitecture. Larger caches are an example of the improvements that enhance the performance of Intel HT Technology on today's Intel microarchitectures.

Intel® HT Technology requires a computer system with:

- A processor that supports Intel® HT Technology

- Intel® HT Technology enabled chipset

- Intel® HT Technology enabled system BIOS

- Intel® HT Technology enabled/optimized operating system

It is important to understand that not all cores are equal. That is to say that a logical core isn't the same as a physical core, and core architectures, features, and capabilities vary between processor families. For optimum performance it's up to the operating system to make the best thread scheduling decisions based on the topology of the cores, and for the software developer to design code that effectively exploits the parallel execution capabilities of Intel architecture processors.

Processor resource utilization is at the heart of performance and the difference between Intel HT Technology, and Intel dual-core and multi-core technologies. An illustration of single processor resource utilization and Intel HT Technology is shown in Figure 9.1. The illustration is used for conceptual purposes only. The diagrams represent single core superscalar processors. A superscalar processor is a CPU architecture that provides instruction level parallelism, which means it can execute multiple instructions in the same clock cycle. The number of instructions that can be executed in one clock cycle depends on the instruction width of the execution engine.

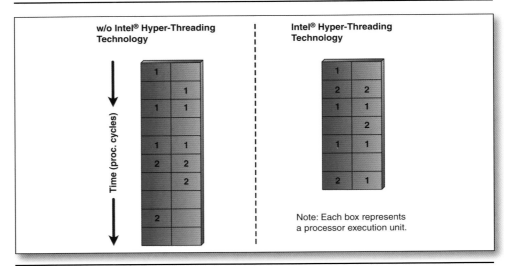

Figure 9.1   Processor Resource Utilization

In the case of the example in Figure 9.1, the figure depicts superscalar processors having 2-wide execution engines. Each small square represents a processor execution unit. Each row of squares is one processor clock cycle, and several clock cycles are executed over time from top to bottom. Squares numbered 1 and 2 are used to show the execution of two different threads, thread 1 and thread 2, and empty squares represent processor execution units that are unused in a clock cycle. Each clock cycle uses various processor resources.

The superscalar processor on the left of Figure 9.1 does not enable Intel HT Technology. Consequently, this processor can only execute one thread at any given time. Notice that thread 1 executes first and for a number of clock cycles, and after it runs for a while it stops executing and then thread 2 starts executing. The example shows that nearly half of the processor execution resources were unused during the time two threads executed.

The superscalar processor on the right of Figure 9.1 enables Intel HT Technology. Notice that with Intel HT Technology two threads can execute simultaneously because the second thread makes use of unused processor execution unit resources, allowing the two threads' instructions to be executed within the same clock cycle. The result is that the processing of the two threads is completed in fewer clock cycles than on the processor without Intel HT Technology. The net effect is an increase in processor resource utilization, resulting in higher instruction throughput, greater performance[5], and enhanced energy efficiency.

Intel® Dual-Core Technology

Intel dual-core technology provides dual independent execution cores and pipelines contained within one packaged processor assembly and delivers full parallel execution of two software threads, enabling higher levels of performance. The implementation can be based on two processors that share the last level of on-die cache, or in the case of today's dual-core Intel Atom processors, as two complete processors that have completely independent processor execution resources. Today's Intel Atom processors based on dual-core also support Intel Hyper-Threading Technology.

A conceptual illustration of a dual-core processor with Intel HT Technology is depicted in Figure 9.2. Notice that two single-core processors are contained within one physical processor package. Also, with Intel HT Technology each logical core has its own architecture state and Advanced Programmable Interrupt Controller (APIC), and the logical cores share the execution units and other resources, such as level 2 cache. Therefore, the dual-core processor with Intel HT Technology has a hardware thread count of four.

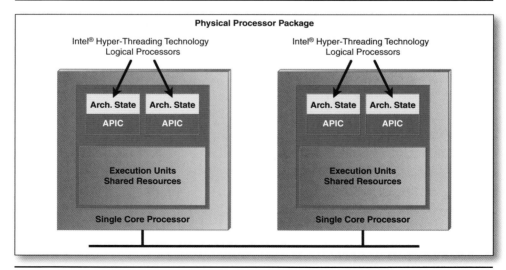

Figure 9.2 Dual-Core Processor with Intel® Hyper-Threading Technology

---

[5] Performance results are based on certain tests measured on specific computer systems. Any difference in system hardware, software or configuration will affect actual performance. For more information go to http://www.intel.com/performance.

An illustration of dual-core processor resource utilization and Intel HT Technology is shown in Figure 9.3. Intel HT Technology is not enabled on the dual-core processor on the left of Figure 9.3, while Intel HT Technology is enabled on the dual-core processor on the right of Figure 9.3. Notice in the processor without Intel HT Technology, two threads execute simultaneously, one thread on each core. When Intel HT Technology is added to the example as shown in the figure on the right, four threads are able to execute simultaneously.

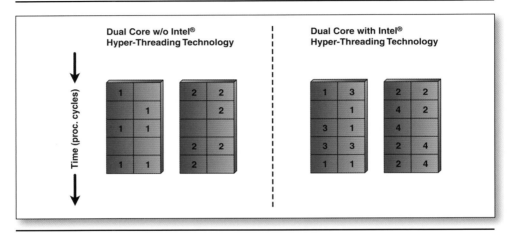

Figure 9.3 Dual-Core and Processor Resource Utilization

This completes the overview on how Intel HT Technology works and the difference between Intel HT Technology and dual-core technology. Keep in mind that in either case an SMP OS is required to recognize the extra cores and to schedule threads to the cores. Depending on the SMP OS and its optimization for Intel HT Technology and dual-core technology, it will likely try to schedule one thread to each physical processor before scheduling the processors to execute additional threads. This is illustrated by the thread numbers in Figure 9.3. First thread 1 is scheduled to run, and then thread 2, and so on.

Intel® Multi-Core Technology Solutions

What solution should be used to adopt dual-core or Intel HT Technology on Intel Atom processor platforms? Several factors will guide the migration plan for adopting the extra cores, including the starting point design of the original source code, as well as migration goals and constraints. The choices include symmetric multiprocessing (SMP), asymmetric multiprocessing (AMP), and virtualization. Each method has its own strengths, so it's important to understand goals and constraints of the migration to choose the method that best fits those requirements. The ideal situation is to have SMP, AMP, and virtualization at your disposal.

> The best strategy is whenever possible try to use performance libraries that are already enabled for Intel HT Technology or Intel multi-core technology.

If the software is already architected to distribute processing to multiple processors then running on Intel Atom processor-based platforms with additional cores should benefit with minimum, if any, changes in the software. However, it's a different story for legacy software that is designed for a uniprocessor (UP) system. For serial code, a couple of options can be considered for a system design that will take advantage of platforms enabled with Intel multi-core technology. The challenge is for cases where the application is not well suited for parallelization. For these cases AMP or virtualization could be cost-effective and viable solutions for leveraging the extra processing capabilities of the additional cores. The best strategy is whenever possible try to use performance libraries that are already enabled for Intel HT Technology or Intel multi-core technology. Using performance libraries will require the least amount of changes in the serial code and could be possibly the only change required to reap the benefits of extra cores. These highly optimized library APIs include functions for video, imaging, compression, cryptography, audio, speech recognition, and signal processing functions and codec component functions for digital media and data-processing applications. Refer to Chapter 7 for more information about threaded performance libraries and tips for applying the libraries to Intel architecture technologies.

A vast number of articles and books have been written about multithreading and multi-core software development. Here are a few good references that are directly related to Intel architecture:

- Shameem Akhter, Jason Roberts. 2006. *Multi-Core Programming*, Hillsboro, OR: Intel Press.

- Clay Breshears. 2009. *The Art of Concurrency*, Sebastopol, CA: O'Reilly Media.

- Max Domeika. 2008. *Software Development for Embedded Multi-core Systems*, Elsevier, Inc.

- Timothy G. Mattson, Beverly A. Sanders, Merna L. Massingill. 2005. *Patterns For Parallel Programming*, Boston, MA: Person Education, Inc.

- Stewart Taylor. 2007. *Optimizing Applications for Multi-core Processors Using the Intel® Integrated Performance Primitives, Second Edition.* Hillsboro, OR: Intel Press.

Symmetric Multiprocessing

SMP operating systems treat all cores as equals and distribute the workload/processing to the available cores. An SMP design is a very performance-efficient way to take advantage of multi-core and/or thread-level parallelism (Intel HT Technology) in the hardware. SMP applications can be written to scale performance automatically as the number of processing cores increase, but SMP requires code to be specifically architected to take advantage of multiple CPUs, also referred to as a parallel application or parallel code.

Most of the popular commercial operating systems have SMP products, and more real-time operating systems are now providing support for SMP. Examples of RTOS products that provide real-time SMP support for Intel architecture include:

- Green Hills Integrity[†]

- LynuxWorks LynxOS[†]

- QNX Neutrino[†]

- Wind River VxWorks[†]

SMP is not always the first choice in taking advantage of multi-core architecture. If the code is not already designed for parallel processing the code needs to be updated and validated, and parallel code can be complex because the software design must decompose the problem into sub-problems that can safely execute simultaneously. Threads are used to execute the concurrent processing. Multithreaded software implementations are prone to data race conditions, stalls, and deadlocks, whether running on SMP or UP processors. Along with breaking down the problem into sub-problems, access to any data that is shared and changeable between the threads must be controlled with synchronized access to the data to prevent data races. Synchronization itself impacts performance, and if implemented incorrectly can cause stalls and deadlocks, but without synchronization data races will occur and thus the processing results are not deterministic. Table 9.2 lists the design and software development tradeoffs of multithreading.

Table 9.2 Multithreading Design and Software Development Tradeoffs

Multithreading Benefits	Multithreading Considerations
Provides best performance for multi-core systems.	Multithreading is prone to bugs.
	Multithreading can be complex.
Provides best scalability for multi-core systems.	Multithreading requires the most development and validation time.

OS-based SMP Affinity

In the case of dual-core Intel Atom processors, each with Intel HT Technology, there are four logical cores within the processor. However, for best performance careful consideration should be made about how the threads are assigned to the cores. Performance can degrade when threads contend for the same processor resources. The SMP OS kernel scheduler assigns threads that are ready to execute to run on the next available core. However, the developer can take control by using processor affinity mechanisms to assign specific cores to specific tasks/threads.

SMP affinity can improve performance on multi-core platforms by improving data locality in cache, which in turn can improve the cache hit rate. The technique involves pinning threads that share a lot of data to cores that share cache. This methodology can also be used to dedicate specific processing to certain cores. Refer to the Intel® Software Network article by Foong, Fung, and Newell, 2008[6] "Improved Linux SMP Scaling: User-directed Processor Affinity" for details about user directed affinity. Table 9.3 provides some tradeoffs that should be considered when using SMP affinity.

Table 9.3   SMP Affinity Tradeoffs

SMP Affinity Benefits	SMP Affinity Considerations
Simply leverages Linux scheduling capabilities.	Obstructs the operating system's ability to treat all cores as equals and distribute balanced workload/ processing to the cores.
Resources may be dynamically assigned using scripts or based on current load conditions.	

Multithreading Software Development Tools

Similar to dual-core, Intel HT Technology benefits from code architected for SMP. Code that is already designed for SMP should be well suited to take advantage of these extra cores. For serial code that will be modified for SMP, consider using software development tools that make it easier to implement threads into the code. Threading tools, such as Intel® Thread Checker, find bugs in threaded code such as deadlocks, data races, and stalls, and Intel® Thread Profiler analyzes threads, showing any thread workload imbalances and synchronized access to data that might limit the potential of the thread's performance. Refer back to Chapter 4 for more information about software development tools and choices.

Library-based Multithreaded Methodologies

Libraries, such as the Intel® Integrated Performance Primitive Library and Intel® Math Kernel Library, make it easier to extract multi-core performance from applications. These libraries provide APIs that are thread-safe and many of the APIs are provided in multithreaded versions. As a result, it's possible to create an SMP implementation of your software and gain the benefits of extra cores just by calling the threaded APIs of this library.

---

[6] Annie Foong, Jason Fung, Don Newell. 2008. Improved Linux* SMP Scaling: User-directed Processor Affinity. http://software.intel.com/en-us/articles/improved-linux-smp-scaling-user-directed-processor-affinity/

Implicit Multithreading Methodologies

There are various implicit threading solutions available for developers who prefer to program threads manually but would like to ease the effort and maintain portability of the code. OpenMP and Intel® Thread Building Blocks are two examples of implicit threading solutions.

OpenMP. If the design of the processing is suited for data parallelism, consider implementing threads into the code with the OpenMP method. "…OpenMP is a portable, scalable model that gives shared-memory parallel programmers a simple and flexible interface for developing parallel applications." (OpenMP organization Web site mission statement, 2010). OpenMP uses a fork/join model as shown in Figure 9.4, whereby the master thread spawns a team of threads for processing each parallel task as a parallel region. When all of the tasks complete the threads are joined back to the master thread.

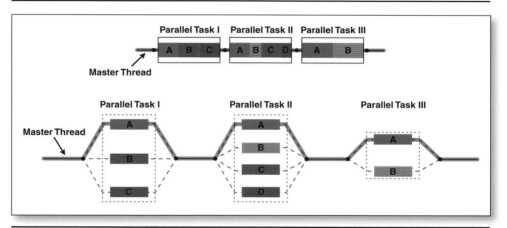

Figure 9.4   Fork/Join Thread Model

OpenMP uses compiler directives to multithread code. Creating a threaded `for` loop can be as simple as inserting one pragma into the code. OpenMP provides a long list of thread controls including constructs and directives used for specifying parallel regions, work sharing, synchronization and data environment, and also includes runtime library functions and environment variables. An example of thread creation and parallelizing a region of code with OpenMP is shown in Figure 9.4.

The code in Figure 9.5 provides an example of using OpenMP to parallelize image processing. Notice the `pragma omp parallel` statement on the first line of code, which directs the compiler to parallelize the region of code that follows the `pragma omp` statement. The code uses a doubly nested `for` loop for processing the image of a given pixel width and height. The OpenMP statement also uses the `private` clause to direct the compiler to use a private copy of the variables pixelX and pixelY for each thread.

```
#pragma omp parallel for private(pixelX,pixelY)
for (pixelX = 0; pixelX < imageHeight; pixelX++)
{
   for (pixelY = 0; pixelY < imageWidth; pixelY++)
   {
     newImage[pixelX,pixelY] =
              ProcessPixel (pixelX, pixelY, image);
   }
}
```

Figure 9.5   Example of OpenMP Thread Creation

Table 9.4 lists the OpenMP and software development tradeoffs.

Table 9.4   OpenMP and Software Development Tradeoffs

OpenMP Benefits	OpenMP Considerations
OpenMP does not require serial code to be changed for threading. Compiler directives, pragmas, are added, keeping the original code intact.	Loops that are flow-dependent (results are used by other iterations of the loop) will not work correctly with OpenMP.
Code can be compiled as multithreaded or serial by simply enabling or disabling the compiler's OpenMP switch respectively.	OpenMP does not determine the correctness of code. Therefore, the developer must understand the dependencies of a loop before using OpenMP to parallelize it.
Code can be parallelized incrementally. That is, OpenMP pragmas can be added to localized portions of the code without consequence to other portions of the source code. Once the effectiveness of one set of pragmas is established, other parts of the code can be considered.	OpenMP does not provide the fine control mechanisms (such as thread priority) of explicit threading methods like Pthreads.
OpenMP does a lot of the threading work that would require much more time to write in an explicit threading implementation.	
OpenMP code is portable to any system with an OpenMP-compliant compiler.	

Intel® Thread Building Blocks. For processing that is more suitable as task parallelism consider the Intel® Thread Building Blocks (Intel® TBB). The Intel TBB library uses common C++ templates and coding style to eliminate tedious threading implementation work. In essence, Intel TBB abstracts the low-level threading details. As a result Intel TBB requires fewer lines of code to achieve parallelism than other threading models, and fewer lines of code means less opportunity for bugs in the threaded code.

Figure 9.6 and Figure 9.7 show the difference between explicit threading with Windows† API threads and implicit threading with Intel TBB. The code shows two versions of the same algorithm. Intel TBB is a higher level of abstraction requiring fewer lines of code to accomplish the same work as the explicitly threaded Windows API thread version of the code. With explicit threading, the developer has more control of the implementation and so could potentially write code that executes faster than the Intel TBB implementation. There is a natural tradeoff between thread control and ease of thread programming, similar to the tradeoff between programming in assembly language verses a higher level programming language.

```
Thread Setup and Initialization
CRITICAL_SECTION MyMutex, MyMutex2, MyMutex3;
int get_num_cpus (void) {
    SYSTEM_INFO si;
    GetSystemInfo(&si);
    return (int)si.dwNumberOfProcessors;}
int nthreads = get_num_cpus ();
HANDLE *threads = (HANDLE *) alloca (nthreads * sizeof (HANDLE));
InitializeCriticalSection (&MyMutex);
InitializeCriticalSection (&MyMutex2);
InitializeCriticalSection (&MyMutex3);
for (int i = 0; i < nthreads; i++) {
    DWORD id;
    &threads[i] = CreateThread (NULL, 0, parallel_thread, i, 0, &id);
}
for (int i = 0; i < nthreads; i++) {
    WaitForSingleObject (&threads[i], INFINITE);
}

Parallel Task Scheduling and Execution
const int MINPATCH = 150;
const int DIVFACTOR = 2;
typedef struct work_queue_entry_s {
    patch pch;
    struct work_queue_entry_s *next;
} work_queue_entry_t;
```

```
work_queue_entry_t *work_queue_head = NULL;
work_queue_entry_t *work_queue_tail = NULL;
void generate_work (patch* pchin) {
    int startx, stopx, starty, stopy;
    int xs,ys;
    startx=pchin->startx; stopx= pchin->stopx;
    starty=pchin->starty; stopy= pchin->stopy;
    if(((stopx-startx) >= MINPATCH) || ((stopy-starty) >= MINPATCH)) {
      int xpatchsize = (stopx-startx)/DIVFACTOR + 1;
      int ypatchsize = (stopy-starty)/DIVFACTOR + 1;
      for (ys=starty; ys<=stopy; ys+=ypatchsize)
        for (xs=startx; xs<=stopx; xs+=xpatchsize) {
            patch pch;
            pch.startx = xs;
            pch.starty = ys;
            pch.stopx  = MIN(xs+xpatchsize-1,stopx);
            pch.stopy  = MIN(ys+ypatchsize-1,stopy);
            generate_work (&pch);
        }
    } else {
      /* just trace this patch */
      work_queue_entry_t *q =
        (work_queue_entry_t *) malloc(sizeof(work_queue_entry_t));
      q->pch.starty = starty; q->pch.stopy = stopy;
      q->pch.startx = startx; q->pch.stopx = stopx;
      q->next = NULL;
      if (work_queue_head == NULL) {
        work_queue_head = q;
      } else {
        work_queue_tail->next = q;
      }
      work_queue_tail = q;
    }
}
void generate_worklist (void)
{
    patch pch;
    pch.startx = startx;
    pch.stopx = stopx;
    pch.starty = starty;
    pch.stopy = stopy;
    generate_work (&pch);
}
bool schedule_thread_work (patch &pch)
{
    EnterCriticalSection (&MyMutex3);
    work_queue_entry_t *q = work_queue_head;
    if (q != NULL) {
        pch = q->pch;
        work_queue_head = work_queue_head->next;
```

```
    }
    LeaveCriticalSection (&MyMutex3);
    return (q != NULL);
}
generate_worklist ();


void parallel_thread (void *arg)
{
    patch pch;
    while (schedule_thread_work (pch)) {
        for (int y = pch.starty; y <= pch.stopy; y++) {
            for (int x=pch.startx; x<=pch.stopx; x++) {
                render_one_pixel (x, y);}}
        if (scene.displaymode == RT_DISPLAY_ENABLED) {
            EnterCriticalSection (&MyMutex3);
            for (int y = pch.starty; y <= pch.stopy; y++) {

                GraphicsDrawRow(
                    pch.startx-1,
                    y-1,
                    pch.stopx-pch.startx+1,
                    (unsigned char *) &global_buffer[
                        ((y-starty)*totalx+(pch.startx-startx))*3]
                );
            }
            LeaveCriticalSection (&MyMutex3);
        }
    }
}
```

Figure 9.6   Windows API Thread Setup and Initialization

```
Thread Setup and Initialization
#include "tbb/task_scheduler_init.h"
#include "tbb/spin_mutex.h"
tbb::task_scheduler_init init;
tbb::spin_mutex MyMutex, MyMutex2;


Parallel Task Scheduling and Execution
#include "tbb/parallel_for.h"
#include "tbb/blocked_range2d.h"
class parallel_task {
public:
    void operator() (const tbb::blocked_range2d<int> &r) const {
        for (int y = r.rows().begin(); y != r.rows().end(); ++y) {
            for (int x = r.cols().begin(); x != r.cols().end(); x++) {
```

```
                    render_one_pixel (x, y);
                }
            }
            if (scene.displaymode == RT_DISPLAY_ENABLED) {
                tbb::spin_mutex::scoped_lock lock (MyMutex2);
              for (int y = r.rows().begin(); y != r.rows().end(); ++y) {
                  GraphicsDrawRow(startx-1, y-1, totalx, (unsigned char
                      *) &global_buffer[(y-starty)*totalx*3]);
                }
            }
        }
    }
    parallel_task () {}
};
parallel_for (tbb::blocked_range2d<int> (starty, stopy + 1,
            grain_size, startx, stopx + 1, grain_size),
            parallel_task() );
```

Figure 9.7   Intel® Thread Building Blocks Thread Setup and Initialization

Explicit Threading Methodologies

Explicit threading, the use of native threading APIs, requires the developer to manually write all required code to manage threads that interface to a specific library. This code is responsible for creating and freeing the resources associated with each thread, as well as synchronizing and managing shared thread resources. Explicit threading requires in-depth knowledge of thread management and the thread API functions, but such methods are well suited for task decomposition. Windows and POSIX† thread APIs are examples of explicit threading methods. Table 9.5 lists the explicit threading software development tradeoffs.

Table 9.5   Explicit Threading Software Development Tradeoffs

Explicit Threading Benefits	Explicit Threading Considerations
Explicit threading allows for fine control of threads and processing based on thread function or status of specific variables.	Explicit threading requires more code modification than implicit threading methods.
The priority of individual threads can be changed.	Explicit threading alters the serial code implementation forever. Once multithreaded, always multithreaded. It can't be turned on and off.
Explicit threading allows developers to write their own scheduler for fine control over threading operations.	Explicit threading requires the developer to guess at the optimum number of threads to use, and then test performance to narrow to the best number.
	Explicit threading typically requires much more time to write than an implicit implementation.
	Explicit threading uses a more complex implementation, which makes it more difficult to maintain.
	Since explicit threading libraries are tied to the operating system, code that uses these methods is not as portable as code using implicit methods.

Which Threading Methodology Is Right for Your Application?

For many applications, OpenMP is sufficient. Applications with compute-intensive and independent loop iterations are especially well-suited. While it takes more programming effort, explicit threading methods can be used to encapsulate the execution of independent loops for execution by threads.

Explicit threading is preferred for processing that scales with the number of independent tasks or if those tasks are dissimilar. Clean task decomposition makes a program better suited to explicit threading. However, OpenMP 3.0 has added facilities to create independent computational tasks that can be assigned to threads.

The good news is that this is not necessarily a choice of one or the other. Applications can use a mixture of implicit and explicit threading methods, allowing the best of both worlds to be realized. No matter which threading methodology is implemented, the code needs to be tuned for multithreading performance.

For detailed guidelines on multithreading applications refer to the recently published Intel educational papers series titled *Intel® Guide for Developing Multithreaded Applications*.

Asymmetric Multiprocessing

Asymmetric multiprocessing (AMP) has started to show up in product descriptions for embedded processors. The term is used to refer to a case where multiple OS images are run on a system with multiple cores. The term is used to distinguish from the SMP case where all of the software on the system runs on a single OS image.

AMP is an interesting Intel multi-core technology adoption design choice for serial applications that for one reason or another cannot be multithreaded. AMP requires no application changes to leverage the benefits of multi-core platforms. In an AMP design multiple cores are leveraged by running multiple instances of the OS and application in separate partitions that are dedicated to specific cores, PCI devices, and system memory areas. AMP requires a boot loader that can partition the hardware resources and make OS and application paired assignments to the partitions. The OS must also meet requirements to support AMP, such as the OS must be relocateable, which means it must be able to restrict its memory region, and the OS must only operate on its assigned PCI devices. Table 9.6 lists the software development tradeoffs that should be considered for AMP software implementations.

Table 9.6   Asymmetric Multiprocessing Software Development Tradeoffs

AMP Benefits	AMP Considerations
Requires no application changes.	Requires special capability in the OS and boot loader.
Allows very tight control over the environment, including support for different operating systems.	Requires reconfiguration to scale as the number of cores change.
Allows easy mapping from existing processing environments.	Resources are statically assigned with no support for dynamic configuration.
Provides system partitioning without the overhead of a virtual machine manager.	Applications are not isolated in secure partitions as with a virtual machine manager.

Green Hills Integrity† *AMP Support for Intel® Architecture*

Green Hills Integrity provides AMP support for Intel architecture processors, including Intel Atom processors, running a separate instance of Integrity on each core. The initially booted core's instance has special logic in the Integrity board support package that manages the launch of each instance of Integrity on the cores. Integrity provides a wide suite of IPC mechanisms that can be used to coordinate execution between applications on each instance. Integrity AMP and SMP operating systems are integrated with a comprehensive multicore debugging and system analysis suite, Green Hills Multi[†].

Wind River VxWorks[†] AMP Support for Intel® Architecture

In 2009 Wind River released a VxWorks AMP solution for Intel architecture processors enabled with Intel multi-core technology. The product allows combinations of the VxWorks uniprocessor and VxWorks SMP operating systems to reside side-by-side on the same system. VxWorks 6.7 is the first embedded AMP product commercially available for Intel architecture. This AMP solution allows legacy serial VxWorks designs to take advantage of Intel multi-core technology, keeping the legacy software unmodified while running new and future parallelized code in a VxWorks SMP partition. Check with Wind River for the latest information on Intel architecture product support.

Intel® Virtualization Technology (Intel® VT)

Today, most embedded systems use a single operating system, typically real-time, general-purpose, or homegrown. Although one OS is sufficient for most devices, some developers are choosing to run multiple operating systems in secure partitions using virtualization. Similar to an AMP design, virtualization allows systems to execute legacy software with little or no modification. This enables them to simplify the porting of legacy applications onto new platforms. Virtualization with Intel VT is also a very effective multi-core technology adoption strategy for applications that are constructed from multiple application components that are independent and CPU-bound, and not bound by contention to shared resources.

Operating systems and applications are partitioned to run within virtual machines (VMs) managed by the virtual machine manager (VMM). The VMM manages the assignment and access between the VMs and platform resources. There are several use cases for partitioning, such as system leveraging the additional processing power of multi-core enabled hardware by replicating the applications and operating systems across multiple cores, consolidation, and OS co-location, which provides the ability for real-time and general-purpose operating systems to run simultaneously, as shown in Figure 9.8. The OS co-location use case provides both fast response for time-critical code and many standard features for application development. For example, if the guest

OS running the GUI crashes, the RTOS and the time-critical functions will continue to run deterministically because they are isolated and protected.

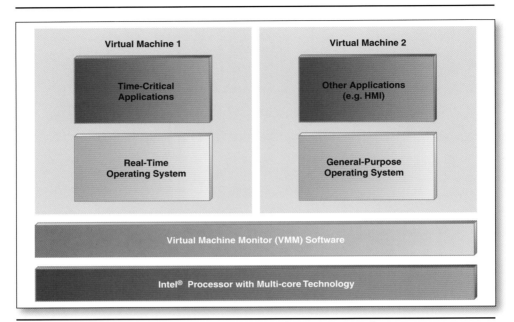

Figure 9.8 Embedded Virtualization OS Co-location Example

Hardware-Assisted Virtualization

By employing Intel VT, software developers have greater control over operating systems and applications with respect to their mix, performance and security. Intel VT makes VMM development easier and enhances performance of virtualized systems enabled with the technology. Intel VT increases the determinism of time-critical functions and improves the security and stability of safety-critical code in virtualization implementations. Applications requiring a higher level of security can be isolated in secure VMs, whose memory space is protected by hardware features in Intel processors including Intel VT. This means that software running in a VM only has access to its own code and data regions, unable to page outside the memory boundaries specified by the VMM. The Intel VT capabilities and benefits are listed in Table 9.7.

Table 9.7   Intel® Virtualization Technology Capabilities and Benefits

Capabilities	Benefits
Isolates applications in secure partitions.	Increases system reliability and stability.
Runs RTOS on a dedicated processor core.	Eases software migration and consolidation.
Performs virtualization tasks in hardware.	Improves real-time performance[7].
	Decreases loop jitter, increases determinism.
	Decreases VMM load on the processor.
	Reduces VM-to-VM switching time.

Intel has developed different versions of Intel VT to improve the fundamental flexibility and robustness of software-based virtualization solutions. Intel VT for IA-32, Intel® 64 and Intel® architecture (Intel® VT-x) speeds up the transfer of platform control between the VMM and guest operating systems by using hardware-assist to trap and execute certain instructions on behalf of guest operating systems, relieving the VMM of such duties. These commonly used virtualization operations are very secure because they are performed in hardware and thus unalterable by hackers. Intel VT has several extended features including Intel® Virtualization Technology for Directed I/O (VT-d) chipset focus and Intel Virtualization Technology for Connectivity (Intel VT-c). However, the Intel Atom processor–based systems support only the processor focus, Intel VT-x capability.

The VMM choice for given migration project could be made on the basis of which OSs will be involved on the target platform, and the real-time requirements are of the project. VMM vendors and products that support real-time and Intel VT features are:

- Green Hills Integrity Secure Virtualization[†]

- LynuxWorks LynxSecure[†]

- TenAsys eVM[†]

- VirtualLogix VLX[†8]

---

[7] Performance results are based on certain tests measured on specific computer systems. Any difference in system hardware, software or configuration will affect actual performance. For more information go to http://www.intel.com/performance.

[8] VirtualLogix, Inc.[†] was recently acquired by Red Bend Software[†] http://www.redbend.com/.

- ■ Wind River Hypervisor[†]

- ■ Real-Time Systems GmbH[†] Real-Time Hypervisor[†]

Green Hills Software, Inc., is a leader in software development tools, real-time operating systems, and virtualization solutions for developers of embedded systems. The following is a summary provided by David Kleidermacher, which discusses the evolution of hypervisor architecture, including both software and hardware trends, and how they affect the security and practicality of system virtualization. David Kleidermacher is chief technology officer at Green Hills Software where he has been responsible for operating system and virtualization technology over the past decade and has managed the team responsible for implementing Intel-based solutions, including operating systems, hypervisors, and compilers.

Methods and Applications of System Virtualization Using Intel® Virtualization Technology

The information in this summary discusses a range of compelling applications for secure virtualization across a variety of communities of interest, and captures how Intel Virtualization Technology (Intel VT) is leveraged to assist the capabilities of the Green Hills Integrity Secure Virtualization hypervisor.

Introduction

The motivations for system virtualization technology in the data center are well known, including resource optimization and improved service availability. But virtualization technology has broader applications throughout the enterprise and in the home, including security-enabled mobile devices, virtual appliances, secure servers, personal/corporate shared use laptops, trusted web-based transactions, and more. This vision is made possible due to Intel VT, which is hardware virtualization technology that scales from embedded and mobile devices up to server-class computing.

Computer system virtualization was first introduced in mainframes during the 1960s and 1970s. Although virtualization remained a largely untapped facility during the 1980s and 1990s, computer scientists have long understood many of the applications of virtualization, including the ability to run distinct and legacy operating systems on a single hardware platform.

At the start of the millennium, VMware† proved the practicality of full system virtualization, hosting unmodified, general purpose, *guest* operating systems such as Windows on common Intel architecture–based hardware platforms.

In 2005, Intel launched Intel VT, which both simplified and accelerated virtualization. Consequently, a number of virtualization software products have emerged, alternatively called virtual machine monitors or hypervisors, with varying characteristics and goals.

While Intel VT may be best known for its application in data center server consolidation and provisioning, Intel VT has proliferated across desktop- and laptop-class chipsets, and has most recently found its way into Intel Atom processors, built for low power and designed for embedded and mobile applications.

The availability of Intel VT across such a wide range of computing platforms provides developers and technologists with the ultimate open platform: the ability to run any flavor of operating system in any combination, creating unprecedented flexibility for deployment and usage. This summary introduces some of these emerging uses, with an emphasis on the latest platforms enabled with Intel VT, which target embedded and mobile. Because embedded and mobile platforms often have resource and security constraints that differ drastically from enterprise computing platforms, this summary also focuses on the impact of hypervisor architecture upon these constraints.

Applications of System Virtualization

Mainframe virtualization was driven by some of the same applications found in today's enterprise systems. Initially, virtualization was used for time sharing, similar to the improved hardware utilization driving modern data center server consolidation. Another important usage involved testing and exploring new operating system architectures. Virtualization was also used to maintain backward compatibility of legacy versions of operating systems.

Environment Sandboxing

Implicit in the concept of consolidation is the premise that independent virtual machines are kept securely separated from each other. The ability to guarantee separation is highly dependent upon the robustness of the underlying hypervisor software. As we'll soon discuss, researchers have found flaws in commercial hypervisors that violate this separation assumption. Nevertheless, an important theoretical application of virtual machine compartmentalization is to "sandbox" software that is not trusted. For example, a web browser connected to the Internet can be sandboxed in a virtual machine so that Internet-borne malware or browser vulnerabilities are unable to infiltrate or otherwise adversely impact the user's primary operating system environment.

Virtual Security Appliances

Another example, the virtual security appliance, does the opposite: sandbox trusted software away from the user's operating system environment. Consider anti-virus software that runs on a mobile Internet device (MID). A few years ago, the *Metal Gear* Symbian Trojan was able to propagate itself by disabling the mobile device's anti-malware software[9]. Virtualization can solve this problem by placing the anti-malware software into a separate virtual machine, as shown in Figure 9.9.

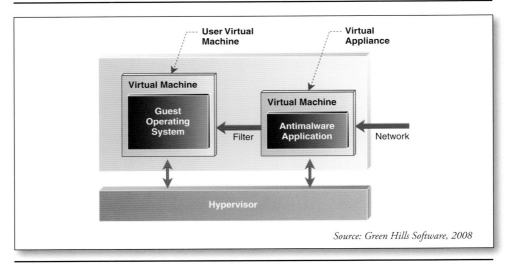

Source: Green Hills Software, 2008

Figure 9.9　Virtual Security Appliance

The virtual appliance can analyze data going into and out of the user's environment or hook into the user's operating system for demand-driven processing.

---

[9] Larry Garfield. "'Metal Gear' Symbian OS Trojan disables anti-virus software". http://www.infosyncworld.com/, 2004.

Hypervisor Architectures

Hypervisor architectures vary along several dimensions. Some are open source, others are proprietary. Some comprise thin hypervisors augmented with specialized guest operating systems. Others employ a monolithic hypervisor that is fully self-contained. In this section, we shall compare and contrast currently available architectures.

Monolithic Hypervisor

Hypervisor architectures seen in commercial applications most often employ a monolithic architecture, as shown in Figure 9.10. Similar to monolithic operating systems, the monolithic hypervisor requires a large body of operating software, including device drivers and middleware, to support the execution of one or more guest environments. In addition, the monolithic architecture often uses a single instance of the virtualization component to support multiple guest environments. Thus, a single flaw in the hypervisor may result in a compromise of the fundamental guest environment separation intended by virtualization in the first place.

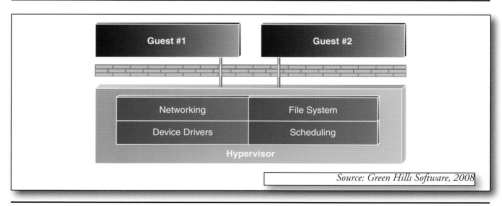

Figure 9.10 Monolithic Hypervisor Architecture

Console Guest Hypervisor

An alternative approach uses a trimmed down hypervisor that runs in the microprocessor's privileged mode but employs a special guest operating system partition to handle the I/O control and services for the other guest operating systems Thus, a complex body of software must still be relied upon for system security. As shown in Figure 9.11, a typical console guest, such as Linux operating system, may add far more code to the virtualization layer than found in a monolithic hypervisor.

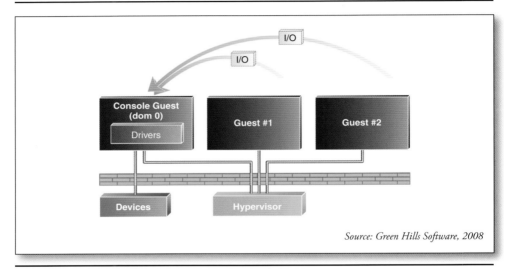

Source: Green Hills Software, 2008

Figure 9.11   Console Guest Hypervisor Architecture

Microkernel-based Hypervisor

The newest hypervisor architecture was designed specifically to provide robust separation between guest environments. Figure 9.12 shows the microkernel-based hypervisor architecture.

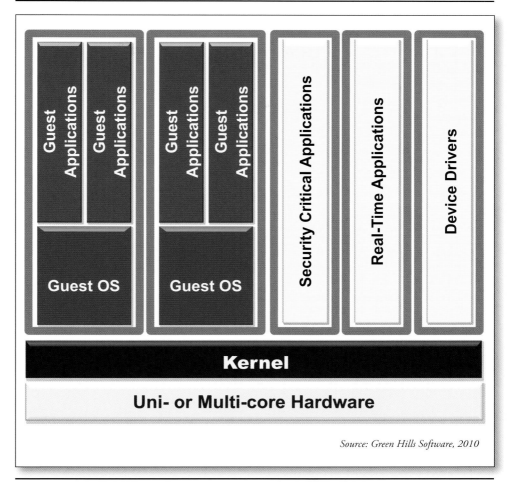

Figure 9.12 Microkernel-based Hypervisor Architecture

This architecture places the computer virtualization complexity into user-mode processes outside the trusted operating system microkernel, as, for example, in Green Hills Software's Integrity. A separate instance of the virtualization layer is used for each guest environment. Thus, the virtualization layer need only meet the equivalent (and, typically, relatively low) robustness level of the guest itself.

Paravirtualization

System virtualization can be implemented with full virtualization or *paravirtualization*, a term first coined in the 2001 Denali project[10]. With full virtualization, unmodified guest operating systems are supported. With paravirtualization, the guest operating system is modified in order to improve the ability of the underlying hypervisor to achieve its intended function.

Paravirtualization is often able to provide improved performance and lower power consumption. For example, device drivers in the guest operating system can be modified to make direct use of the I/O hardware instead of requiring I/O accesses to be trapped and emulated by the hypervisor.

Contrary to enterprise computing requirements, most of the virtualization deployed within low power embedded systems have used paravirtualization. This trend is likely to change, however, due to the inclusion of Intel VT in low power chipsets. The advantage to full virtualization is the ability to use unmodified versions of operating systems that have a proven fielded pedigree and do not require the maintenance associated with custom modifications. This maintenance savings is especially important in embedded devices where I/O peripherals tend to vary dramatically across designs.

Leveraging Intel® Virtualization Technology

Intel VT has been a key factor in the growing adoption of full virtualization throughout the enterprise computing world. Intel VT for IA-32, Intel® 64 and Intel® Architecture (Intel VT-x) provides a number of hypervisor assistance capabilities. For example, true hardware hypervisor mode enables unmodified ring-0 guest operating systems to execute with reduced privilege. Intel VT-x will also prevent a guest operating system from referencing physical memory beyond what has been allocated to the guest's virtual machine. In addition, Intel VT-x enables selective exception injection, so that hypervisor-defined classes of exceptions can be handled directly by the guest operating system without incurring the overhead of hypervisor software interposing.

> True hardware hypervisor mode enables unmodified ring-0 guest operating systems to execute with reduced privilege

---

[10] Whitaker, et al. "Denali: Lightweight Virtual Machines for Distributed and Networked Applications". USENIX Annual Technical Conference. 2002.

Early Results with Intel® Virtualization Technology

In 2006, Green Hills Software demonstrated virtualization using Intel VT-x. Prior to this, in 2005, Green Hills demonstrated a full virtualization solution on platforms without Intel VT capabilities. This was implemented by using selective dynamic translation techniques conceptually similar to that employed by original versions of VMware.

> General PC benchmarks showed an approximate factor of two performance[11] improvement for Intel VT-x over earlier platforms.

Green Hills Software's previous desktop solution was able to support no more than two simultaneous full-motion audio/video clips, each in a separate virtual machine, without dropping frames. With Intel VT-x on similar class desktops, the number of simultaneous clips was limited only by the total RAM available to host multiple virtual machines. General PC benchmarks showed an approximate factor of two performance[11] improvement for Intel VT-x over earlier platforms. In addition, the Green Hills virtualization layer was radically simplified due to the Intel VT-x capabilities.

> Intel VT has enabled Green Hills Software and other technology suppliers to leverage the power of full system virtualization across a wide range of hardware platforms, vertical industries, and emerging usage scenarios.

Recent Improvements

In 2008, Green Hills Software demonstrated its virtualization technology enabled by Intel VT-x on Intel Atom processors, thereby taking advantage of the scalability of Intel VT-x across low power embedded systems, laptops and desktops, and server-class systems.

---

[11] Results have been estimated based on internal Intel analysis and are provided for informational purposes only. Any difference in system hardware or software design or configuration may affect actual performance.

Intel does not control or audit the design or implementation of third party benchmark data or Web sites referenced in this document. Intel encourages all of its customers to visit the referenced Web sites or others where similar performance benchmark data are reported and confirm whether the referenced benchmark data are accurate and reflect performance of systems available for purchase.

Hypervisor Security

Some tout virtualization as a technique in a "layered defense" for system security. The theory postulates that since only the guest operating system is exposed to external threats, an attacker who penetrates the guest will be unable to subvert the rest of the system. In essence, the virtualization software is providing an isolation function similar to the process model provided by most modern operating systems.

Published Hypervisor Subversions

However, common enterprise virtualization products have not met security requirements for high robustness and were never designed or intended to meet these levels. Thus, it should come as no surprise that the theory of security via virtualization has no existence proof. Rather, a number of studies of virtualization security and successful subversions of hypervisors have been published.

In 2006, the SubVirt project demonstrated hypervisor rootkits that subverted both VMware[†] and VirtualPC[†12].

The BluePill[†] project took hypervisor rootkits a step further by demonstrating a malware payload that was itself a hypervisor that could be installed on-the-fly, beneath a natively running Windows operating system[13].

Tavis Ormandy performed an empirical study of hypervisor vulnerabilities. The researchers generated random I/O activity into the hypervisor, attempting to trigger crashes or other anomalous behavior. The project discovered vulnerabilities in QEMU[†], VMware Workstation and Server, Bochs, and a pair of unnamed proprietary hypervisor products[14].

Clearly, the risk of an *escape* from the virtual machine layer, exposing all guests, is very real. This is particularly true of hypervisors characterized by monolithic code bases. As one analyst has said, "Virtualization is essentially a new operating system …, and it enables an intimate interaction between underlying hardware and the environment. The potential for messing things up is significant."[15]

---

[12] Samuel King, et al. "SubVirt: Implementing malware with virtual machines." IEEE Symposium on Security and Privacy. 2006.

[13] Joanna Rutkowska. "Subverting Vista Kernel for Fun and Profit." Black Hat USA. 2006.

[14] Tavis Ormandy. "An Empirical Study into the Security Exposure to Hosts of Hostile Virtualized Environments."

[15] Denise Dubie. "Security concerns cloud virtualization deployments."

At the 2008 Black Hat conference, security researcher Joanna Rutkowska and her team presented their findings of a brief research project to locate vulnerabilities in Xen[†16]. One hypothesis was that Xen would be less likely to have serious vulnerabilities, as compared to VMware and Microsoft[†] Hyper-V, due to the fact that Xen is an open source technology and therefore benefits from the *many-eyes* exposure of the code base.

Rutkowka's team discovered three different and fully exploitable vulnerabilities that the researchers used to commandeer the computer by way of the hypervisor. Ironically, one of these attacks took advantage of a buffer overflow defect in Xen's Flask layer. Flask is a security framework that is the same one used in SELinux[†]. It was added to Xen to improve security.

Rutkowka's results further underscore an important principle: software that has not been designed for and evaluated to high levels of assurance must be assumed to be subvertible by determined and well-resourced entities.

High Assurance Approach

However, the hypervisor need not hamper security efforts. For example, Integrity is an operating system that has achieved a high assurance Common Criteria security certification[17]. Designed for EAL 7, the highest security level, Integrity meets what the National Security Agency deems is required for *high robustness*, protection of high value resources against highly determined and sophisticated attackers.

The Green Hills Software operating system is being used in NSA-approved cryptographic communications devices, avionics systems that control passenger and military jets, life-critical medical systems, secure financial transaction systems, and a wide variety of other safety and security-critical systems.

Green Hills has found that a security kernel can provide domain separation with virtualization duties relegated to user-mode applications. This approach achieves a high level of assurance against hypervisor escapes.

Integrity[†] provides a full-featured applications programming interface (API) and software development kit (SDK), enabling the creation and deployment of secure applications that cannot be trusted to run on a guest. Thus, critical security applications and data such as firewalls, databases, and cryptographic

---

[16] Joanna Rutkowska, Alexander Tereshkin, and Rafal Wojtczuk. "Detecting and Preventing the Xen Hypervisor Subversions"; "Bluepilling the Xen Hypervisor"; "Subverting the Xen Hypervisor". Black Hat USA. 2008.
[17] Common Criteria Validated Products List. http://www.niap-ccevs.org/, 2008.

subsystems can be deployed both alongside and securely separated from general purpose operating environments such as Windows or Linux.

The combination of virtualized and native applications results in a powerful hybrid operating environment, as shown in Figure 9.13, for the deployment of highly secure yet richly functional systems. The following section discusses how this hybrid architecture is especially critical for the flexibility required in embedded systems.

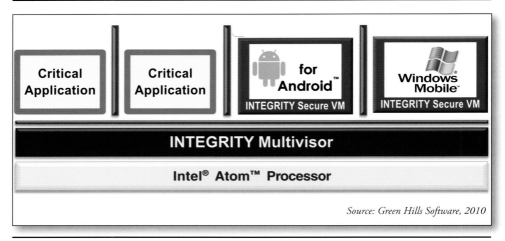

Figure 9.13   Virtualized Environments alongside Native Applications

Emerging Applications for Virtualization

The use of virtualization outside of traditional enterprise PC and server markets is nascent, and yet presents a significant opportunity. This section discusses a sample of emerging applications with significant promise.

Electronic Flight Bag

Electronic Flight Bag (EFB) is a general purpose computing platform that flight crews use to perform flight management tasks, including calculating take-off parameters and viewing navigational charts more easily and efficiently. EFBs replace the stereotypical paper-based flight bags carried by pilots. There are three classes of EFBs, with class three being a device that interacts with the onboard avionics and requires airworthiness certification.

Using the hybrid virtualization architecture, a class three EFB can provide a Windows environment (including common applications such as Microsoft Excel) for pilots while hosting safety-critical applications that validate parameters before they are input into the avionics system. Virtualization enables class three EFBs to be deployed in the portable form factor that is critical for a cramped cockpit.

In-Vehicle Infotainment

Demand for more advanced infotainment systems is growing rapidly. In addition to theater-quality audio and video and GPS navigation, wireless networking and other office technologies are making their way into the car. Despite this increasing complexity, passenger expectations for "instant on" and high availability remain. At the same time, automobile systems designers must always struggle to keep cost, weight, power, and component size to a minimum.

Although it's not uncommon for desktop operating systems to crash occasionally, automobile passengers expect the radio and other traditional *head-unit* components never to fail. In fact, a failure in one of these components is liable to cause an expensive (for the automobile manufacturer) visit to the repair shop. Even worse, a severe design flaw in one of these systems may result in a recall that wipes out the profit on an entire model year of cars. Exacerbating the reliability problem is a new generation of security threats: bringing the Internet into the car exposes it to all the viruses and worms that target networked Windows-based computers.

The currently deployed solution, found on select high-end automobiles, is to divide the infotainment system onto two independent hardware platforms, placing the high-reliability, real-time components onto a computer running a real-time operating system, and the Windows component on a separate PC. This solution is highly undesirable, however, because of the need to tightly constrain component cost, size, power, and weight within the automobile.

Multiple instances of Windows, powered by multiple instances of the virtual machine, can run simultaneously on the same computer.

The hybrid virtualization architecture provides an ideal solution. Head unit applications running under control of the real-time kernel are guaranteed to perform flawlessly. Because the real-time kernel is optimized for the extremely fast boot times required by automotive systems, instant-on requirements are met.

Multiple instances of Windows, powered by multiple instances of the virtual machine, can run simultaneously on the same computer. In the back seat, each passenger has a private video monitor. One passenger could even reboot Windows without affecting the second passenger's email session.

Next Generation Mobile Internet Devices

Using the hybrid virtualization architecture, mobile device manufacturers and service providers can leverage traditional operating systems and software, such as the Linux-based MeeGo[18] platform, while guaranteeing the integrity, availability, and confidentiality of critical applications and information shown in Figure 9.14.

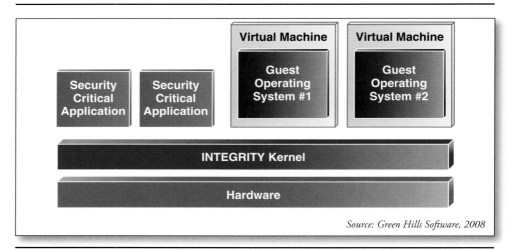

Source: Green Hills Software, 2008

Figure 9.14 Virtualization Environment for Mobile Internet Devices (MID)

We bring our mobile devices wherever we go. Ultimately, consumers would like to use mobile devices as the key to the automobile, a smart card for safe Internet banking, a virtual credit card for retail payments, a ticket for public transportation, and a driver's license and/or passport. There is a compelling world of personal digital convenience just over the horizon.

The lack of a high security operating environment, however, precludes these applications from reaching the level of trust that consumer's demand. High assurance secure platform technology, taking maximum advantage of

---

[18] MeeGo.com. http://meego.com.

Intel silicon features such as Intel VT, enables this level of trust. Furthermore, security applications can be incorporated alongside the familiar mobile multimedia operating system on one chip (SoC), saving precious power and production cost.

Reducing Mobile Device Certification Cost

A certified high assurance operating system can dramatically reduce the cost and certification time of mobile devices, for two main reasons. First, because it is already certified to protect the most sensitive information exposed to sophisticated attackers, the operating system can be used to manage the security-critical subsystems. The certified operating system comes with all of its design and testing artifacts available to the certification authority, thus precluding the cost and time of certifying an operating system.

Second, the operating system and virtualization software take advantage of Intel VT and the Intel architecture Memory Management Unit (MMU) to partition security-critical components from the user's multimedia environment. For example, a bank may require certification of the cryptographic subsystems used to authenticate and encrypt banking transaction messages, but the bank will not care about certifying the system's multimedia functions.

Split Mobile Personalities

With secure virtualization technology, the mobile device can host multiple instances of mobile operating systems. For example, the device can incorporate one instance of Linux that the consumer uses for the phone function, e-mail, and other "critical" applications. A second instance of Linux can be used specifically for browsing the Internet. No matter how badly the Internet instance is compromised with viruses and Trojans, the malware cannot affect the user's critical instance. The only way for files to be moved from the Internet domain to the critical user domain is by using a secure cut and paste mechanism that requires human user interaction and cannot be spoofed or commandeered. A simple key sequence or icon is used to switch between the two Linux interfaces.

Secure virtualization can also be used to provide a MID with multiple operating system personalities, enabling service providers, phone manufacturers, and consumers to provide and enjoy a choice of environments on a single device. Furthermore, by virtualizing the user environment, personas (personal data, settings, and so on) can be easily migrated across devices, in much the same way that virtual machines are migrated for service provisioning in the data center.

In an article discussing the growth of mobile devices in corporate environments, *USA Today* stated that "mobile devices represent the most porous piece of the IT infrastructure."[19] The same problems that plague desktops and servers are afflicting mobile devices. Secure operating systems and virtualization technology provide a solution to the demand for enhanced security in the resource-constrained environment of portable consumer devices.

> Secure communications components, including network security protocols and key management, can be securely partitioned away from the gaming multimedia environment.

Gaming Systems

Gaming systems manufacturers are promoting the use of open network connectivity in next-generation gaming systems and properties. This vision provides for some exciting possibilities, yet the security challenges that arise in this architecture are not unlike other network-centric initiatives, such as the military's Global Information Grid (GIG). In both cases, formerly isolated assets are being connected to networks at risk of cyber attack. Clearly, gaming systems are an attractive target for well-resourced hostile entities.

The same hybrid virtualization architecture previously discussed can enhance user-to-game and game-to-server interactions. Secure communications components, including network security protocols and key management, can be securely partitioned away from the gaming multimedia environment (such as Linux, for example), which is hosted in a virtual machine using Intel VT. This is done in both the game console clients as well as in the servers, providing secure end-to-end encryption, authentication, and transaction verification.

Virtualization Trends for Embedded

In the past decade, virtualization has reemerged as a disruptive technology in the enterprise. However, due to resource constraints and different usage scenarios, virtualization has seen slower adoption in other areas of the computing world, in particular mobile and embedded systems. This is likely to

---

[19] Byron Acohido, "Cellphone security seen as profit frontier." http://www.usatoday.com/, 2008.

change, due to two significant recent innovations. First, low power, Intel Atom processors now incorporate the same kind of hypervisor hardware acceleration enjoyed by desktop and server processors. Second, the advent of a powerful hybrid architecture incorporating certified high robustness security kernels, augmented with secure virtualization using Intel VT, represents a better fit for resource-constrained systems that often have rigorous safety, security, reliability, real-time, memory-efficiency, and/or power-efficiency requirements. The future for Intel VT–enabled applications is indeed bright.

Intel® 64 Architecture

Intel® 64 architecture is an enhancement to Intel® IA-32 architecture, which delivers 64-bit computing when combined with supporting software[20]. With Intel 64, software developers can theoretically address up to one terabyte of physical memory, paving the way for greater performance by eliminating paging penalties associated with smaller memory spaces. However, the maximum physical address space for a given platform is much lower.

For applications requiring complex calculations and a high level of precision, developers may consider writing 64-bit code. These applications can yield vastly improved performance over their 32-bit counterparts. Intel's approach to extended memory technology allows the processor to run either 32-bit or newly written 64-bit code.

Intel Software Development Tools enable developers to automatically benefit from high-performance features, such as the additional and wider registers available to applications built for 64-bit mode under Intel 64. Intel® Integrated Performance Primitives (Intel® IPP) replace common operations, like MP3 encoding and encryption, with highly optimized equivalents that have been hand-tuned for Intel® processors. Refer to Chapter 7 for more information about the Intel IPP library.

Figure 9.15 summarizes the Intel 64 architecture ingredients that were detailed in Chapter 3.

---

20 64-bit computing on Intel® architecture requires a computer system with a processor, chipset, BIOS, operating system, device drivers, and applications enabled for Intel® 64 architecture. Processors will not operate (including 32-bit operation) without an Intel® 64 architecture-enabled BIOS. Performance will vary depending on your hardware and software configurations. Consult with your system vendor for more information.

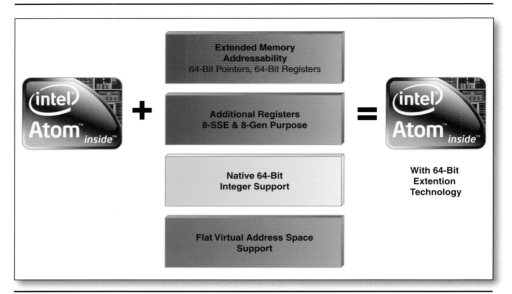

Figure 9.15   Intel® Atom™ Processor with Intel® 64 Ingredients

Porting Applications to Intel® 64 Architecture

Porting an application to a 64-bit operating system requires consideration of the follow items:

■ Software development and testing tools for the 64-bit operating system.

■ The availability of 64-bit compliant third-party libraries supported by the operating system and required by your application.

■ The conversion of the size of stored data so that data size changes that occur when moving from 32-bit to 64-bit are handled, such as data saved to disk.

■ Any code that assumes it knows the size or precision of pointer, handle, integer, or other common types, such as size_t, will need to be thoroughly examined. GUI or text display routines, hash algorithms, integer to floating-point conversions, load and save routines, and so on are vulnerable to such code assumptions and may fail catastrophically if the code makes such assumptions. In many cases, the 64-bit compiler can help find such issues.

■ Porting a 32-bit application to 64 bits can increase the data size in memory, as well as on disk. This can result in performance issues such as increased I/O and storage requirements, increased cache misses, and cache layout issues. These issues must be addressed to prevent performance degradation when the application runs on the 64-bit operating system. Optimize the software for 64-bit performance.

Efficient Programming for the Intel® 64 ISA

The following tips summarize efficient programming when using the Intel 64 ISA:

■ Use the 32-bit versions of instructions in 64-bit mode to reduce code size unless the 64-bit version is necessary to access 64-bit data or additional registers.

■ When needed to reduce register pressure, use the 8 extra general purpose registers and 8 extra XMM registers for floating-point.

■ Prefer 64-bit by 64-bit integer multiplies that produce 64-bit results over multiplies that produce 128-bit results.

■ Sign extend to 64-bits instead of sign extending to 32 bits, even when the destination will be used as a 32-bit value.

■ Use the 64-bit versions of multiply for 32-bit integer multiplies that require a 64-bit result.

■ Use the 64-bit versions of add for 64-bit adds.

■ Use 32-bit versions of CVTSI2SS and CVTSI2SD when possible.

Resources for Intel® 64 Programming

The Intel Press book titled *Programming with Intel® Extended Memory 64 Technology: Migrating Software for Optimal 64-bit Performance* (Binstock, 2006) is a good reference to use for in-depth details of porting 32-bit software to Intel 64.

The Intel® 64 and IA-32 Architectures Software Developer's Manuals provide information about the Intel 64 instructions.

The Intel Press book titled *The Software Optimization Cookbook; Second Edition* (Gerber, Bik, Smith, Tian, 2006) includes comprehensive information for optimizing software for Intel 64, formerly known as Intel® Extended Memory 64.

Community support also exists at the *Intel 64-bit Programming Forum* at http://software.intel.com/en-us/forums/64-bit-programming/.

Summary

The Intel® Atom™ processors have features beyond low power benefits that provide the ability to unleash further capabilities through a variety of Intel product technologies. Following the migration design guide explained in Chapter 4, these technologies should be considered as part of software migration plan.

This chapter provided an overview of a few of the key product technologies provided by the Intel Atom processors and suggested methodologies, techniques, and software development tips for adopting these technologies. The information was tied together with a virtualization summary provided by Green Hills Software Inc., which discussed the evolution of hypervisor architecture, including both software and hardware trends, and how they affect the security and practicality of system virtualization.

Ask yourself how your product can extend its capabilities and possibilities by leveraging the product technology features of the low power Intel Atom processors. For more information refer to the Intel® Product Technologies Web site at the Intel® Embedded Design Center (EDC).

Chapter **10**

Embedded Software Debugging

Debugging is twice as hard as writing the code in the first place. Therefore, if you write the code as cleverly as possible, you are, by definition, not smart enough to debug it.

— Brian W. Kernighan

Embedded platforms tend to be highly customized. In addition, they tend to be complex; in many cases they comprise a heterogeneous mix of different micro-engines and specialized architectures performing dedicated tasks. This functionality may be implemented at the platform level; however the trend is towards increasing levels of integration resulting in many system-on-chip (SoC) designs.

The form-factor constraints and specialized use cases of embedded designs frequently imply cross-development. Cross-development in embedded systems is where the development host is a standard workstation or personal computer based on Intel® architecture. This development host is then connected to the embedded target system, which is the system that will ultimately be available to customers. The development host may consist of a mix of a variety of architectures. If the general purpose processor of the target system happens to be an Intel® Core™ or Intel® Atom™ processor, this can lead to some simplifications, because the development host is likely to have a similar architecture. The basic premise of different host and target software stack requirements will however stay intact, although to a lesser degree.

In this chapter, an in-depth look at embedded software debugging for Intel Atom processors is presented. Topics discussed include identifying coding issues, debugging techniques for embedded systems, and techniques to aid bringing varying components of the embedded software stack to maturity.

Software Debug Overview

Software debug and coding issue resolution has always been one of the most time consuming aspects of writing and maintaining complex and multi-layered applications or systems. The simplest methods range from monitoring register contents and bus signals to using `printf` debugging in an attempt to monitor execution flow. These approaches may be useful if the developer is highly familiar with all layers of the software stack or if the problem in question is expected to be isolated to a single well-known piece of source code. Frequently, the situation is much more complicated. Defects turn out to have unexpected dependencies on other components in the software stack. Keeping track of all of the dependencies with these simple mechanisms can be difficult. Therefore a wide range of debug utilities and feature rich debuggers have been developed and have become widely adopted. The variety of available debug tools start with the IDE integrated debuggers such as Microsoft Visual Studio for Windows† operating systems and the widely used command-line debug tools with various GUI extensions based upon GNU GDB for Linux and other embedded operating systems. Figure 10.1 shows a screen capture of a GDB session.

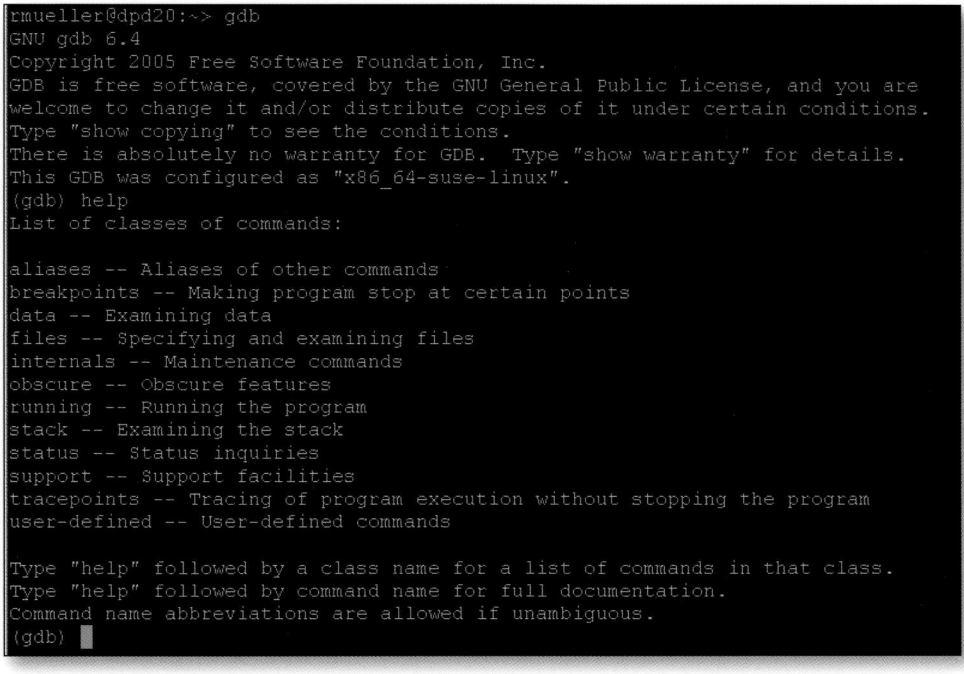

```
rmueller@dpd20:~> gdb
GNU gdb 6.4
Copyright 2005 Free Software Foundation, Inc.
GDB is free software, covered by the GNU General Public License, and you are
welcome to change it and/or distribute copies of it under certain conditions.
Type "show copying" to see the conditions.
There is absolutely no warranty for GDB.  Type "show warranty" for details.
This GDB was configured as "x86_64-suse-linux".
(gdb) help
List of classes of commands:

aliases -- Aliases of other commands
breakpoints -- Making program stop at certain points
data -- Examining data
files -- Specifying and examining files
internals -- Maintenance commands
obscure -- Obscure features
running -- Running the program
stack -- Examining the stack
status -- Status inquiries
support -- Support facilities
tracepoints -- Tracing of program execution without stopping the program
user-defined -- User-defined commands

Type "help" followed by a class name for a list of commands in that class.
Type "help" followed by command name for full documentation.
Command name abbreviations are allowed if unambiguous.
(gdb)
```

Figure 10.1   GDB Command Interface

These and many other similar debug tools cover most of the needs for traditional application software development.

Standard features of these tools include:

■   High level language symbolic debugging.

■   Runtime control of the debug target.

■   Data displays for arrays, pointers, structures and templates.

■   Callstack analysis enabling the developer to analyze the execution flow and function and process level dependencies.

Support for debug of multithreaded programs is increasing in importance. Features like thread grouping and thread- or thread-group-specific run control are important. First class support for viewing parallelism structures for implementations like OpenMP[†], Cilk, Ct technology, Microsoft native threads, PThreads, or Intel® Threading Building Blocks (TBB) is also important.

Embedded systems add an additional layer of complexity and thus amplify the need for advanced tools. There are two aspects that make debugging on embedded systems unique.

The first is the frequent need for cross-development and cross-debug environments. This aspect will be covered in more detail later in the chapter. The second is that since embedded systems tend to be highly customized the requirement to be able to debug and customize the system level software stack is more commonplace in embedded development.

Frequently, embedded systems are heterogeneous and consist of multiple processor cores with different ISA that need to communicate. This requires firmware, bootcode and BIOS adjustments. It also requires debug access to memory and signal busses shared by the different processor cores.

A discussion about these needs and how they can be addressed for platform designs based on the Intel Atom processor appears later in the chapter.

Debugging Software Ecosystem

Despite the high prevalence of real-time operating systems (RTOS) employed in the embedded market segments, two broadly adopted development tools ecosystems are based on what is commonly available for desktop Linux† and Microsoft Windows. Developers writing code for Windows† Embedded most commonly employ Microsoft Visual Studio and the debug tools integrated into it. Developers writing for a Linux target frequently employ GDB and any of the variety of graphical user interface add-ons that exist for it.

These common debug tools and their capabilities do however only touch on some of the needs of embedded developers. Some debuggers targeting multithreaded development are commonly employed by embedded developers. In the Linux and open source community the following tools are employed:

■ Valgrind (http://www.valgrind.org). Valgrind is a framework for debug and platform analysis tools with a focus on memory management analysis and profiling to help with the detection of threading issues and memory leaks.

■ TotalView Technologies offers a highly configurable and programmable debugger (http://www.totalviewtech.com/) that is focused on the analysis of serial, multi-threaded, or multi-process applications.

■ The MemoryScape[†] memory debugger (http:///www.totalviewtech. com/) is an additional utility for the analysis of memory usage and automated detection of memory errors such as leaks and bounds errors in serial, multi-threaded, or multi-process applications. The ReplayEngine[†] add-on to the TotalView[†] debugger records program execution, capturing hard to reproduce error scenarios and allowing the developer to follow clues backwards through execution history from the failure to the cause.

■ Allinea DDT[†] (Distributed Debugging Tool) (http://www.allinea. com/) is another graphical debugger for scalar, multi-threaded, and large-scale parallel applications that are written in C, C++, or Fortran.

None of the debug tools mentioned thus far takes into account the unique needs of the embedded developer, such as the need for cross-development and system level debug. Many of these embedded-specific debug needs are addressed by operating system vendors (OSVs) and silicon vendor tools and recommendations. Many of the embedded OSVs and tools vendors support multiple architectures thus making it possible for a developer working on an embedded project to work primarily with one set of tools only substituting for feature gaps on occasion. Examples of embedded OSVs that offer software development tools targeting the embedded market segments include:

■ GreenHills Software[†] (http://www.ghs.com)

■ Windriver Systems[†] (http://www.windriver.com)

■ Mentor Graphics[†] (http://www.mentor.com)

These vendors offer debug tools that integrate into their respective IDEs (GreenHills Multi[†] IDE, Windriver Workbench[†], EDGE Developer Suite[†]) and offer debug solutions that allow for extended embedded cross-development targeting Linux, OS-independent code, and RTOS code. In fact, all of the aforementioned vendors offer their own families of real-time operating systems (Integrity[†], VxWorks[†], Nucleus OS[†]) and Linux real-time kernel and scheduler adaptation kits. An adaptation kit enables source level debug of operating systems. These customizable real-time operating systems are designed to run on the commonly employed embedded microarchitectures from ARM[†], MIPS[†], PowerPC[†] and Intel architecture. GreenHills Software and Windriver Systems both offer JTAG-based system and platform debug tools supporting connections across TCP/IP as well as USB. These JTAG devices support Intel Atom processor–based platforms as well.

Finally, Linux-based operating system platforms targeting handheld devices and other small form-factor mobile Internet and location based services devices also include customized power optimization and debug analysis tools. These are frequently based on and are expanding upon GNU GDB. Examples include the Android[†] SDK, the Maemo[†] SDK, the MeeGo[†] SDK, and QT Creator[†]. These various development and debug frameworks are available supporting ARM as well as Intel architectures.

Intel offers two sets of tools that include debug tools and target Linux and MeeGo SDK development:

■ Intel® Embedded Software Development Tool Suite for Intel® Atom™ processor

■ Intel® Application Software Development Tool Suite for Intel® Atom™ processor

These tool suites allow for integration with the Moblin[†] SDK and MeeGo SDK, which include their own Linux-hosted Eclipse[†] GUI cross-debug solution. The supported JTAG debug solutions include the Intel® XDP-ITP (eXtended Debug Port – Integrated Target Probe) and Macraigor Systems[†] (http://www.macraigor.com) usb2Demon[†] device.

Linux Ecosystem

Aside from the traditional real-time operating systems like VxWorks, Integrity, Nucleus OS or µ-ITRON, Linux is trending towards broader deployment in embedded systems and has its own set of commonly employed debug tools.

For open source tools, a complete embedded development debug tool is hard to find. There is a wide variety of individual debug tools and GDB extensions that address some of the needs of embedded debug. For example, there are software debug adaptations to convert GDB to enable JTAG debug. Many developers employ gdbserver executing as an OS independent debug agent and integrated into their firmware. Another option is to execute gdbserver and a debug agent application under Linux. CodeSourcery[†] (http://www.codesourcery.com) is a tools provider for custom embedded cross-development and debug tools based on standard GNU tools.

For embedded Linux, Windriver Systems, MontaVista†, and GreenHills create integrated development tools which include debug tools. In particular, Windriver Systems and GreenHills fulfill many of the requirements for truly embedded debug development.

The MeeGo SDK and Android SDK offer a set of application interface (API) templates and tools. These include debug tools that complement the GNU tools and enable development for their unique software stack and platforms. For a complete cross-debug solution in these scenarios, another option to consider is the Intel® Application Debugger and the Intel® JTAG Debugger included in the Intel® Embedded Software Development Tool Suite for the Intel Atom processor.

Microsoft Windows Ecosystem

Microsoft Windows is quite important in two areas of embedded software development, namely as a host development system and as an embedded target. Many system-level and JTAG debug solutions from vendors such as

- American Arium† (http://www.arium.com)

- Lauterbach† (http://www.lauterbach.com)

- Sophia Systems† (http://www.sophia.com)

- Windriver Systems (http://www.windriver.com)

primarily offer Windows-hosted JTAG system debug tools for firmware, BIOS, and other embedded software developers. This particular niche of embedded development traditionally is Windows-hosted.

Market segment–specific applications such as many industrial embedded applications, handheld applications for the medical industry, warehousing, and logistics also rely upon Windows as the target device operating system. The operating system of choice for these target devices tend to be Microsoft Windows Embedded or Windows CE in either its basic variant or in the slightly more feature rich Windows Mobile variety.

As is the case in the desktop developer world, Microsoft provides a debugger and development tools ecosystem for Windows CE and Windows Embedded. The Microsoft Platform Builder tool provides means to customize a Windows CE or Windows Embedded build with the exact features needed for the embedded environment. In addition, they provide TCP/IP- and USB-based remote debug tools for those embedded devices. Debugging a Windows CE or Windows Mobile application executing on an Intel Atom processor would be handled via the traditional Microsoft Visual Studio integrated debugger in conjunction with a Microsoft remote debug add-on and a debug agent (that is, Microsoft ActiveSync†). All of the relevant header files, APIs, and libraries necessary to resolve OS dependencies correctly are provided. The whole package required to develop and debug an application running on Windows CE is included in a software development kit (SDK) that plugs into Microsoft Visual Studio.

When discussing development on a Microsoft Windows host for a Windows Embedded or Windows CE target, this is still a cross-targeted build environment and a cross-debug solution, regardless of whether the microarchitecture on host and target are closely related.

Native and Cross-Debug Concepts

As mentioned in the introduction, a key difference between embedded software development and standard personal computer development is the frequent necessity to use cross-development. The target system, which is the platform on which an application and OS is intended to ultimately run, often does not and is not supposed to have any development tools installed on it. Its software stack and even the underlying platform architecture are different enough that code written for the development host would not execute on the target system without significant modifications.

This simple fact of embedded development implies that the code intended to execute on the target system will have to be built inside a protective isolating wrapper, basically a division between host environment and the target environment. In embedded Linux, this is commonly termed a *jailroot-* or *chroot-based* environment. Part of this protection implies compilation build options forcing the compiler and linker to pull in the target OS–specific libraries instead of the host system libraries.

When developing for the Intel Atom processor, the architecture level differences between the host and target system are probably minimal, however it is advisable to ensure that there is no pollution of system software between the host and target. In some cases, the fact that the host and target system are similar can be a negative because some host code may link and execute correctly on the target most of the time, albeit not all of the time, which is a problem.

Two options exist for a cross development target: 1) a real hardware target device or 2) a virtual runtime environment. If you are developing on an Intel Core processor for example and both your host and target environment are Linux-based, a GUI simulation layer like Xephyr† may be sufficient. In this case one would debug locally inside a chroot environment with a traditional native GDB debugger.

Most of the time however, it is best to either remotely connect to real target hardware or to connect via TCP/IP to a virtual machine that executes the target environment software stack. In this manner, the target environment is cleanly isolated and the potential for cross environment pollution is minimized. For hardware platform optimization it will of course be necessary to have real hardware at hand so the baseline data and measured performance and power consumption improvements do indeed reflect the user experience on the real target.

Although it may be tempting when debugging an application for the Intel Atom processor to assume native development, it is best to employ a cross-development environment especially when the host system and target system differ significantly.

Cross-Debugging Setup

The first step in setting up for cross-debugging is to have the source of the code base accessible on the debug host. In addition, for source level debugging, symbol information of the compiled code is also required. For a Windows target platform, this implies that the application executable and DLL files are located on the host for symbol information resolution and source file mapping to the target memory layout of the code. The associated PDB symbol information files are also required. PDB files contain the debug information for compiled objects.

On a Linux target platform and most other RTOS target platforms, required components include the source tree, the linker output files or executables, and any shared objects. The debug information is stored inside of the object code and is typically in the DWARF format. Before deployment, it may be necessary to strip the symbol information out especially if it is not desirable to have symbol information on the target.

The source directory layout stored in the symbol information (that is, as seen by the build environment at build time), may differ from the layout of the system executing the debugger. One fairly common cause is where the application is built on a different system than where it is debugged. Another cause can be as simple as the build environment being inside a chroot wrapper or inside a cygwin type environment, whereas the debugger may be launched external to such an environment.

In order to correctly map the directory information stored in the symbol file to the debug environment, a source path substitution feature of a debugger is employed. An example of such a feature is depicted in Figure 10.2. This feature enables modification of the directory structure that has been loaded into the debugger dynamically and ensures the mappings inside the debugger are correct, thus enabling symbolic high level language debugging even for the most complex embedded cross-debug environments.

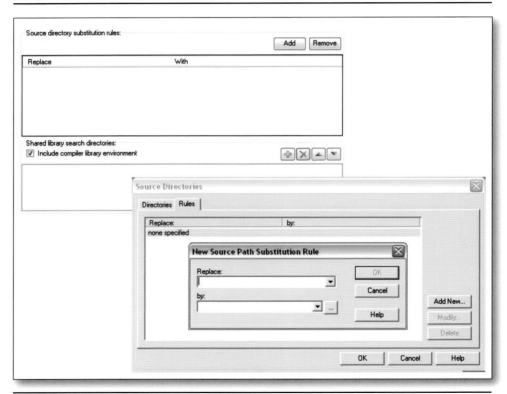

Figure 10.2 Source Path Substitution

The second step during setup is to download the process to debug right onto the target device and launch execution remotely. A dialog box that enables this action is depicted in Figure 10.3.

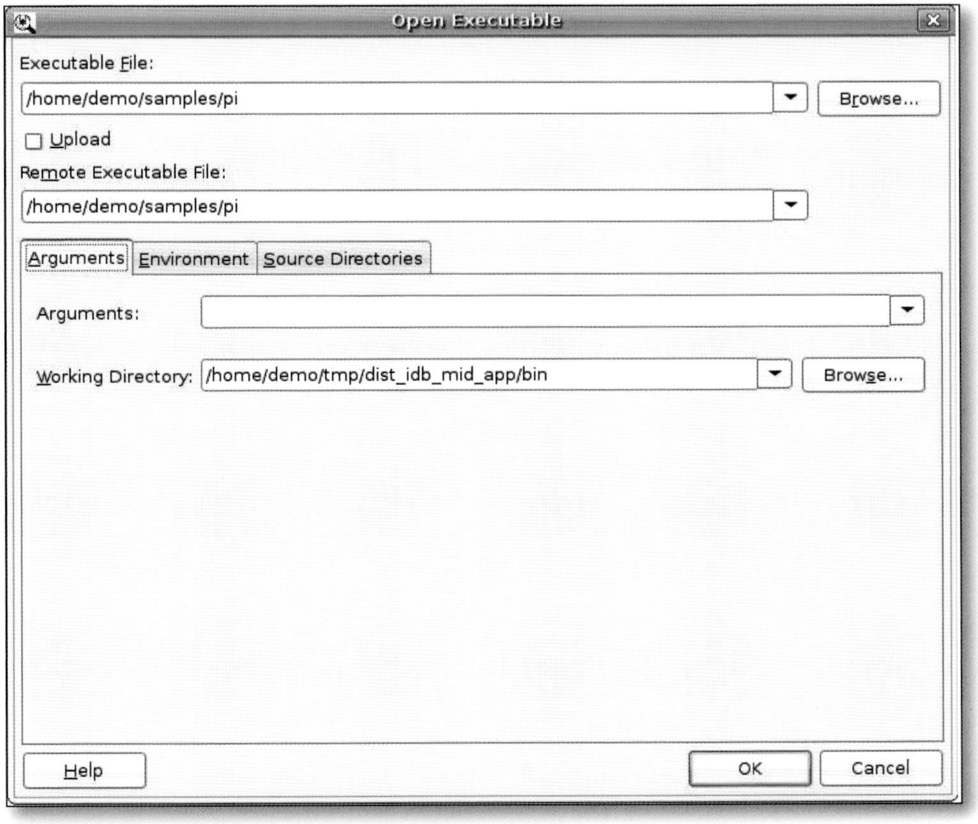

Figure 10.3 Upload and Launch Application

Next, it is desirable to either explicitly select the symbol information file associated with the remote process or attach to the remote process directly. This action is depicted in Figure 10.4. In the latter case, the target OS environment must export the active process list to the host side via a debug agent like gdbserver.

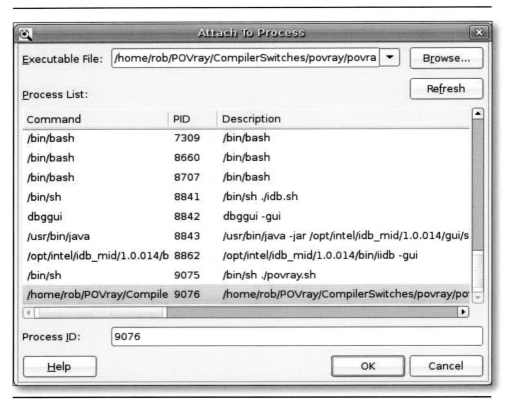

Figure 10.4 Remotely Attach to a Running Process

Lastly, for cross-debugging it is desirable to have detailed insight into the software environment on the target. A good debug tool enables the sharing of information such as target OS constructs, active processes, kernel modules, and kernel threads.

One point to be aware of when cross-debugging remotely via TCP/IP, USB, or even JTAG is that because the execution control handling occurs via a debug agent (or an on-chip communication state machine) application behavior is different than it may be when executing in a native debug environment. When the application under debug is released execution control is handed over completely to the target. It is not until an interrupt is encountered (this could be an OS signal, hardware interrupt, or breakpoint) that control is handed back to the host system. If a break-all command is issued from the host this implies that a break request needs to be sent to the debug agent on the target, which will then issue the debug-break interrupt. In short, there could be a delay in response. While execution control has been handed over from the debugger to the target, status information such as register contents or thread status information will not be updated. This information is only updated once control has been handed back over to the debugger at a breakpoint or interrupt.

Cross-Debug: Intel® Atom™ Processor and ARM† Architecture

Many developers targeting the Intel Atom processor for an embedded handheld or embedded industrial design may have experience developing primarily for RISC architectures with fixed instruction length. MIPS and ARM are prime examples of ISAs with a fixed length. In general, the cross-debug usage model between an Intel Atom processor and ARM architecture processor is very similar. Many of the conceptual debug methods and issues are the same.

Developing on an Intel architecture-based development host for an Intel Atom processor target does, however, offer two big advantages, especially when the embedded operating system of choice is a derivative of one of the common standard operating systems like Linux or Windows. The first advantage is the rich ecosystem of performance, power analysis, and debug tools available for the broader software development market on Intel architecture. The second advantage is that debugging functional correctness and multithreading behavior of the application may be accomplished locally. This advantage will be discussed later in the chapter.

There are a few differences between Intel Atom processors and ARM processors that embedded developers should know. These differences are summarized in the next two subsections.

Variable Length Instructions

The IA-32 and Intel 64 instruction sets have variable instruction length. The impact on the debugger is that it cannot just inspect the code in fixed 32-bit intervals, but must interpret and disassemble the machine instructions of the application based on the context of these instructions; the location of the next instruction depends on the location, size, and correct decoding of the previous. In contrast, on ARM architecture all the debugger needs to monitor is the code sequence that switches from ARM mode to Thumb mode or enhanced Thumb mode and back. Once in a specific mode, all instructions and memory addresses are either 32-bit or 16-bit in size. Firmware developers and device driver developers who need to precisely align calls to specific device registers and may want to rely on understanding the debugger's memory window printout should understand the potential impact of variable length instructions.

Hardware Interrupts

One other architectural difference that may be relevant when debugging system code is how hardware interrupts are handled. On ARM architecture the exception vectors

- 0 Reset

- 1 Abort

- 2 Data abort

- 3 Prefetch abort

- 4 Undefined instruction

- 5 Interrupt (IRQ)

- 6 Fast interrupt (FIRQ)

are mapped from address 0x0 to address 0x20. This memory area is protected and cannot normally be remapped. Commonly, all of the vector locations at 0x0 through 0x20 contain jumps to the memory address where the real exception handler code resides. For the reset vector that implies that at 0x0 will be a jump to the location of the firmware or platform boot code. This approach makes the implementation of hardware interrupts and OS signal handlers less flexible on ARM architecture, but also more standardized. It is easy to trap an interrupt in the debugger, by simply setting a hardware breakpoint at the location of the vector in the 0x0 through 0x20 address range.

On Intel architecture a dedicated hardware interrupt controller is employed. The interrupts

- 0 System timer

- 1 Keyboard

- 2 Cascaded second interrupt controller

- 3 COM2 - serial interface

- 4 COM1 - serial interface

- 5 LPT - parallel interface

- 6 Floppy disk controller

- 7 Available

- 8 CMOS real-time clock

- 9 Sound card

- 10 Network adapter

- 11 Available

- 12 Available

- 13 Numeric processor

- 14 IDE -- Hard disk interface

- 15 IDE -- Hard disk interface

cannot be accessed directly through the processor memory address space, but are handled by accessing the Intel 8259 Interrupt Controller. As can be seen from the list of interrupts, the controller already allows for direct handling of hardware I/O interrupts of attached devices which are handled through the IRQ interrupt or fast interrupt on an ARM platform. This feature makes the implementation of proper interrupt handling at the operating system level easier on Intel architecture especially for device I/O. The mapping of software exceptions like data aborts or segmentation faults is more flexible on Intel architecture as well and corresponds to an interrupt controller port that is addressed via the Interrupt Descriptor Table (IDT). The mapping of the IDT to the hardware interrupts are definable by the software stack. In addition, trapping these exceptions cannot as easily be done from a software stack agnostic debug implementation. In order to trap software events that trigger hardware interrupts on Intel architecture, some knowledge of the OS layer is required. It is necessary to know how the OS signals for these exceptions map to the underlying interrupt controller. Most commonly, even in a system level debugger a memory mapped signal table from the operating system will trap exceptions instead of attempting to trap exceptions directly on the hardware level.

Single Step

ARM architecture does not have an explicit single step instruction. On Intel architecture, an assembly level single step is commonly implemented in the debugger directly via such an instruction. On ARM, a single instruction step is implemented as a "run until break" command. The debugger is required to do some code inspection to ensure that all possible code paths (especially if stepping away from a branch instruction or such) are covered. From a debugger implementation standpoint this does generate a slight overhead but is not excessive, since this "run until break" implementation will be frequently needed for high level language stepping anyways. Software developers in general should be aware of this difference since this can lead to slightly different stepping behavior.

Virtual Memory Mapping

The descriptor table and page translation implementation for virtual memory mapping is surprisingly similar, at least conceptually. On Intel architecture, the Global Descriptor Table (GDT) and Local Descriptor Table (LDT) enable nested coarseness adjustments to memory pages are mapped into the virtual address space. Figure 10.5 uses the page translation feature of the debugger to graphically represent the linear to physical address translation on Intel architecture.

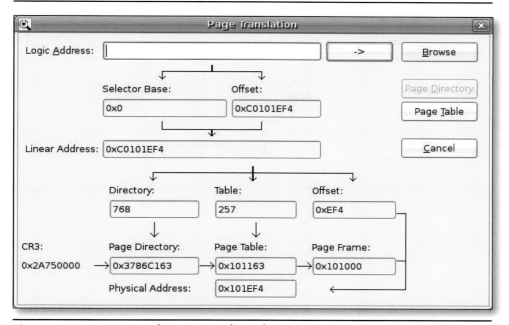

Figure 10.5 Page Translation on Intel® Architecture

On ARM, the first level and second level page tables define a more direct and at maximum, a one or two level deep page search for virtual memory. Figure 10.6 shows a sample linear address to physical address translation.

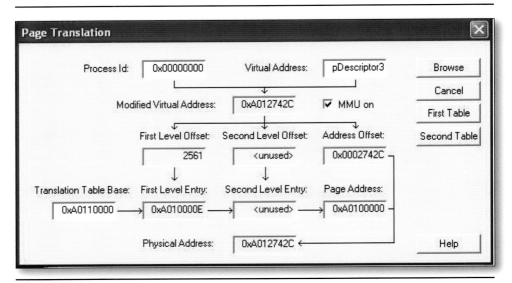

Figure 10.6   Page Translation on ARM

Intel architecture offers multiple levels of coarseness for the descriptor tables, page tables, 32-bit address space access in real mode, and 64-bit addressing in protected mode that's dependent on the selector base:offset model. ARM does not employ base:offset in its various modes. On Intel architecture, the page table search can implicitly be deeper. On ARM, the defined set is two page tables. On Intel architecture, the descriptor tables can actually mask nested tables and thus the true depth of a page table run can easily reach twice or three times the depth on ARM.

The page translation mechanism on Intel architecture provides for greater flexibility in the system memory layout and mechanisms used by the OS layer to allocate specific memory chunks as protected blocks for application execution. However, it does add challenges for the developer to have a full overview of the memory virtualization and thus avoid memory leaks and memory access violations (segmentation faults). On a full featured OS with plenty of memory, this issue is less of a concern. Real-time operating systems with more visibility into memory handling may be more exposed to this issue.

Initalization and System Boot

On ARM architecture, memory initialization and basic system boot can commonly be achieved within a few hundred lines of code. The boot process usually involves basic platform initialization via firmware followed by a handover to OS boot code that has been loaded from some external storage device such as NAND flash, NOR flash, or a USB flash file system. The boot code then handles the loading and unpacking of the operating system itself into initialized memory. This is in principle not much different than on Intel architecture. With the more complex memory initialization sequence and transition from real mode to protected mode addressing and execution modes during processor initialization and memory setup, the initialization code tends to be significantly larger. On the positive side for Intel architecture, this BIOS or firmware will have already initialized a significant part of the peripheral devices on the platform ready for handoff to the OS. On ARM, these tasks are commonly handled by the OS bootloader.

I/O and Drivers

The I/O bus used for Intel architecture is a de facto industry standard for a vast range of embedded hardware designs, making it easy to develop device drivers or to reuse slightly modified device drivers that are already available in the Linux and open source community. This vast driver ecosystem enables easy adaption of the embedded software stack on Intel architecture quickly to the latest peripheral devices. For an embedded SoC hardware design it also enables easy integration of the I/O bus system and the corresponding I/O bridge chipset into the design.

For ARM a slightly different approach is employed that requires device memory mapping and does not in a general sense (beyond the processor specs itself) provide a standardized I/O bus. ARM does employ a coprocessor model for tightly integrated SoC devices that allows for a standard to directly access the device and configure it through the processor's main bus system via a small set of coprocessor instructions.

Monitoring and Trace

Lastly, both architectures and surrounding software ecosystems enable bus signal monitoring, performance monitoring via event counters, and various instruction and execution trace facilities. As with the other items discussed previously the implementation on hardware may differ sufficiently to be of concern for the developer of firmware and device driver code. The list of similarities and differences is however too vast to be enumerated here in detail. Let it suffice to say that for the average application developer even in an embedded environment the differences are small enough to not be an issue on a daily basis.

Both the ARM and Intel architecture ecosystems are rich in the number of debug tools available. Many of the software debug tools are offered by similar vendors, which eases any migration effort. The previous sections discussed a number of differences to consider when debugging. Many of these differences also apply in transitioning to Intel architecture from other architectures such as MIPS or PowerPC.

Multi-Core Debugging for Intel® Atom™ Processor

This section discusses considerations of multi-core debugging on an Intel Atom processor.

Debugging Single-Core versus Debugging Multi-Core Systems

The key difference between debugging on single-core and multi-core systems is in the distribution of the program execution onto multiple cores. The application or system code developer must be aware which pieces of code are executing on each processor core. Another question to consider: are all cores sharing a common memory map or are the memory locations different? If program flow relies upon cached data, then it is important to understand which cache levels are shared between the different processor cores and which ones are not.

Furthermore, how does the code take advantage of the parallel execution power offered by the multi-core platform? Parallelism could be implemented on a process level or on a thread level. The software workload could be partitioned to the different processor cores based upon functional blocks or logical blocks. Alternatively, partitioning could involve executing the same code on all cores, but operating on different data sets.

The impacts of multi-core processors on the debugger are several fold. First and foremost, execution control and breakpoint handling has an additional layer of complexity. In addition to knowing which memory address or data value dependency a breakpoint has, the debugger now also needs to track the association of processor core, OS thread, or application thread with individual breakpoints. Thread management and core affinity management is generally handled by the OS which implies that for application debug purposes it will be important to track the OS thread identifier for each application thread synchronized with the memory location.

Second, debugging a heavily multithreaded application in a debugger that lacks thread awareness can be a challenge. For example, if a breakpoint is set while executing in the context of one thread, there is a risk that the breakpoint is reached by another thread, thus preventing effective debug of the execution flow of your thread.

A debugger that supports thread awareness such as the screenshot depicted in Figure 10.7, will execute the breakpoint, but then check the thread identifier that is associated with the active thread that reached the breakpoint. If the thread identifier is not for the desired thread, program execution will simply continue.

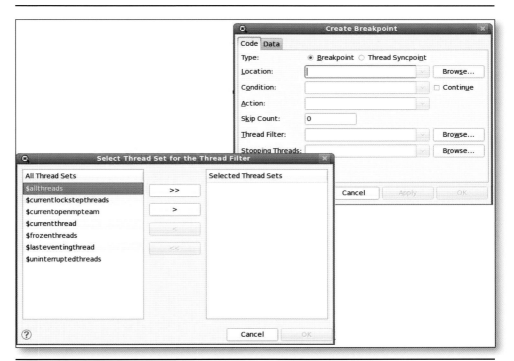

Figure 10.7   Thread Grouping and Thread-Aware Debugging

Similarly, a thread-aware debugger will enable stopping and starting individual threads, colloquially known as *freezing* and *thawing* respectively. Freezing a thread enables the developer to minimize potential interference between threads when analyzing an execution flow.

The third consideration in multi-core processor debugging is the realization that all local variables and even the cache contents are most likely thread-specific. This observation stresses the need for awareness of the code and its execution context including processor and specific thread. This issue is also true for a heavily multithreaded application executing on a single processor core system, except for the cache line considerations.

Multi-core debugging at system level adds additional complexity, especially below the OS layer focusing on firmware or bootloader debugging.

When debugging OS-independent code on a multi-core system it is important to know which processor cores have set breakpoints. Questions to consider:

- Will a breakpoint stop execution of all cores or only of one specific core?

- If memory is shared between the processor cores and execution reaches a breakpoint, is there a core context switch?

The debugger on a multi-core system should notify when changes occur in the processor core context. Processor core affinity on a homogeneous multi-core system will typically be implemented the same way as the breakpoint thread affinity discussed in the previous paragraphs. In this case, the breakpoint is reached by all processor cores, but if the core identifier does not match, execution continues.

Considerations for Intel® Hyper-Threading Technology

From a debugging perspective there is really no practical difference between a physical processor core and a logical core that has been enabled via Intel Hyper-Threading Technology. Enabling hyper-threading occurs as part of the platform initialization process in your BIOS. Therefore, there is no noticeable difference from the application standpoint between a true physical processor core and an additional logical processor core. Since this technology enables concurrent execution of multiple threads, the debugging challenges are similar to true physical multi-core processors.

Homogeneous and Heterogeneous Multi-Core Environments

Thus far, debugging in a multi-core environment with a multi-core–aware debugger seems fairly straightforward. A heterogeneous multi-core processor, where the individual processor cores differ in terms of ISA, adds another layer of complexity. Some of the processor cores may simply be microengines dedicated to encoding or decoding specific data streams. Other systems, for example a handheld device may house dedicated communication processors for voice and data transmission. These accelerators are then tied to the general purpose processor, which typically coordinates the processing. These complicated heterogeneous multi-core designs are typical of designs based on the Intel Atom processor Z6xx or on the Intel Atom processor CE4100. Figure 10.8 shows the component processor cores comprising an Intel Atom processor CE4100. For the embedded application level developer the behavior of a debugger on a heterogeneous multi-core system is still very similar to that of an application running on a standalone general purpose processor. The only difference is that there is a defined software API that handles the information exchange with the other processor cores. Its functionality is however implemented on the device driver and system level and thus completely hidden from the application developer. System developers engaging in debugging are not so lucky and need to understand the impact of these other processor cores.

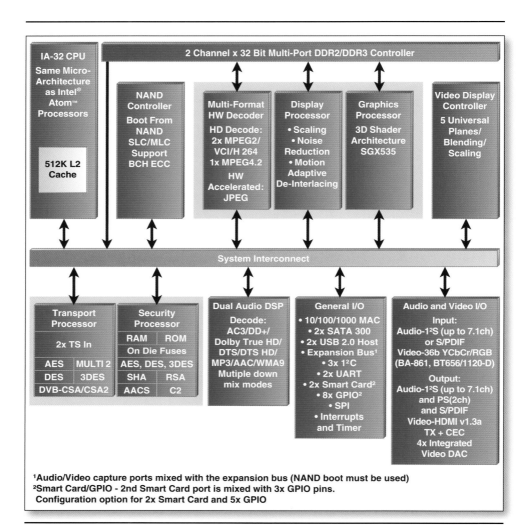

Figure 10.8 Intel® Atom™ processor CE4100

The first and obvious question for the embedded system developer is what is the initialization or boot sequence of these different cores? Usually, one of the processor cores on the chip is assigned the task to power up first. It prepares the memory layout for the other processor cores that then power up in a carefully orchestrated sequence. There may be several different JTAG interfaces or debug agents involved for each of the processor cores. This makes debugging considerably more difficult. In addition, if a breakpoint is reached and execution halted on one processor core, this does not imply that the other processor cores will stop at the same time. If there is no breakpoint monitoring and synchronization unit on the chipset that triggers an interrupt for the other processor cores as soon as the first one is halted, these other processor cores may have executed several hundreds of instructions before halting execution. This synchronization issue makes true heterogeneous multi-core debugging complicated.

Furthermore, on these designs the different processor cores tend to have their own execution space and memory. They execute as mostly autonomous systems. There will however, be some shared memory to upload data and runtime code from the general purpose processor core to a secondary processor core. This data or assembly code usually only makes sense as seen from one of these processors. One processor sees it as write-only and the other one as read-only memory.

This complex setup, which by design offers very limited visibility into the data streams exchanged between the different processor cores, makes platform bus signal monitors and debug tools like SVEN (System Visible Event Nexus) desirable. Such a tool can fill in the gaps about how all of the different data streams and platform events are communicated and processed.

A heterogeneous multi-core-aware debugger may be sufficient to cover debugging the main general purpose processor, the data initialization processor, the security processor, and perhaps the communication processor on a handheld device. Hardware-assisted execution control synchronization may enable the debugger to handle breakpoints correctly. The debugger may be able to monitor the shared memory between those processors. However, this is the limit of a debugger. In order to provide a full comprehensive debug view of complex systems with multiple I/O processors and microengines, it is desirable to monitor the data bus and actively debug the data streams or what is termed transactional memory. These concepts are even gaining popularity for homogeneous multi-core systems. The later section that covers SVEN will discuss these details.

Real-Time Debug Response Requirements

Coordination of debug breakpoints and events between processor cores in a heterogeneous processor is critical. The decision to break and halt execution needs to happen within a few cycles of the break that occurred on that encountered the breakpoint. Thus, many embedded designs employ a debug synchronization unit. The ability to stop and start all processor cores synchronously is extremely valuable for multi-core systems that have inter-process communication or shared memory. To ensure that this synchronization is within a few cycles, a cross-trigger mechanism should be added on the chipset itself.

The configuration registers of the debug synchronization unit enable the developer to select the required cross-triggering behavior. In other words, the developer can specify which cores are halted on a breakpoint. On the other hand, if the processor cores have widely separated and non-interfering tasks, it may be sufficient to synchronize stops and starts with the debug tools. In other words, the debugger can handle synchronization of breakpoints as well, but with a little less fidelity.

Inevitably, this will lead to hundreds of cycles of what is termed *skid* between the halting of processor cores. The synchronous starting of processor cores can be achieved with either a cross-triggering mechanism or via the test access port (TAP) controller of each core.

AMP versus SMP Support in an Embedded OS

Let us now examine these multi-core environments from one level higher in the software stack. In many embedded multi-core designs it may be desirable to assign a few processor cores to a dedicated real-time task. In this case, a careful comparison should be made between asymmetric multiprocessing, bound multiprocessing, and symmetric multiprocessing.

Table 10.1 Features and Properties of Multiprocessing Models that Impact Debug

Feature	SMP	BMP	AMP
Seamless resource sharing	Yes	Yes	No
Scalable beyond dual CPU	Yes	Yes	Limited
Legacy application operation	In most cases	Yes	Yes
Mixed OS environment	No	No	Yes
Dedicated processor by function	No	Yes	Yes
Inter-core messaging	Fast	Fast	Slower
Thread synchronization between CPUs	Yes	Yes	API limited
Load balancing	Yes	Yes	No
System-wide debugging and optimization	Yes	Yes	Limited

In *symmetric multiprocessing* (SMP) a single copy of the main operating system executes on all processor cores. Once the OS is running, thread distribution and workload distribution is almost completely handled by the OS. For effective debugging, it is important to know the unique thread identifier—which core is executing particular threads.

An OS that supports SMP has insight into activities occurring on the system and allocates resources on the multi-core processors with little or no input from the embedded developer. The native threading layer of an OS will probably provide interfaces that enabled safe data sharing between cores and threads. Since an SMP OS has this oversight over all activities on the system, it can dynamically allocate resources to specific applications rather than to processor cores, thereby enabling greater utilization of available processing power. It also lets system tracing tools gather operating statistics and application interactions for the multiprocessing system as a whole, providing valuable insight into how to optimize and debug applications.

In *bound multiprocessing* (BMP) a single OS manages all of the processor cores, but during application initialization, a setting determined by the system designer forces all of an application's threads to execute only on a specified processor core. This effectively isolates a workload and can eliminate the cache thrashing that can reduce performance in an SMP system by allowing applications that share the same data set to execute exclusively on the same processor core. BMP offers a simpler application debugging environment than SMP since all execution threads within an application run on a single processor core. It helps legacy applications that use poor techniques for synchronizing shared data to execute correctly, again by letting them run on a single processor. BMP can be very useful if you have one or two high priority applications that need to be isolated, either for legacy reasons or for prioritization reasons. BMP support is very OS specific. Examples of real-time operating systems that offer support include VxWorks and QNX†. One drawback with BMP is that it does not permit the use of idle resources on an unused processor core, thus artificially restricting performance gain through parallelism.

Asymmetric multiprocessing (AMP) is the software equivalent of heterogeneous multi-core platform development. The different processors execute their own dedicated OS. Data sharing is limited to shared memory and defined messaging APIs. In the simplest scenario the dedicated OS layers are carbon copies of each other. More commonly, this approach is used for heterogeneous hardware designs. The main purpose of this approach may be the need to use special purpose operating systems on a special purpose chip. For example, a handheld device or a SoC implementation targeting in-car infotainment (IVI) may comprise a digital signal processor (DSP) or GPS chip that execute its own RTOS or firmware code. An RTOS like Nucleus, VxWorks, or µ-Itron may be executing on a general purpose processor handling real-time background tasks like phone-call switching and telephone tower registration. This RTOS would also control the messaging API between the general purpose processor and the DSP. Lastly, a full Linux-based OS like Android or MeeGo may be executing the application user interface for the end user.

To successfully debug application or device driver code, debug access to the multiple processor cores may be required. One means of achieving this is to have two separate debuggers that debug aspects of the code executing on different processor cores. If this debugging occurs in shared memory a potential problem can occur if one debugger set breakpoints that the other debugger then encounters and breaks. What if the breakpoint instruction from one core is alien enough to the other core that it triggers an invalid instruction exception and needlessly crashes the execution of the entire application?

For the system level debugger an additional complication is that an AMP software stack design probably has a custom messaging API between the various processors. The application developer probably has no other choice but to rely on the API to behave as intended. There will however, be a system level developer who has to first implement the messaging API. With highly customized embedded designs it may not be possible to adopt an existing API from elsewhere. The developer of this API may need to use multiple debuggers for the different architectures involved simultaneously.

An improvement to employing multiple debuggers is to have a heterogeneous multi-core debugger implementation that can monitor multiple processor cores simultaneously while having a hardware cross-trigger mechanism in place that allows for breakpoint and debugger execution control synchronization between the cores. Such a debugger would at the application layer export information from the API that can be used for messaging, bus monitoring, and debug. At the system level, the debugger would literally be in a bus signal probing tool that allows for signal timing optimization and handover correctness checks.

Debugging the boot sequence of an AMP software stack in a heterogeneous multi-core system is always going to be challenging, although luckily this is a task usually handled by the silicon vendor. Boot performance is frequently not quite as critical (in-car applications and emergency applications are exceptions), allowing for more freedom in signal timing.

Picking the right combination of application level OS, specialized RTOS, and microengine or DSP API is critical for efficient debug. It is strongly encouraged to look at the available debug solutions as part of the decision process when choosing a chipset combination for the embedded design.

Debugger: Application and JTAG

After examining the impact on debugging of different types of OS combinations, software stacks, and chipset combinations, it makes sense to example the embedded debug models themselves. What does cross-debug for embedded targets look like for system debug as well as application debug?

Debug Agent and I/O Driver–based Debug

When cross debugging either via a virtual machine or to a real target hardware device a debug communication channel between host and target needs to be established.

For Windows CE or Windows Embedded, the Microsoft Visual Studio Remote Debugger for TCP/IP based debugging or ActiveSync for Windows CE and USB-based debugging are employed.

For Linux gdbserver, the open source remote debug agent of GDB, is commonly employed. Gdbserver has been adapted for many environments and there are implementations available that allow it to be loaded as a kernel module, which enables Linux kernel system debug as well as adaptations for JTAG support of low-cost JTAG solutions.

These debug agent approaches require that a communication stack for the interface chosen for debug is available. It thus will occupy and block an I/O port that may be needed for another purpose. In addition it is influenced by the timing behavior of the underlying OS or RTOS scheduler. The debug agent is implemented as a low overhead exception handler. When a debug exception is triggered, the OS or minimal software stack on the system will hand over control to the debug agent via an IRQ. Once the thread or process to debug is halted, information can then be read out through the standard OS interfaces and APIs provided for this purpose. When complete, control or a debugged process is handed back to the OS. This process is repeated whenever a debug event such as a breakpoint, watchpoint, or single step occurs. In the most basic implementation this type of debug handler could also execute as a small self-booting mini-RTOS on a system. It could even be implemented as part of the firmware.

This debug method relies on a software stack to set up basic platform configuration, memory access, register access, and information about the available software infrastructure. Thus, it is ideally suited for application debugging or debugging of simple microengines or DSPs.

If the debug agent is implemented as a Ring 3 user mode application it will benefit from full access to all of the exported OS constructs including OS threads, processes, and application load locations. On Windows the agent could access system level information through the Microsoft Windows IOCTL API. On Linux such a debug agent could be implemented as a kernel module and thus provide information about the initialization methods and cleanup methods for device drivers.

The drawback is that this approach does not work for debugging an environment that is not already up and running. Instead, a debug agent can be implemented as part of a dedicated platform debug chip, that is available and up and running from the startup. The other approach is to have a debug state machine integrated on the processor itself either in the form of a small microcode program or in the form of a simple serial I/O signal driven state machine. This is where JTAG solutions for system debug and firmware as well as bootcode development are appropriate.

JTAG: Concepts, Advantages, and Disadvantages

The Joint Test Action Group (JTAG) IEEE 1149.1 standard defines a "Standard Test Access Port and Boundary-Scan Architecture for test access ports used for testing printed circuit boards." This standard is commonly simply referred to as the JTAG debug interface. From its beginnings as a standard for circuit board testing it has developed into the de facto interface standard for OS independent and OS system level platform debug. Figure 10.9 shows a JTAG debug probe connected to an Intel processor.

Figure 10.9 JTAG Device and Connector

When used as a debugging tool, it enables a developer to access an on-chip debug module, which is integrated into the CPU via the JTAG interface. JTAG revolutionized low level platform debug capabilities for the embedded software development community providing a direct serial link from the target processor to the host development machine. Figure 10.10 shows where JTAG connects on a processor bus.

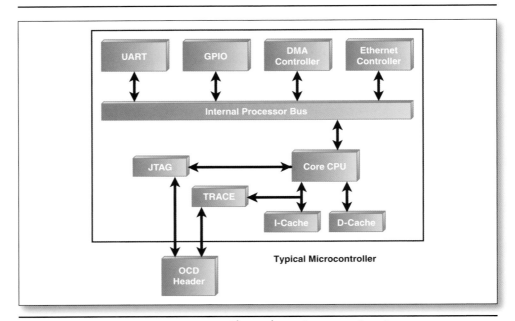

Figure 10.10 JTAG Communication Channel into Processor Bus System

Products employing the JTAG interface for debugging exist today in two forms. First, there are the more advanced JTAG devices that frequently contain a MIPS or ARM architecture processor and memory of their own. These devices may provide additional features like extended execution trace or data trace. Usually these devices offer remote debug connectability via TCP/IP. Second, the simpler JTAG debug interfaces usually contain a small application-specific integrated circuit (ASIC) that handles the communication protocol and translates the serial JTAG signals for transmission over a USB connection. Figure 10.11 illustrates the connection between the debugger host and target hardware via USB or TCP/IP.

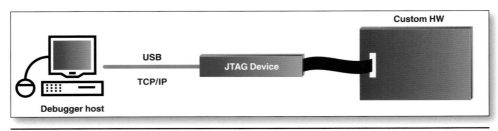

Figure 10.11 Basic Remote JTAG Debug Setup

JTAG debugging has traditionally been used for hardware bring-up and more recently to expand the capabilities of agent-based debugging. However, JTAG based on-chip debug capabilities play a more significant role debugging SoCs. In this role, they help debug the operating system and middleware by isolating complex interactions between the software executing on one or more processor cores.

Following the concepts introduced when discussing AMP on heterogeneous multi-core systems, an ideal method of employing JTAG for SoC debugging is to employ a single JTAG debugger capable of support the different processor cores of your SoC design. If all of the devices in your design are daisy-chained in the same JTAG scan chain, the debugger can leverage the existing JTAG interface to communicate with all the processors of interest. This support of multiple processor core debugging through a single JTAG interface is diagrammed in Figure 10.12.

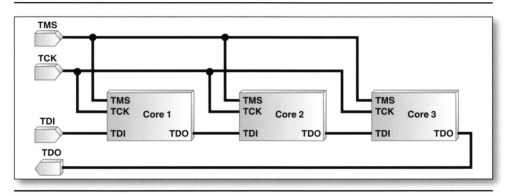

Figure 10.12 Multiple Cores on a Single JTAG Scan Chain

The JTAG interface usually supports at least four signals that are actively being processed by a processors JTAG interface: TDI, TDO, TCK, and TMS. For the purpose of connecting to the JTAG interface in multi-core debugging, the relevant wires are the TDI and TDO. In daisy-chaining, the output of the first core is connected to the input of the second core, and so on to reach the maximum number of cores. The daisy-chain methodology is standards-based, widely used, and will work in all of the multi-core debugging scenarios: single die, multiple processor cores on a board, and complex systems. It also works well in a heterogeneous multi-core processor in which more than one processor family and operating system is used for development such as in the mobile handset and consumer electronics devices.

The issue with daisy-chained JTAG is that the amount of data to transmit at one of the communications stages depends on the number of devices on the scan chain as well as the instruction register (IR) length of each device. The command sequences that need to be sent down the scan chain can reach considerable length if it contains numerous devices.

One concern with multi-core debugging on an embedded AMP system is the ability to use a stop request signal to stop a core immediately or a stop indication signal to stop a core and then synchronize the stopping of all cores. Individual commands issued to a processor core over JTAG require hundreds of JTAG operations. While these appear to execute very quickly (the JTAG scan chain may typically perform serial scans at 10 MHz to 40 MHZ) to a user, this is actually a very slow process in comparison to a processor core executing at several GHz. To avoid instruction skid a hardware on-chip cross-trigger unit between the processors is required. There is, however, the possibility to implement a JTAG server that can issue a stop request signal to stop a core immediately or a stop indication signal to stop a core and then synchronize the stopping of all cores. This can alleviate some of the issues with instruction skid. For example, the Wind River Workbench on-chip debugging solution can start and stop multiple cores simultaneously.

The alternative to using a single debugger is JTAG multiplexing. This extends the IEEE JTAG specification to support the use of an independent debugger for every core that is connected through a shared JTAG interface. Multiplexing technology enables the developer to access multiple discrete cores on a single die by registering, through a single JTAG interface, the desired core to debug. The main advantage of this approach is its connection and debugging performance. The multiplexing technology connects to each core individually and thus does not have the bit shifting challenge of the daisy-chaining method. This approach does not address the issue with simultaneous start and stop of the cores and instruction skid. With a multiplexer, stopping all the cores requires the developer to stop each core sequentially, which introduces the dreaded skid. Multiplexing technology may also not be available on all of the cores present in a heterogeneous system. Thus this only provides a partial solution.

Linux User Mode Debug versus Kernel Mode Debug

Debugging Linux has one unique challenge because of the strict separation of user mode (Ring 3) and kernel mode (Ring 0). User mode cross debugging with a debug agent like gdbserver or the Intel IDB idbserver is quite straightforward.

Linux exports very detailed OS signal, process, and thread information into user mode. Therefore, it is possible for an application level debugger to debug a multithreaded application and display information about the environment. Figure 10.13 is a screenshot of the Intel IDB debugger showing thread awareness capabilities.

Figure 10.13 GUI and Thread Awareness of the Intel® Debugger

Some access to kernel level information is required to obtain the following information:

■ Kernel threads

■ Intel® Atom™ processor instruction trace

■ memory location of kernel module initialization and cleanup methods

One method for debugger support is to instrument the targeted kernel module and let it notify you. Another method is to patch the kernel to force the export of this information into user mode or at least into kernel mode. Both of these approaches are not very elegant.

A better method and one that has become more common is to augment the regular application debugger with kernel modules for information export and JTAG debug solutions.

One such complementary JTAG debug tool is the Intel® JTAG Debugger available with the Intel® Embedded Software Development Tool Suite for Intel® Atom™ processor. It supports Linux OS kernel awareness and instrumentation free kernel module debugging as show in Figure 10.14. In addition, this debugger supports detailed OS signal, interrupt and on-chip instruction trace awareness as highlighted in Figure 10.15.

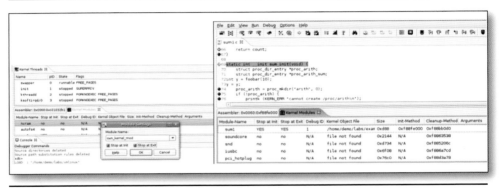

Figure 10.14 OS Awareness and Kernel Module Debugging

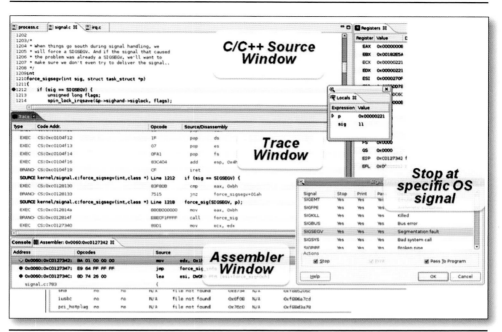

Figure 10.15 OS Signal Awareness and On-Chip Instruction Trace

Using a user mode application debugger in conjunction with a kernel mode JTAG debugger adds additional complexity since the two debug tools employ completely independent debug communication paths and are unaware each other's actions. In short, a breakpoint set in either one of the debuggers may be hit by the other one. This possibility requires a high level of discipline when debugging. Since the JTAG debugger is not aware of application level multithreading it may also trigger breakpoints when it is not desirable for them to be hit. The JTAG debugger will halt the entire processor when reaching a breakpoint including any applications that run on it, whereas the application debugger will of course only halt the target application and the executing process or threads therein.

Developers should be aware of the interactions that multiple debuggers can have within a single embedded system when launched in parallel.

Case Study: Application Debugging on Intel® Atom™ Processor

This case study provides a brief overview over an actual application debug session in a cross-debug environment highlighting the debug methodology and capabilities on an Intel Atom processor-based system.

Application Preparation

For the initial debugging of an application it is recommended to compile it with debug information and no optimization. It is also convenient to rename the output to something different than a.out. A sample command line that achieves these objectives is as follows:

```
$ icpc -g -O0 -o ouput_file_name input_file_name
```

This command line employs the Intel C++ Compiler. Other compiler options may be used depending on the application. Consider a more concrete example on a sample program that computes the value of pi. Assume the source file is named *pi.cpp*. Compile and verify that the program is working by executing the following commands:

```
$ icpc -g -O0 -o pi pi.cpp <cr>
$ ./pi <cr>

Program Output: The value of PI is 3.141592653589
```

When employing a standalone target system make sure that the application is made available to the target OS. One method would be to establish a shared drive with access from the host and target or use the scp command.

Starting the Debugger

When the remote server on the target system is started it will respond by printing a sign-on message on the console of the target system:

```
Intel(R) Debugger Remote Server for IA32 Linux, Version 1.0.0
Copyright (C) 2006-2008 Intel Corporation. All rights reserved.

Waiting for connection with "tcpip:2000"...
```

The Application Debugger is now ready to be started on the host system. Examine the *idb.sh* file in the /opt/intel/atom/idb/2.0.xxx/bin directory. The following command starts the Application Debugger:

```
$ cd /opt/atom/intel/idb/2.0.xxx/bin <cr>
$ ./idb.sh <cr>
```

As displayed in Figure 10.16 the Application Debugger will open up the first time with an empty window, a menu line with most buttons grayed out, and a Console window. If it has been used before it opens with the same window layout as when it was closed. Only the Console window will contain any data—the sign in message.

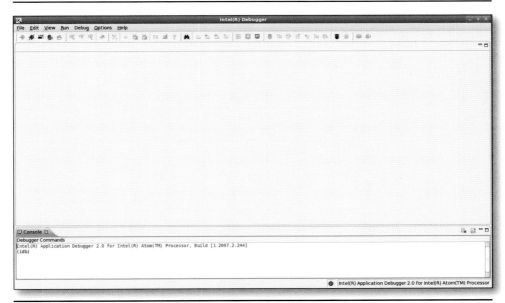

Figure 10.16 Application Debugger Startup

Below the console window appears a status bar. In the middle of the status bar there is a symbol that indicates the debugger's mode of operation. These indicators are summarized in Table 10.2.

Table 10.2   Debugger Status Indicators

Indicator		Description
⊗	Red cross in circle	Disconnected from the target (default state right after debugger launch).
●	Grey dot	Connected to target.
○	Yellow dot	Application loaded or attached.
◉	Green dot	Application active and in running state.
◉	Red dot	Application stopped (e.g. sitting at breakpoint).

Table 10.3 summarizes other icons used by the debugger. In the menu a few symbols are active.

Table 10.3   Debugger Menu Button Icons

Indicator		Description
⟜	Connect	Connect debugger to debug server agent running on target.
⟜	Disconnect	Disconnect debugger from debug agent running on target.
LOAD	Load	Upload application executable onto target platform.
📎	Paper clip	Attach to existing application process running on the target platform.
📂	Half opened folder with arrow	Open source file.
👁x	Eye with X	Evaluate variables.
👁	Eye	Open evaluation window.
👁L	Eye with L	Open local variables window.
▥	Ram chip	Open memory window.
⋈	Mapping tangle	Display source files window.

	Yellow arrow	Set scope to current execution location.
	Up arrow	Set scope one stack frame up.
	Down arrow	Set scope one stack frame down.
	Treeview list	Display threads window.
		Display callstack window.
	Stop sign	Breakpoint dialog - Display breakpoints window.
	Binoculars	Find/Replace.
	Bookmark	Toggle source bookmark.
	Right pointer bookmark	Jump to next bookmark.
	Left pointer bookmark	Jump to previous bookmark.
	X bookmark	Clear bookmarks.
	01010101	Display assembler window.
	R on chip background	Display registers window..
	Display monitor	Display console window.
	Green traffic light	Continue execution.
	Step into	Step one source line entering a function if required (same as F11).
	Step over	Step one source line proceeding through function calls (same as F12).
	Run until caller	Run until caller (same as Shift + F11).
	Run until	Enables execution and break on a specific location.
	Assembly step into	Step one assembly instruction entering a function if required (same as F6).

	斤i	Assembly step over	Step one assembly line proceeding through function calls (same as F7).
	⬤	Red traffic light	Stop/Pause.
	◉	Green arrow on target ring	Restart - run or rerun application.
	▣	Blue camera	Show instruction trace.
	▣	Blue camera with yellow T	Enable/Disable instruction trace.
GDT IDT LDT		Descriptor table	Display descriptor tables (global, interrupt, local).
▢ ▢ ▢		Page translation	Display page translation table and associated configuration table entries.

One of them is the Connect button which is a black and blue button. Click on this symbol to connect to the remote server on the target. An Open Connection dialog appears where the IP address of the target system should be entered as shown in Figure 10.17. It is also possible to debug an application executing on the host system. In this case, the remote server (on the host system) is still started and connected to it via the IP address.

Figure 10.17 Remote Connection Setup for Intel® Application Debugger

The port number should be the same as the one used when the remote server was started. It is possible to have more than one application debugger running; each would be connected to a remote server with a different port number. This enables debug of an application on the host and target at the same time.

If the following error message is displayed:

```
connect refused by remote server
(idb)
```

most likely the IP address or port specified in the Open Connection dialog is incorrect. When the connection is established the remote server provides the following message to the target system console:

```
Intel(R) Debugger Remote Server for IA32 Linux, Version 1.0.0
Copyright (C) 2006-2008 Intel Corporation. All rights reserved.

Waiting for connection with "tcpip:2000"...
Connected
```

On the host system the debugger GUI is updated to illustrate that the buttons to enable attaching to a running process and load a new application are enabled. A summary of each appears below.

Load and Debug a New Application

Consider the pi application once again. To upload the application to the debugger, click on the Load button. A new popup window appears as shown in Figure 10.18 where the application binary is specified along with any environment variables needed to execute the binary correct.

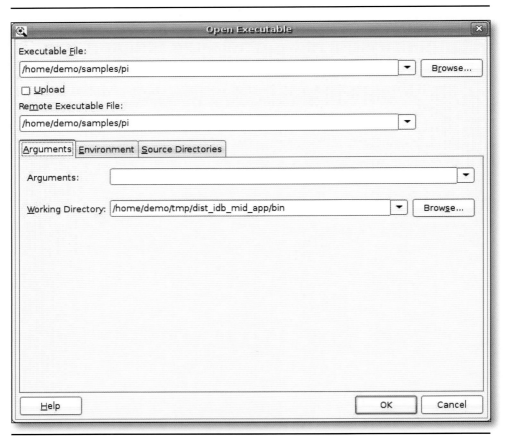

Figure 10.18 Open and Downloading Executable

Next, check the Upload box to instruct the debugger to copy the file over to the target system. In the Target Executable File field, enter the location on the target where the executable should be stored. Make sure that all of the specified directories already exist on the target system and that the file name is the same as specified in the Executable File field. The location on the host and target can be different but the file name should be the same. Click on the OK button and wait until the status indicator changes color to yellow. At this point, debugging can begin.

The first action to take is to examine the list of source files and modules available to view. Click the View menu and select Source Files and the source file window opens. Figure 10.19 shows the debugger source view after double-clicking pi.cpp in the source file listing window.

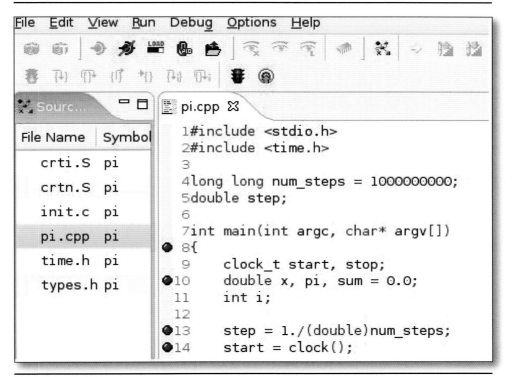

Figure 10.19 Debugger Source View

A breakpoint is set by just double-clicking on any of the blue dots to the left of the line numbers in the Source window. Be careful when enabling breakpoints near the beginning of functions. Note that if a breakpoint is enabled at line 8 in Figure 10.20, no visibility into local variables on the stack would be available once the breakpoint is reached during debugging.

Another very useful window is the Callstack window as shown in Figure 10.20, which shows the path through the function calls taken to reach the current position in the code. The Callstack window is viewed by clicking the View menu and selecting the Callstack option or by typing Ctrl+Alt+R.

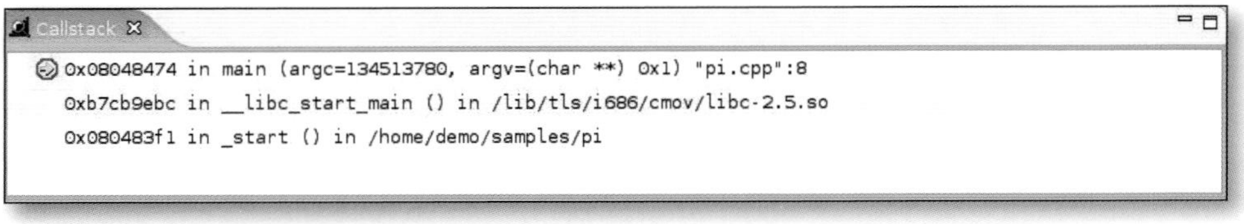

Figure 10.20 Callstack Window

Additional useful windows include the following:

■ *The Register window.* Opened by selecting the Register option from the View menu or by typing Ctrl+Alt+G. It shows the current values of the segment registers, general purpose registers, floating point registers, and the XMM registers.

■ *The Locals window.* Displays local variables and is opened by selecting the Locals option on the View menu and or by typing Ctrl+Alt+V.

■ *The Thread window.* This window is particularly useful for debugging a multithreaded application. It displays which thread is currently under debug. Enabled by selecting the Threads option from the View menu and or by typing Ctrl+Alt+T.

Working with the Debugger

One of the most important capabilities of a debugger is the mechanism for stepping through the code.

The Run Until button enables execution until a specific location is reached. When clicked the dialog box shown in Figure 10.21 appears to enable the specified location to be entered.

Figure 10.21 Run Until Selection Dialog

An alternative to setting a breakpoint by double-clicking the source line is shown in Figure 10.22. This dialog block enables fine-grained breakpoint specification and is selected by clicking the Set Breakpoint option on the Debug menu.

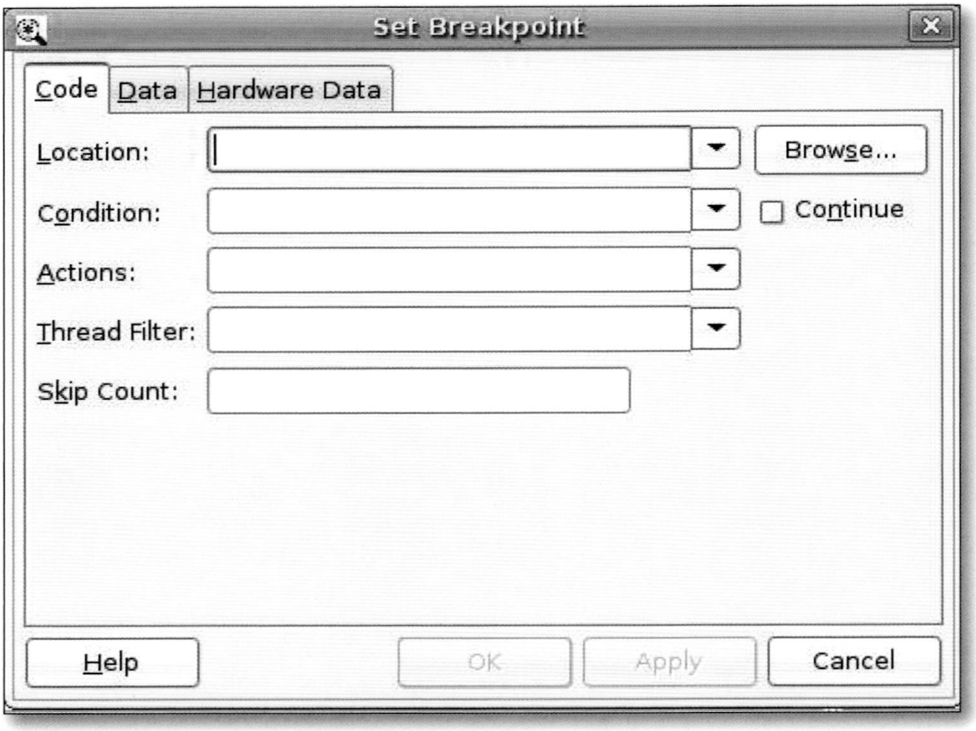

Figure 10.22 Breakpoint Dialog

This dialog enables the setting of breakpoints based on conditions. Furthermore, it is possible to configure a breakpoint to trigger on after it has been reached a specified number of times (by using Skip Count). This feature is also useful for multithreaded applications as the breakpoint can be thread specific (by using Thread Filter). This dialog also supports Data breakpoints and Hardware Data breakpoints. The different between the two is that a hardware data breakpoint employs the processor debug registers directly and thus a very limited number can be active. The data breakpoint requires more internal work in the debugger. As such, data breakpoints impact execution time performance while debugging.

Once the break point is set, the Continue (green traffic light) and Stop (red traffic light) buttons can be employed to continue execution after a breakpoint and to stop execution respectively.

Case Study: Driver Debugging Using the Intel® JTAG Debugger

This section details how to debug a driver using a JTAG debugger. Specifically, the example driver is an Ethernet driver executing under Linux. The specific debugger employed in this case study is the Intel® JTAG Debugger.

The first step in debugging is to ensure that the kernel modules are built with symbol information generation enabled so that the debugger can map the sources to machine instructions once the memory load location is specified. In the debugger, the Linux OS awareness plug-in needs to know where to find the kernel module sources. The following commands enable this:

```
set directory "/usr/linux-2.6.31.i686/drivers/net/\"
 OS "setdir \"/usr/linux-2.6.31.i686/drivers/net/\""
```

Second, the debugger needs to take control and halt the boot process as soon as the Ethernet driver is loaded by the operating system and the Ethernet connection is being established. To do this the OS boot sequence needs to be modified so that `idbntf.ko` is loaded before the device driver targeted for debugging. Next, the Linux kernel OS awareness plug-in is instructed to stop at the driver initialization method by entering the following command at the debugger console window:

```
OS "stopinit e1000 /on"
```

An alternative method for setting up the driver for debugging is to use the kernel module window. Figure 10.23 shows the result of right-clicking on the e1000 kernel module in kernel module window. A dialog appears, which enables specifying the module name and the ability to break at the initialization method.

Figure 10.23 Module Settings Dialog

As soon as the Ethernet driver is initialized, execution will be halted at the `init_method` function and symbol information is loaded enabling viewing of the driver source code. Scroll down in the sources and set a breakpoint at a specific function (that is, IP address acquisition).

At this point, the Restart button and the Run button can be employed to reboot the OS and stop execution at the Ethernet driver load and the specified breakpoint.

Kernel Modules Loaded after Boot Process

The process for debugging a device driver or kernel module loaded after completion of the boot process is similar to the discussion in the previous section. For example, consider an arbitrary kernel module named `scull.ko` as an example.

In the debugger, the Linux OS awareness plug-in is instructed where to find the kernel module sources using the debugger console window:

```
set directory "/home/lab/scull/\"
OS "setdir \"/home/lab/scull/\""
```

Next open the Linux Modules window, right-click and select "add" from the pull-down menu. All of the other kernel modules already loaded during the boot process will be listed; however most of them will state the particular file associated with each is missing. In the next dialog type in "scull", select "Stop at Init" and "Stop at Exit". At this point, begin execution on the target by pressing the Run button.

Next, use PuTTy/SSH or Telnet to connect to the target system. Change directories to the scull directory and initialize the kernel module by typing

```
./scull.init start
```

The debugger as expected halts execution at the `scull init` method. Set a breakpoint at the `scull_read` function and enable execution on the target system once again. Send an echo to the `/dev/scull0` device. The debugger halts execution and further debugging is now possible.

Whole Platform Signal and Event Debug

Earlier in this chapter, the issue of understanding transactions and messaging between the various components on an asymmetric multiprocessing system was highlighted. One valuable approach to debugging is to employ an event tracing API that enables signals and messages to be tracked during execution time. This section discusses the issue in more details and introduces the SVEN tool which enables such event tracing.

SoC and Interaction of Heterogeneous Multi-Core

Dozens of software components and hardware components interacting on SoCs increase the amount of time it takes to root-cause issues during debug. Interactions between the different software components are often timing sensitive. When trying to debug a code base with many interactions between components single-stepping through one specific component is usually not a viable option. Traditional printf debugging is also not effective in this context because the debugging changes can adversely affect timing behavior and cause even worse problems (also known as "Heisenbugs").

SVEN (System Visible Event Nexus)

SVEN is a software technology (and API) that collects real-time, full-system visible software "event traces." SVEN is currently built into all media/display drivers and is the primary debug tool for the Intel® Media processor CE3100 and Intel Atom processor CE4100 platforms providing debug, performance measurement, and regression testing capabilities.

Ultimately, SVEN is simply a list of software events with high resolution timestamps. The SVEN API provides developers a method of transmitting events from any operating system context and firmware. The SVEN Debug infrastructure consists of a small and fast "event transmit" (SVEN-TX) library and a verbose capture and analysis (SVEN-RX) capability.

This so called System Visible Event Nexus in the form of the SVEN-TX library provides an instrumentation API with low and deterministic overhead. It does not cause any additional timing dependent effects. There are no changes in the behavior of the system because of the instrumentation observation. In other words, there is no software Heisenberg effect. The events to monitor can be issued by any software component on the entire platform. These can be interrupt service routines (ISRs), drivers, application, even firmware.

A real-time monitor interface named SVEN-RX provides real-time and offline analysis of the data exported by the SVEN-TX API. SVEN-RX is an interface that can monitor a executing system and analyze failures on the executing application. In addition, it provides detailed information for fine-grained performance tuning.

Lastly, the SVEN Debug console is a command line utility that attaches to the Nexus and observes all events being generated by the SVEN-TX instrumented code (drivers, user-apps, libraries). A scriptable filter dynamically accepts or rejects any describable event category (for example, only record events from MPEG decoder). Scriptable "triggers" stop recording of events to halt local capture of events leading up to a failure. A "Reverse Engineer" feature transfers all register reads/writes from physical address to the unit and External Architecture Specification (EAS) registers.

The SVEN debug console can save all the recorded events collected from the entire SoC to a disk file for offline debugging.

Signal Encode/Decode Debug

The SVEN Debug console has a built-in Streaming Medias Decoder (SMD) buffer flow monitor that checks on SMD ports/queues for data flow between drivers. It also samples the SMD circular buffer utilization over time. Its health monitor is capable of triggering an execution stop and data capture if it for example, fails to detect video flip or an audio decode within a specified period of time.

SVEN Benefits

SVEN enables an accelerated platform debug process providing the developers with all of the required evidence for problem triage. The included automation tools can diagnose most of the common system failures automatically. In short, it speeds up the development cycle on complex Intel Atom processor–based SoC designs by reducing the time it takes the developer to understand issues that occur in the data exchanges and handshake between all of the system components.

Platform Simulation Best Practices

One primary advantage of developing on an Intel architecture–based host system targeting an Intel Atom processor–based system is the similarity between the host and target. Software stack components that do not have a strong dependency on the specific platforms can be developed and debugged on the host system. This is especially true if your host and target environment are executing closely related operating systems. For the discussion in this section, assume that the host environment is executing Linux and the target environment is executing MeeGo, Android, or Windriver Linux for Embedded.

Usage and Limitations of Virtual Machines (VMs)

Your target system software stack may run within a GUI simulation environment such as the Xephyr[†] X-Server with redirection on Linux launched inside a chroot environment. Alternatively, a virtual machine environment such as KVM[†], VMWare software, or Sun[†] xVM VirtualBox may be employed. The build environment itself is most likely external to the virtual machine. In the case of simple GUI redirection the debugger is most likely executing outside of the chroot environment so it can take full advantage of the rich GTK[†] or Gnome[†] GUI that the host development system provides. If testing the application inside a virtual machine (VM) it is still desirable to use the virtual TCP/IP interface of the VM to debug. The reason is the same as for simple X-Server redirection. The power of full GTK or Gnome-based Linux GUI of the host system is quite attractive.

The usage model for this application debug scenario would closely follow the application debug use case from earlier in the chapter. The only difference is that the remote TCP/IP connection to the target goes through a virtual Ethernet port and that idbserver runs inside a virtual machine.

The Intel Application Software Development Tool Suite for Intel Atom processor supports download and install from the idbserver running within the virtual machine, by individually downloading it from a dedicated yum repository. In this manner, there is no need to install unnecessary tool suite components on the target environment. The desired components for the target can be downloaded and installed individually.

Another big advantage is that the entire ecosystem of desktop-centric development, debug, and analysis tools is available for use on the virtual test system.

Except for the software stack components that have direct dependencies on the SoC hardware components, the entire software stack can run inside a virtual machine complete with all of the system monitors and analysis tools needed.

Functional Platform Simulation

Virtual machines and GUI redirection reach their limits when SoC shared memory and data exchange message handling between multiple SoC components are involved. This is where functional simulation solutions like the Virtio[†] IO and functional device simulations from Synopsis provide value. The KVM project offers some interesting interfaces to these simulations as well.

System Bring-up

As expected, system bring-up of an Intel Atom processor–based platform relies heavily on JTAG debug capabilities. Macraigor Systems, Green Hills, Windriver Systems, American Arium, and Lauterbach provide JTAG debug tools to facilitate system level debug and board bring-up for Intel Atom processor–based designs.

Firmware and Bootloader

The first step in bringing up the platform is to define and implement the platform boot process. If an Intel architecture custom boot loader is employed, then the Intel JTAG Debugger can be used for debugging. In general, the JTAG debugger should be attached shortly after reset.

The next step is to load the symbol ELF Dwarf2 linker output file from the bootloader build into the JTAG Debugger. This step enables symbolic debugging and provides more information than disassembly output alone. Another technique to perform functional testing on the platform is to use the pre-loaded platform firmware to initialize target memory. Next instruct the JTAG debugger to upload the test firmware into target RAM, set the EIP instruction pointer register to the upload location of your code, and commence debugging.

It is recommended to change the debugger settings to force the use of only hardware breakpoints if the firmware is debugged directly in boot-ROM. During the early initialization phase of the platform any attempt to query uninitialized memory or write a breakpoint instruction into invalid memory can disrupt the boot process.

OS Kernel

Once the firmware or BIOS and the bootloader are finished loading the operating system kernel is loaded into the target RAM and unpacked. Execution then commences from the operating system kernel entry point. On Linux the start function is `start_kernel()`. Typically, at this point software breakpoints in a JTAG debugger are operational. In addition, memory access monitoring from within the debugger should be safe.

At the end of this chapter, a detailed case study shows how to use the Intel JTAG Debugger to debug perform system and OS bring-up of a Moblin or MeeGo compliant OS on the Intel Atom processor.

Model Specific Registers and Bitfield Editors

Memory mapped peripheral platform registers are used for configuring I/O devices. Access and visibility into these registers can aid device driver developers. A bitfield editor such as depicted in Figure 10.24 can help monitor side effects of modifications to these registers. A bitfield editor can also provide easy access to documentation on individual bits for the following types of registers in an Intel processor platform:

- Model Specific Registers (MSRs)

- Peripheral chipset registers

■ Processor core registers

■ Local and Global Descriptor Tables

Most advanced system debug solutions provide a list of these registers and a menu item to easily modify them. The Intel® JTAG Debugger goes one step further with the bitfield editors which enables monitoring and toggling register bits individually and an integrated online help to provide possible settings and the purpose of the registers.

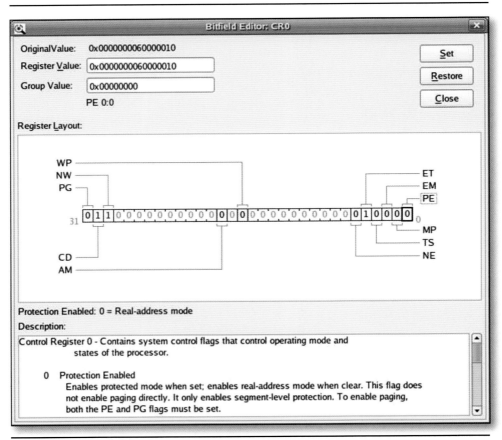

Figure 10.24 Bitfield Editor

In addition, the bitfield editor can monitor the local descriptor table (LDT) and global descriptor table (GDT) permitting full in-depth understanding of the virtual memory setup.

The same detailed level of access to the performance monitoring unit (PMU) configuration registers enables the developer to write basic performance analysis scripts for the debugger and identify bottlenecks in select routines.

On-Chip Instruction Trace

The Intel Atom processor has an on-chip instruction trace feature. This can be very useful for speeding up the process of tracking down problems in OS kernel or driver code.

This feature can be employed to identify application-level runtime defects. For example, assume a scenario where an application contains an array or a matrix that executes incorrectly. Isolating the problem involves monitoring the values in the array beginning at initialization. If it could be verified that the initialization was not complete or the values assigned during the initialization are incorrect, then the execution trace feature can be employed. Based upon the trace the exact incorrect execution path in the code could be identified. Figure 10.25 shows an instruction trace gathered using the on-chip trace feature.

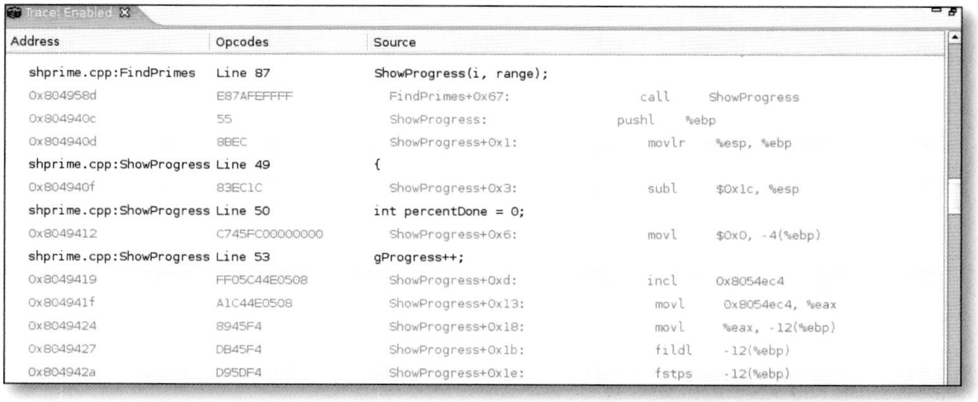

Trace: Enabled

Address	Opcodes	Source		
shprime.cpp:FindPrimes	Line 87	ShowProgress(i, range);		
0x804958d	E87AFEFFFF	FindPrimes+0x67:	call	ShowProgress
0x804940c	55	ShowProgress:	pushl	%ebp
0x804940d	8BEC	ShowProgress+0x1:	movlr	%esp, %ebp
shprime.cpp:ShowProgress	Line 49	{		
0x804940f	83EC1C	ShowProgress+0x3:	subl	$0x1c, %esp
shprime.cpp:ShowProgress	Line 50	int percentDone = 0;		
0x8049412	C745FC00000000	ShowProgress+0x6:	movl	$0x0, -4(%ebp)
shprime.cpp:ShowProgress	Line 53	gProgress++;		
0x8049419	FF05C44E0508	ShowProgress+0xd:	incl	0x8054ec4
0x804941f	A1C44E0508	ShowProgress+0x13:	movl	0x8054ec4, %eax
0x8049424	8945F4	ShowProgress+0x18:	movl	%eax, -12(%ebp)
0x8049427	DB45F4	ShowProgress+0x1b:	fildl	-12(%ebp)
0x804942a	D95DF4	ShowProgress+0x1e:	fstps	-12(%ebp)

Figure 10.25 Instruction Trace of an Interrupt Handler Routine

Similarly, the execution trace can be employed to track down the source of an exception by setting a breakpoint at the exception handler entry point and looking at the execution trace of the directly preceding instructions. This can help to identify the root causes for segmentation faults, memory leaks, and stack overflows in your system level code.

Case Study: Moblin Kernel Bring-up and Debugging

This section details a case study that employs the Intel JTAG Debugger to assist with Moblin Kernel bring-up and debugging. These first steps highlight how to configure the debugger in order to begin.

1. Check that the Macraigor usb2Demon (http://www.macraigor.com) JTAG probe is firmly connected to the eXtended Debug Port marked "JTAG" on the target board. Also check that the probe is connected to the USB cable and USB port on the host computer.

2. Change to the debugger directory:
   ```
   > chdir /opt/intel/atom/xdb/2.x.xxx
   ```

3. Launch the XDB Debugger:
   ```
   > ./xdb.sh
   ```

4. Check Linux Console Window on Connection Failure

Once connected, the JTAG interface takes control of the target device. For example, the target system will not respond if the mouse is moved or commands are entered on the keyboard. At this point, the symbol information needs to be loaded into the debugger.

This is accomplished by clicking on the Load button in the debugger menu bar and navigating to the vmlinux kernel ELF/Dwarf2 file in the Linux kernel source tree that matches the Linux image running on the target.

Alternatively, the following console commands perform the equivalent:

```
LOAD /SEGMENT /DEBUG /NOLOAD /GLOBAL OF "/usr/
linux-2.6.31.i686/vmlinux"
```

While the debugger is loading and interpreting the large OS kernel file it may seem unresponsive for a few moments.

It is necessary to instruct the debugger on the location of the top level directory of the source tree for the debug host system. To map the paths for the location of the sources associated with the symbol info on the debug host system correctly, select Source Directories from the Options menu.

After selecting the Rules tab and clicking on Add New… the dialog box shown in Figure 10.26 appears enabling entry of the correct source mapping.

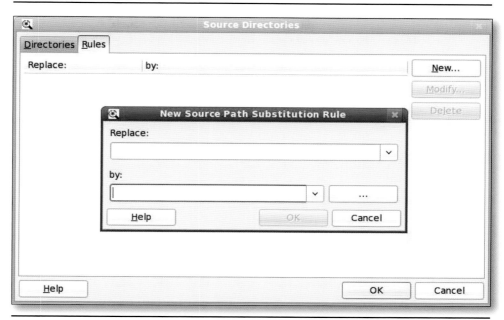

Figure 10.26 Source Path Substitution Dialog

Alternatively in the debugger console window, the following command line executes the equivalent:

```
SET DIRECTORY /SUBSTITUTE = ""''/usr/linux-2.6.22.i686/"
```

At this point, full symbol debug capabilities for the Linux OS kernel are enabled and actual debugging the kernel can commence from the Linux kernel entry point.

To do so place the target processor back into reset by issuing the restart command in the debugger console window. Next, a hardware breakpoing is placed at the Linux kernel startup function called `start_kernel()`. The breakpoint must be a hardware breakpoint instead of a software breakpoint because the system's RAM is not fully configured this early in the boot process. To be on the safe side when it comes to single stepping through the boot code, instruct the debugger to treat all breakpoints as hardware breakpoints for now. This is enabled by typing the following command on the console window:

```
set option /hard=on
```

This breakpoint can be set using the breakpoint dialog or by issuing the following command in the console window:

```
set break at start_kernel hard
```

To run to the kernel entry point, simply click on the Run button or enter run in the debugger console window.

After running through the BIOS and the OS bootloader the target execution will halt at the function entry point for `start_kernel()`. A source window also appears to enable tracking the source location inside the Linux kernel.

Issuing the command:

```
run until sched_init
```

in the debugger console window breaks execution at the scheduler initialization function for the OS. The following command:

```
run until mwait_idle
```

breaks execution at the central OS idle loop.

To understand the OS memory configuration, examine the descriptor tables or go directly to the graphical representation of the physical-to-virtual memory translation by analyzing the page translation table as seen in Figure 10.27.

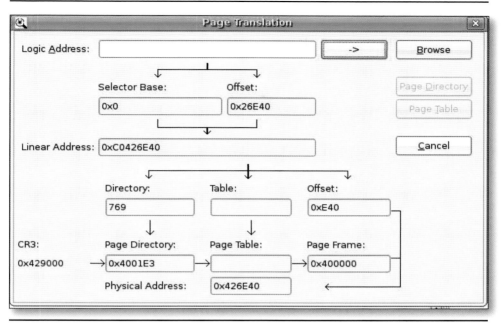

Figure 10.27 Page Translation Table

To get the page translation for the current program counter location check the value of the EIP register and copy and paste the value into the Logic Address field. Clicking on the button to the right of the Logic Address field will then give you a complete representation of the page translation.

If you would like to check the actual page table entries you can then click on Page Table and the table shown in Figure 10.28 will appear.

Index	Value	Comment
0	0x29422067	ADDR=29422000 P=1 R/W=1 U/S=1 PWT=0 PCD=0 A=1 D=1 PS=0 G=0 AVAIL=000
1	0x2909A067	ADDR=2909A000 P=1 R/W=1 U/S=1 PWT=0 PCD=0 A=1 D=1 PS=0 G=0 AVAIL=000
2	0x29B4B067	ADDR=29B4B000 P=1 R/W=1 U/S=1 PWT=0 PCD=0 A=1 D=1 PS=0 G=0 AVAIL=000
3	0x29419067	ADDR=29419000 P=1 R/W=1 U/S=1 PWT=0 PCD=0 A=1 D=1 PS=0 G=0 AVAIL=000
4	0x0000000C	ADDR=00000000 P=0 R/W=0 U/S=0 PWT=0 PCD=0 A=0 D=0 PS=0 G=0 AVAIL=000
5	0x0000000C	ADDR=00000000 P=0 R/W=0 U/S=0 PWT=0 PCD=0 A=0 D=0 PS=0 G=0 AVAIL=000
6	0x0000000C	ADDR=00000000 P=0 R/W=0 U/S=0 PWT=0 PCD=0 A=0 D=0 PS=0 G=0 AVAIL=000

Figure 10.28 Page Translation Table Configuration and Descriptor Table Access

Clicking on any of the index entries will bring up a bitfield editor providing a detailed bit for bit view of the respective page table configuration register and explanation of the current settings.

Summary

There is a rich ecosystem available for debugging software on all layers of the platform software stack running on Intel Atom processor–based designs. For user application debug in single-core, hyper-threaded, or heavily threaded SMP environments. all the well established tools from the Intel architecture ecosystem can be used. For debugging more complex SoC type designs, whether it is for low level system bring-up or messaging API debug, the debug ecosystem for the Intel Atom processor has a solution to address debug concerns. Close collaboration with debugger vendors in the advanced heavily threaded multi-core application debug space as well as the system-level JTAG debug space guarantees the availability of a wide variety of strategies and methodologies that can be used to identify coding problems and correct them quickly.

This chapter provided some guidelines and some tips on how to go about identifying and debugging the kind of problems a developer may run into throughout the development cycle of the different software components running on an embedded system. It should serve as a good starting point for coming up with a solution for debug problems on Intel Atom processor–based embedded designs, whether they be straightforward single-core designs or highly complex SoCs.

Case Study: Migrating Software to the Intel® Atom™ Processor

Each problem that I solved became a rule which served afterwards to solve other problems.

—Rene Descartes (1596–1650), "Discours de la Methode"

For any software architecture migration, processor architecture differences need to be considered and decisions need to be made. Some of those decisions are related to platform-specific features, such as Intel platform technologies. Should you adopt the extra cores that are available? Should you use a symmetric or asymmetric operating system? One very important consideration is meeting real-time requirements.

This chapter is a case study of an ARM† to Intel® Atom™ processor-based architecture migration. The case study follows the migration design guide explained in Chapter 4, and explains the software considerations involved in the migration. Experiments that were conducted to gather data related to these software implications and solution decisions are covered in detail.

The case study involved providing a cable modem front end for the Intel® Atom™ processor CE4100, the newest system-on-chip (SoC) in a family of media processors designed to bring Internet content and services to digital TVs, DVD players, and advanced set-top boxes. A cable modem front end based on the Docsis 3.0 protocol feeds data to the Intel Atom processor CE4100 platform. The cable modem front end architecture and software was originally designed and developed to run on an ARM four-core MP11† processor and then migrated to the Intel Atom processor–based system. The data for this chapter has been derived from this experience.

Ground Conditions of the Case Study

This section describes the ground conditions under which we conducted our experimentation and the various factors that are presented in this case study. The task was to provide a cable modem front end for the Intel® Atom™ processor CE4100. The intent was that all of the processing needed by the cable modem would execute within the Intel Atom processor. For logistical purposes the cable modem solution was prototyped on a four-core ARM MP11–based FPGA solution and then migrated to the Intel Atom processor. In addition, since a new Physical Layer (PHY) was being developed, a FPGA-based development environment was chosen to facilitate quick turn around of PHY revisions.

This provided the opportunity to use the project as an architecture migration case study to achieve the following goals:

■ Capture the software implications, experiments, decisions that needed to be made, and the solutions that were implemented to migrate the software to the Intel Atom processor–based platform. Follow the five-step migration design guide documented in Chapter 4.

■ Determine if the required performance could be achieved using one Intel Atom processor core.

A series of controlled experiments applying a variety of stimulus were used to test the boundary conditions of a proposed architecture solution. If the experiments determined that the performance requirements could be achieved using a single core then an SMP solution would not be required, therefore minimizing the software migration effort and simplifying the operation. If the performance requirements could not be met using one core, then a variety of multi-core solutions would be explored.

There is no direct one-to-one correlation between the stimulus and the variety of proposed multiprocessor solutions. All of the stimuli and the performance experimentation were conducted using one CPU within the ARM MP11 system. The terms *processor* and *core* are used interchangeably in this case study. The flowchart depicted in Figure 11.1 is provided to show how intelligent and informed decisions were made as part of the migration.

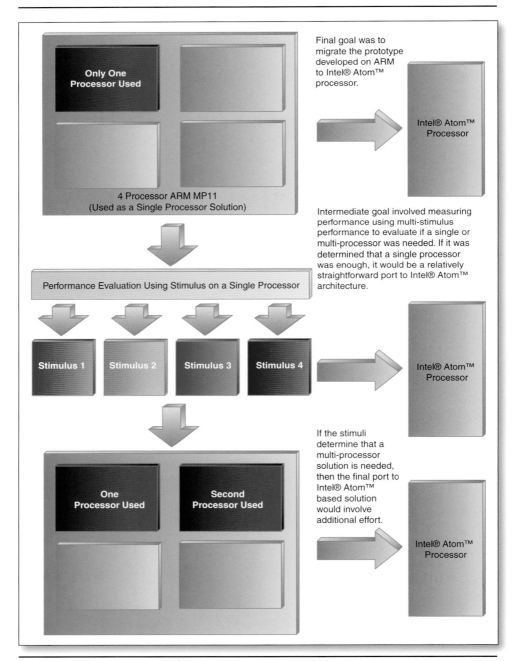

Figure 11.1 Description of Case Study

Step 1: Port Code to the Target Operating System

The performance optimization was conducted on a custom Linux operating system. Extensive investigations were made into the types of real-time operating system (RTOS) available for various ARM platforms and their limitations. Since no RTOS was commercially available for the MP11 when this experiment was conducted, the practical OS choice that would support both the ARM MP11 and the Intel Atom processor was the Linux OS.

The choice of the specific Linux distribution was ARM Linux, and some time was required to customize the OS. The objective was to make ARM Linux as similar to an RTOS as possible. In this direction, various unneeded drivers such as OS drivers related to graphic, video, and audio were removed. The drivers had their own interrupt service routines and even when they were not used, they caused some periodic interrupts that affected the triggering and servicing of the interrupt we were interested in. The kernel was recompiled to use only one processor by disabling SMP in the kernel configuration. The motivation behind this was to use only one processor in the four-processor ARM MP11 system, so that migrating to a single Intel Atom processor at a later stage would be a straightforward task.

Measure Performance on ARM

One of the migration goals was to determine whether a single Intel Atom processor could meet the performance requirements for the cable modem front end. A series of stimulus points and measurement experiments were defined to determine performance and possible alternative solutions based on one processor. We developed our own performance tests, since no tests were available that could be run on both the Intel Atom processor and the ARM MP11. The measurement experiments involved were:

■ Kernel threads switching time

■ Interrupt latency

■ Scheduler latency

- ■ Mutex/semaphore latency

- ■ Processor latency (shared data)

- ■ Actual code processing time

Experiments were also run on the available memory speeds (single read/multiple reads), which showed that the speed was lower, and real-time requirements from the software stack had to be met. Based on the experiment results, the performance design of the software might need to consider various alternatives such as:

- ■ Multiple cores

- ■ Symmetric operating systems

- ■ Asymmetric operating systems

- ■ Scenarios wherein the code ran on a processor without any operating system

- ■ Just firmware

Once the performance tests were developed and the ARM benchmark results recorded, it was time to migrate the software to the Intel Atom processor CE4100 platform.

Step 2: Execute Code Correctly on One Intel® Architecture Processor Core

The source code was developed in C/C++ on the ARM MP11 system and the RealView† tools were used for system as well as debugging and performance measurement. As the code was developed on the single core ARM system it was also compiled on a single-core Intel Atom processor platform. The Eclipse† IDE and the GNU† C/C++ compiler (GCC) were used to compile the code on both architectures.

All cable-specific code was written from scratch. Except for some header file changes, no significant changes were required to compile the code on the Intel Atom processor. There were no endian changes that needed to be dealt with because the code was designed as endian neutral, and the Linux OS provided the architecture abstraction for the network processing software stack.

Design Philosophy

The basic software migration philosophy was to start with a one processor system design and move to a multiprocessor system design only if performance tests warranted the extra CPU performance. Due to the nature of SMP operating systems, there exists a potential of not having direct control of some of the most time-critical aspects of a real-time project. This favored the exploration of a single-processor solution to the fullest before moving to a multiprocessor solution. Development on a multiprocessor system on an embedded project can be complex, and depends a great deal on the available SMP and AMP RTOS choices. Availability of software development tools also plays an important part in successfully migrating from a single processor to multiprocessor design for an embedded project.

This section explains the decision-making process used in determining whether one processor or multiple processors are needed to meet the performance requirements. Figure 11.2 exhibits the basic decision process for the design methodology, which is based on stimulus results, the number of cores required to meet performance, whether or not more than one core is required, and if needed, the multi-core adoption methodology.

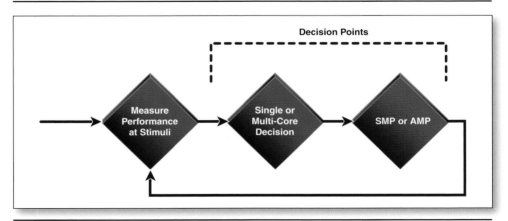

Figure 11.2 Design Methodology Decision Process

The basic principle used in determining whether the Intel Atom processor CE4100 would be a viable cable modem front end involved measuring performance at various stimulus points. Based on the results of the stimulus points, an educated decision was made regarding whether a single core would be sufficient to meet the performance requirements or whether a multi-core solution would be needed instead. Further, if a multi-core solution was required, then a decision would need to be made for the multi-core adoption methodology. The choices include SMP or AMP. These decisions have a significant impact on the overall solution from a firmware, commercial OS choice, software development costs, and validation perspective.

Four stimuli were used in the experiments. The number of stimuli that are relevant to your individual experiment may vary. These stimuli were run on a real-time operating system. The stimuli we experimented with were relevant from an embedded communication perspective (cable modem). A slight variation of these stimuli will work for most of the embedded use cases:

- Stimulus 1: Pertains to meeting the most stringent real-time requirement on one channel.

- Stimulus 2: Pertains to meeting the maximum data rate on one channel.

- Stimulus 3: Pertains to meeting the most stringent real-time requirement on multiple channels.

- Stimulus 4: Pertains to meeting the maximum data rate on multiple channels.

These stimuli translated into four stimuli for the cable modem front end project:

- Stimulus 1: Real-time packet processing is taking more than 200 μs (P1).

- Stimulus 2: Increase the frequency/rate of the control packets to the maximum possible frequency (P1).

■ Stimulus 3: Attempt to do real-time packet processing for multiple channels within 600 μs (P2).

■ Stimulus 4: Test whether the system can handle maximum data rates across four channels (P2).

All of the stimuli were first performed on a single-processor ARM system. The results of the stimuli influenced the decision regarding the need for a multiprocessor system. The following measurements were taken at each of these stimulus points:

■ Kernel thread switching time

■ Interrupt latency

■ Scheduler latency

■ Mutex, semaphore latency, and so on

■ Processor latency (shared data)

■ Actual code processing time

Step 3: Optimize the Code for Performance on One Intel® Architecture Core

The following sections provide details about the stimulus and how the key measurements influenced decisions. The basic idea behind the various stimuli was to test the performance viability using a single processor. A multi-core solution would only be adopted if a single-core solution could not meet the performance requirement.

Stimulus 1: Meet the Most Stringent Real-Time Requirement on One Channel

Value Add of IF Statements

In the practical case, the goal was to process "map packets" within 200 μs. As this experiment ran, various performance measurements were captured and an IF/ELSE list of conditions was built to guide decisions.

The value added is in the IF statements. These problems were encountered on a day-to-day basis. For example, we realized that we could not get any reference on these performance factors:

■ Performance of actual kernel threads

■ Interrupt performance

■ Mutex measurements

■ Semaphore measurements

■ Latency measurements

Custom performance comparisons were conducted to measure these factors. This resulted in making kernel threads a key IF statement in the decision-making flowchart. Also, the decision process was more cognizant of actual memory bandwidth since it was much less than what was encountered in the research.

IF/ELSE Statement for Decision Making on Stimulus 1

If Kernel thread switch timing is more,

Try to merge thread functionality into single thread based on overall design.

If threads cannot be merged,

Move to SMP mode based on processor latency.

If processor latency is too high,

Move to an AMP mode, and experiment and modify the data affinity to a processor.

If interrupt latency is too high,

Move to a preemptive OS.

Move to an AMP mode, with map processing in firmware.

If scheduler latency is too high,

Move to an AMP, wherein we make sure that different high priority threads, ISRs, bottom halves are partitioned on different processors.

Modify the scheduler switching functions (OS do IRQ function) to our needs.

If mutex latency, Semaphore latency, and so on, is high,

Change coding style.

Optimize kernel (OS) to reduce the latency.

Get custom-made patches from a third party source to address these problems.

If processor latency (communication, shared data, and so on) is too high,

Partition data properly and fine tune communication mechanism (such as shared memory) between threads.

If actual code processing time is high,

Optimize coding style, move to assembly if required.

Move to an SMP-based two-processor solution.

If more than one of the conditions above apply to your test, then choose valid solution involving multiple processors, OS or no OS, assembly coding, and/or kernel optimization.

Stimulus 2: Meet the Maximum Data Rate for One Channel

In the cable modem project, the frequency of the control packets were increased to the maximum possible rate. As the experiments were started a list of IF/ELSE conditions to guide our decisions. In the cable modem project, the data was either upstream or downstream. The control packets were packets like map processing, transmit scheduler, and so on.

IF/ELSE Statement for Decision Making on Stimulus 2

If ISRs are coming at such a high rate that we do not have time for data processing,

Find out in hardware if the packet is real-time or not real-time. For real-time packets, raise an IRQ on a separate processor. For non-real-time packets, raise an IRQ on a different processor. For this an AMP solution is needed. In this solution real-time control packets (map and TX scheduler) and upstream data path will be on one processor and the downstream data and other control packets on another processor.

If ISRs are coming at such a high rate that we are not able to process other control packets,

Move to an SMP-based mode with two processors to process interrupts.

If this is not optimal and we see a lot of processor latency,

Move to an AMP-based two processor mode.

If threads are getting starved,

Move to an SMP-based two processor mode.

Stimulus 1 and 2 should be conducted in parallel and based on the data; an amalgamation of the listed possible solutions will be chosen.

Stimulus 3 and 4 details are similar to Stimulus 1 and 2. Results obtained from Stimulus 1 and 2 should be extrapolated to see if it works cross Stimulus 3 and 4 as well.

In our practical example, we came up with the following choices:

■ Stimulus 3: Attempt real-time processing for four channels within 600 μs. The problems and solutions are same as Stimulus 1.

■ Stimulus 4: Attempt to handle maximum data rates across four channels (P2). The problems and solutions are same as Stimulus 2.

There is no 1:1 relationship between stimulus and the suggested split of functionality across processors as shown in Figure 11.3. All the stimulus were carried out on single processor systems and, depending on the performance results, any one of the five suggested processor splits might work for the particular problem that might be encountered.

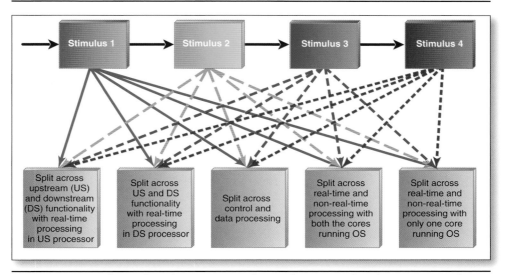

Figure 11.3 Relationships between Stimulus and Suggested Multiprocessor Solution

Step 4: Apply Platform-Specific Software Design Updates

As part of Step 3, if the stimuli points indicate that a multiprocessor solution is required, then the following ideas could be explored to architect a solution. While working on Step 2 and Step 3, it was becoming clear that a single-processor solution would meet performance requirements. Even so, as Step 2 and Step 3 were progressing, potential multi-core solutions were explored. This section reviews all of the multi-core designs that were considered.

Split of Functionality across Processors, on the Basis of US/DS Functionality

The next few sections give some example solutions based on cable modem functionality. Generic terms such as upstream packets, downstream packets, control packets, map packets, and transmit scheduler are used in the following few sections. All of the block diagrams are designed to give the reader an idea of the splits possible. This chapter does not go into detail on the cable modem solution, but rather to use the cable modem solution as an example.

Read this Section before Proceeding

The following is a brief explanation of the overall cable modem design. This explanation will be relevant for the next four sections. The cable modem design has three distinct types of packets: upstream packets, downstream packets, and control packets. All of these packets have time-critical aspects. The most time-critical packets of these are called map packets. Map packets come in the downstream direction and are control packets. Map packets specify the time instance at which the next upstream packet can be sent. In the map packet, the next upstream packet can be specified to be scheduled 200µs from the time the map packet has been received at the cable modem. This creates a real-time requirement of 200 µs in which the map packet must be processed in the downstream direction so an upstream data packet must be prepared and sent out of the cable modem.

Most of this processing was executed using software. A component called Mini-MAC provided a basic level of filtering to understand if a downstream packet is addressed to our cable modem. The rest of the processing, filtering, and building of the packet was performed with software. The PHY was capable of both CDMA and TDMA transmissions.

In this design, all of the upstream processing was executed on one processor, which also performed the real-time map processing. All of the downstream processing is done on a different processor, making use of two processors in this design. The design of this concept is shown in Figure 11.4. We also made use of a symmetric multiprocessing operating system, where different threads were programmed for a particular core affinity.

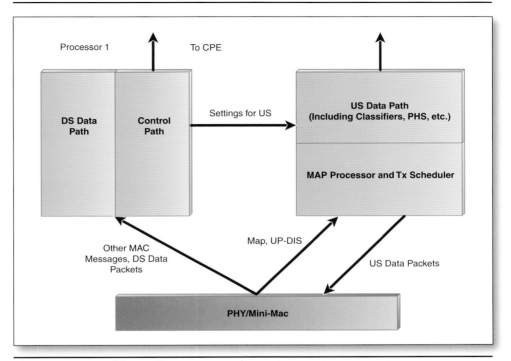

Figure 11.4 Cable Modem Conceptual Design

Figure 11.5 shows the practical design of this two-processor solution. The highlighted area in the picture encapsulates the processing performed on processor 2. The other area shows processor 1.

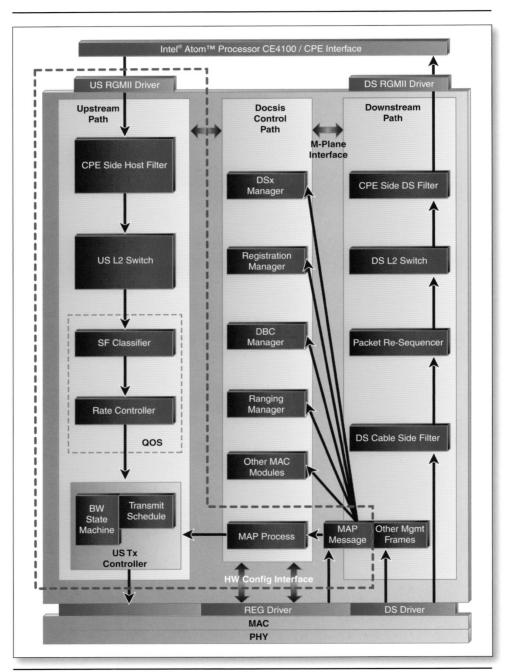

Figure 11.5 Practical Design of Cable Modem Software

Advantages

This approach is optimized across cores, as both processors split the work as well as the communication across the cores.

The communication across cores is minimal and also does not fall in a time critical path.

Disadvantage

This approach needs the Mini-MAC to process classification of MAC control packets. Our hardware was originally designed in a manner where the hardware component (Mini-MAC) would process only destination address filtering. In this design, a hardware change was needed so MAC control packets could be identified in hardware and transferred to a separate queue before the software on a different processor started handling them.

If we need to code MAP/TxScheduler in assembly, then it will get a little trickier. For performance reasons, it might be necessary to code some critical parts of map processing and transmit the scheduler. Writing code in assembly is error-prone and development is usually more cumbersome.

Split of Functionality across Processors, on the Basis of Non-Time-Critical US/DS Functionality

This design is very similar to the earlier design where the functionality has been split on the basis of upstream/downstream functionality. The only difference here is the map processing (the most time-critical functionality) is on the processor where downstream processing is done instead of the upstream processor. The conceptual and practical designs are shown in Figure 11.6 and Figure 11.7 respectively. Symmetric operating system design with processor affinity fixed for key threads was used.

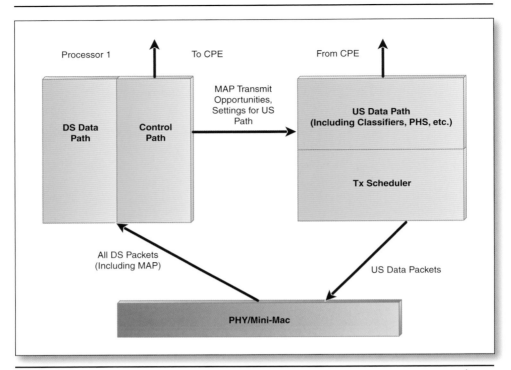

Figure 11.6 Conceptual Design of Split of Functionality across Processors, on the Basis of Non-Time-Critical US/DS Functionality

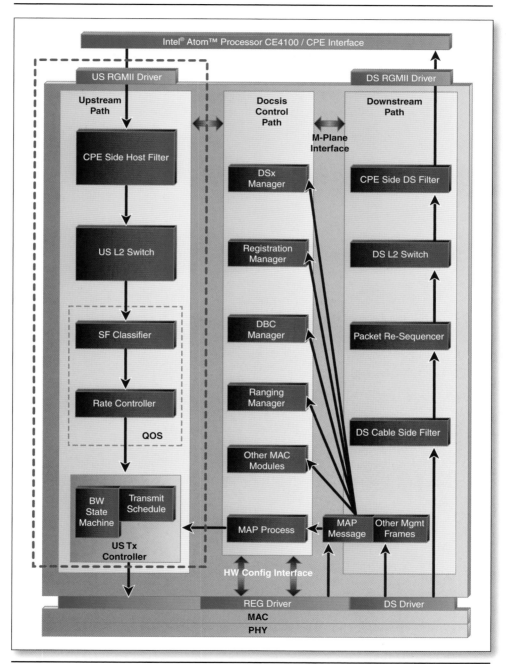

Figure 11.7 Practical Design of Split of Functionality across Processors, on the Basis of Non-Time-Critical US/DS Functionality

Advantages

This approach does not need a modification in Mini-MAC, while still achieving the split across processors. This is because the MAP packets that come in the downstream direction are all processed on the same processor where the MAP processing is done. The filtering of the MAP control packets can be done in software and not in hardware as the earlier design would have warranted.

Disadvantages

If the MAP/TxScheduler must be coded in assembly, then it will get a little trickier. If real-time map processing performance on one channel without the full frequency of packets is bordering around the 200 μs, then it becomes extremely tricky with the full frequency of packets. To increase performance in this case, some critical aspects of map processing and transmit scheduler options will need to be programmed in assembly. However, programming in assembly increases the total development time, debugging, maintenance, and upgrade effort.

Communication across processors is time critical, as MAP information is passed from one processor to another processor. This is a key disadvantage of using multiprocessor systems. Extra effort is needed to make sure that time-critical information is passed in an efficient manner between processors. This is easier said than done because it involves software implications, such as balancing real-time requirements from processor latencies, interrupt latencies, and operating system latencies as well as queue-handling procedures.

Split of Functionality across Processors, on the Basis of Control and Data Processing

This design is based on separating data and control paths on two different processors.

Conceptual and practical designs are shown in Figure 11.8 and Figure 11.9 respectively. A symmetric operating system with fixed processor affinity for key threads was used.

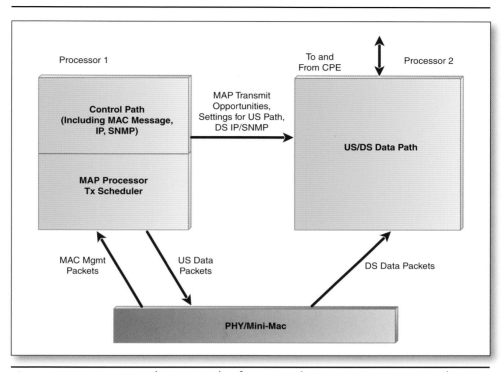

Figure 11.8   Conceptual Design Split of Functionality across Processors, on the Basis of Control and Data Processing

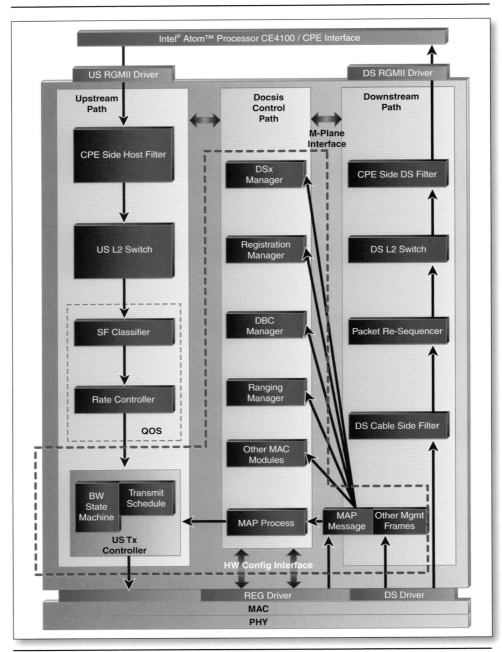

Figure 11.9 Practical Design Split of Functionality across Processors, on the Basis of Control and Data Processing

Advantages

This approach takes advantage of the fact that the control messages (and their processing) do not happen very frequently. So the remaining time of the processor can be used for MAP-TX scheduler.

Communication across the processor is not in the time-critical path.

This approach takes advantage of a separate DMA context for MAC-MGMT and packet data. In our architecture, we had separate DMA contexts for management and regular data packets.

Disadvantages

The Mini-MAC needs to forward the messages received from the MAC-MGMT DMA to processor 1, and messages received from DATA-DMA to processor 2. This translated to some extra functionality on the hardware based Mini-MAC, but this is just incremental functionality on the Mini-MAC.

MAP-Processor/TX-Scheduler on a Separate Processor, with OS

This design is based on having all the real-time processing on one processor and the rest of the processing on a different processor. This design also works on the assumption that there is an asymmetric operating system where the load balancing between the two processors is not chosen by the operating system. The conceptual and practical design diagram is shown in Figure 11.10 and Figure 11.11 respectively.

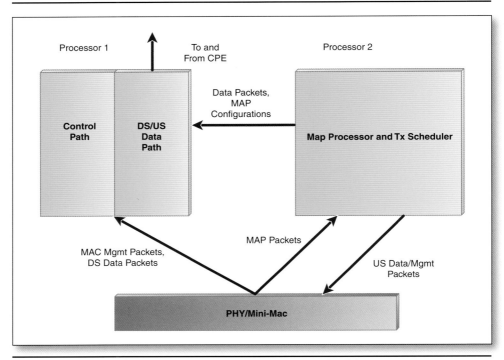

Figure 11.10 Conceptual Design MAP-Processor/TX-Scheduler on a Separate Processor, with OS

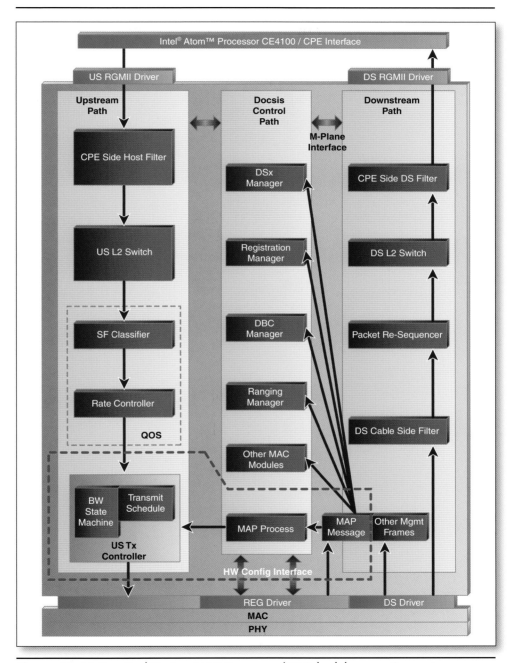

Figure 11.11 Practical Design MAP-Processor/TX-Scheduler on a Separate
Processor, with OS

Advantages

This option is viable if the MAP-TX scheduler (real-time processing) did not meet 200 μs in any of the previous approaches. If the real-time processing is not able to meet the 200 μs target, then it might be worthwhile to have only the real-time processing on one processor and the rest of the processing on a different processor.

Disadvantages

The Mini-MAC (hardware) needs to forward the MAP messages to processor 2. This means that there may be some changes in the hardware functionality.

This also opens the door to move from a two-processor solution to a three-processor solution. If we cannot fit control and data processing in one processor, there might be a need for a third processor.

This also needs an asymmetric operating system executing all real-time functionality on one processor and the non-real-time functionality on another processor. The operating system does not perform any real-time load balancing as this might affect the overall design. With asymmetric operating systems, it is a responsibility of the software developers to coordinate communication between the two cores. This increases software development time, as well as debug and maintenance efforts.

MAP-Processor/TX-Scheduler on a Separate Processor, without OS

This design is very similar to the earlier designs except that all the real-time processing is executed on a dedicated core that does not have an operating system. This means that all the real-time processing will be written as firmware code. The conceptual and practical design diagrams are shown in Figure 11.12 and Figure 11.13.

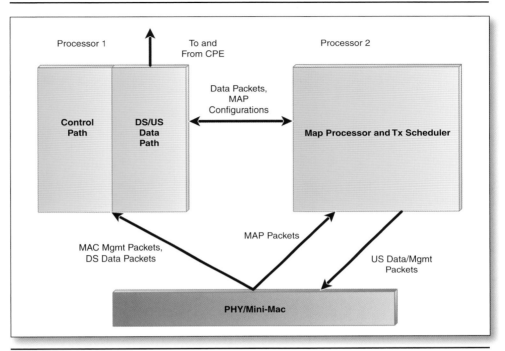

Figure 11.12 Conceptual Design MAP-Processor/TX-Scheduler on a Separate Processor, without OS

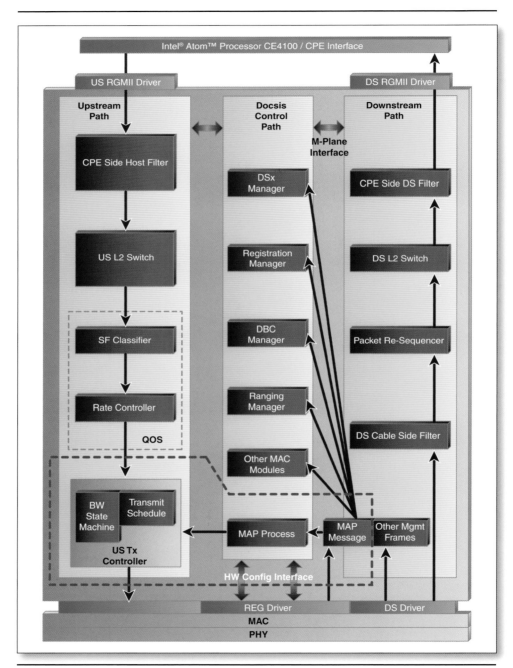

Figure 11.13 Practical Design MAP-Processor/TX-Scheduler on a Separate Processor, without OS

Advantages

This option is viable if the MAP-TX scheduler (real-time processing) did not meet 200 μs in any of the previous approaches. In this approach, there won't be any operating system delays and there won't be any inherent code related latencies because the real-time processing is in firmware code.

Disadvantages

Architecting complex and a huge real-time processing task in firmware is very difficult, making software development a challenge.

Mini-MAC (hardware) needs to forward the MAP messages to processor 2 and will need some modification.

If it is determined that it is not possible to fit control and data processing in one processor, we may need a third processor. This may also require more firmware code.

Step 5: Optimize the Software Design for Multi-Core Intel® Architecture Performance

This section covers the performance tests conducted for the case study, which helped in categorizing the system as a whole.

Performance Measurement

One of the most important challenges that this case study faced was the inability to procure real-time performance data on various aspects of the Linux operating system on the ARM platform. For this, we conducted our own experiments and came up with data similar to what is listed in Table 11.1 below.

Table 11.1   Performance Tests

Details	Status	
Measure using test programs - task switching time using.	All measurements are using Modified Kernel with preemption.	
	Kernel Mode	*User Mode*
Semaphore method	Switch time – 109 microseconds	Switch time – 132 microseconds
Mutex method	Switch time – 106 microseconds	\<Not done\>
Wait queues method	Switch time – 109 microseconds	\<Not done\>
Tasklet method	Creation time – 306 microseconds	\<Not done\>
Interrupt Latency	15 microseconds	N.A.
Interrupt Latency Measurement	ARM Timer is used to measure the interrupt latency.	

Kernel optimization – Identify patches available

- Remove all modules that are not required.	Almost all unwanted modules removed. Preemptive support added. Will do further optimization after test programs are done.
- Identify and do all other finer optimizations possible.	

Performance tests and ratings are measured using specific computer systems and/or components and reflect the approximate performance of Intel products as measured by those tests. Any difference in system hardware or software design or configuration may affect actual performance. Buyers should consult other sources of information to evaluate the performance of systems or components they are considering purchasing. For more information on performance tests and on the performance of Intel products, refer to http://www.intel.com/performance/resources/benchmark_limitations.htm.

Results have been estimated based on internal Intel analysis and are provided for informational purposes only. Any difference in system hardware or software design or configuration may affect actual performance.

Results have been simulated and are provided for informational purposes only. Results were derived using simulations run on an architecture simulator or model. Any difference in system hardware or software design or configuration may affect actual performance.

Results

The results of the performance work indicated that the Intel Atom processor CE4100 would satisfy the performance needs for the cable modem front end. The chief concern of meeting the real-time performance requirement of 200 μs was met. In this case it was relatively straightforward to port the code and architecture to the Intel Atom processor within the Intel Atom processor CE4100, which was handling the media processing as well. The same may or may not be true for the particular case others are dealing with. This chapter is an attempt to provide a framework of performance measurement data to help guide in making an intelligent decision on what works for the individual situation.

This case study resulted in multiple conclusions. The conclusions are discussed in detail in the following subsections.

Design Flexibility

During the course of the experiments, one thing that became increasingly clear was that it is critical to keep the options open and flexible when designing a comprehensive solution. Designing with flexibility ultimately avoids rework and saves crucial resources in terms of time and money. Our iterative approach of performing experiments with various stimuli on ARM-based FPGA helped narrow down on the final design criteria. By adopting four-core architecture for experiments, options were open, when it came to testing the real-time channel requirements for the communications use case.

Real-Time Requirements and Intel® Atom™ Microarchitecture

Though the ultimate aim for doing this exercise was to port the solution to Intel Atom microarchitecture, the experiments did reveal fundamental real-time requirements for a communications solution. Analysis showed that the Intel Atom processor CE4100 is viable as a cable modem front end. Additionally, the results of the migration experiment proved that the Intel Atom processor is capable of handling real-time requirements of communication workloads.

Early Prototyping

One of the key conclusions to be drawn from this exercise is that early prototyping is necessary for any complex solution that has real-time requirements. By choosing to do experimental analysis using stimulus for various cores, we had a good idea of the final solution, once it could be ported to a single core. Tying the results and analysis with flowchart-based decision making aided in coming up with decisions early during the project.

Intel® Architecture Ecosystem (Tools and Software)

Choosing to work with an ARM FPGA–based prototype gave good insight into the availability of tools and software for the work ahead. The experiences and analyses clearly show that when it comes to tools and software availability, Intel architecture is well supported. From the availability of the core operating system to the supporting tools around it, Intel architecture presents various choices to OEMs and design vendors with its legacy of scalable solutions.

Summary

This case study started out with a thorough exercise in analyzing real-time requirements of a communications solution on an ARM-based system solution. The results showed that most stringent real-time requirements posed by a communications system can be addressed using an Intel Atom processor–based platform. Thus, the Intel Atom processor microarchitecture can apply very well to legacy ARM-based solutions in the industry. With a strong software and tools ecosystem around Intel architecture, the Intel Atom processor microarchitecture is positioned to meet and potentially extend the capabilities of the low power embedded design industry.

Glossary

abstraction Abstraction can have several meanings depending on the context. In software, it often means combining a set of small operations or data items and giving them a name. For example, control abstraction takes a group of operations, combines them into a procedure, and gives the procedure a name. As another example, a class in object-oriented programming is an abstraction of both data and control. More generally, an abstraction is a representation that captures the essential character of an entity but hides the specific details. Often we talk about the named abstraction without concern for the actual details, which may not be determined.

ACPI Advanced Configuration and Power Interface.

ARM Advanced RISC Machine, formerly known as Acorn RISC machine.

Amdahl's law A law stating that (under certain assumptions) the maximum speedup that can be achieved on a system of multiple processors is limited by the percentage of code that must remain serial.

AMP Asymmetric multiprocessing.

application programming interface (API) An application programming interface defines the calling conventions and other information needed for one software module (typically an application program) to utilize the services provided by another software module. For example, MPI† is an API for parallel programming. The term API is sometimes used more loosely to define the notation used by programmers to express a particular functionality in a program. For example, the OpenMP† specification is referred to as an API. An important aspect of an API is that any program coded to it can be recompiled to run on any system that supports that API.

ASIC Application-specific integrated circuit.

ASSP Application-specific standard product.

barrier A synchronization mechanism applied to groups of units of execution (UEs), with the property that no UE in the group may pass the barrier until all UEs in the group have reached the barrier. In other words, UEs arriving at the barrier suspend or block until all UEs have arrived. They may then all proceed, for example at the join part of the fork-join.

Also, a memory barrier, or fence, across which certain memory read or write operations are guaranteed to occur.

bi-endian architecture A CPU that is capable of being configured to operate as either big endian architecture or little endian architecture.

big endian architecture Big endian is an order in which the "big end" (most significant value in the sequence) is stored first, at the lowest storage address. The most significant byte is stored in the leftmost position. CPU architectures, such as the Sun SPARC† system, IBM's PowerPC†, and Hewlett-Packard Precision Architecture† systems use a big endian model, where the most significant byte is at the lowest address in memory. See **forward byte ordering**.

BIOS Basic input/output system.

boot loader Minimized specialized firmware stacks created for fast speed, small size, and specific system requirements.

Cache A relatively small memory device close to a processor that mirrors the contents of, and is considerably faster than, the computer's main memory. Cache hierarchies consisting of one or more levels of cache are essential for many algorithms in modern computer systems. Since processors are so much faster than the computer's main memory, a processor can run at a significant fraction of full speed only if the data can be loaded into cache before they are needed, and those data can be reused during a calculation.

Data are moved between the cache and the computer's main memory in small blocks of bytes called *cache lines*. An entire cache line is copied when any byte within the memory mapped to the cache line is accessed. Cache lines are invalidated from the cache when the cache becomes full and space is needed for other data, or when memory represented by the cache line is written by some other processing element (PE) or engine/controller.

In a processor containing multiple cores, each core has its own cache. In many cases, multiple cores share an additional level or two of cache. Keeping the caches coherent (that is, ensuring that all processors have the same view of memory through their distinct caches) is an issue that must be dealt with by computer architects and compiler writers. Programmers must be aware of caching issues when optimizing the performance of software.

CCTV Closed-circuit television.

codec Coder-decoder. Examples of codecs: MPEG1/2/4, H.264, VC1, MJPEG.

concurrent execution A condition in which two or more units of execution (UEs) are active and making progress at the same time. This can be either because they are being executed at the same time on different processing elements (PEs), or because the actions of the UEs are interleaved on the same processing element.

core A core is a distinct processing element inside a processor capable of servicing the full execution needs of a unit of execution (UE). Depending on the processor architecture, a core might have its own cache or share a cache with one or more cores within the processor.

COTS Commercial off-the-shelf.

critical section A region of code manipulating shared resources that must be monitored so that only one unit of execution (UE) has access at a time. Exclusive access avoids race conditions, which might leave data in an inconsistent state, but are also sites for possible contention. Critical sections should be used where needed, but kept as short as possible.

data parallel A type of parallel computing in which the concurrency is expressed by applying a single stream of instructions simultaneously to the elements of a data structure.

data transfer The movement of data from one system to another across a specified transmission medium.

data type Data types are used to access data in different formats. These formats specify the size of the data as well as the location. For example: *char*, *short*, *int*, and *long* all specify the size of machine-defined data sizes. A *structure* defines a custom data type that can contain members of various sizes and residing at specific locations within the structure. A *union* defines a grouping of data types that can be used to access the same data in different formats.

deadlock An error condition common in parallel programming in which the computation has stalled because a group of **units of execution** (UEs) are blocked and waiting for each other in some cyclic dependency.

DSS Digital security and surveillance.

DVR Digital video recorder.

EFI Extensible Firmware Interface.

EDC Intel Embedded Design Center.

endianness The format to how multi-byte data is stored in computer memory.

endian architecture Term is used to refer to the endian architecture of a system, either big endian architecture or little endian architecture.

endian-neutral The code does not assume endian-architecture. All endian sensitive data interfaces are encapsulated by wrappers, such as macros, that access data in a manner respective to the endian-architecture.

endian-specific The code is written explicitly to be either big endian or little endian architecture. endian-specific code will not run correctly on CPUs with the opposite endian-architecture of the implemented code.

external data representation (XDR) A standard (RFC 1832) for the description and encoding of data. It is useful for transferring data between different computer architectures, and has been used to communicate data between such diverse machines as the SUN Workstation†, VAX†, IBM-PC†, and Cray†. XDR fits into the ISO presentation layer, and is roughly analogous in purpose to X.409, ISO Abstract Syntax Notation. The major difference between these two is that XDR uses implicit typing, while X.409 uses explicit typing.[1]

forward byte ordering An addressing scheme in which the lowest address (or leftmost) in a multi-byte value is the most significant byte. Forward byte ordering is equivalent to big endian byte ordering.

HEMS Home energy management system.

IEGD Intel Embedded Graphics Driver

---

[1]Description of XDR from Sun Microsystems, "RFC 1832 - External Data Representation Standard", August 1995, p. 24
ftp://ftp.isi.edu/in-notes/rfc1832.txt

implicitly parallel language A parallel programming language in which the details of what can execute concurrently and how that concurrency is implemented is left to the compiler. Most parallel functional and dataflow languages are implicitly parallel.

ISV Independent software vendor.

IHD In-home display.

IHV Independent hardware vendor.

IOH I/O hub.

IP Internet Protocol

IRQ Interrupt request.

least significant byte (LSB) The byte in a multi-byte value that represents the smallest quantity or weight. On a big endian architecture, the right most byte (high byte) is the LSB. On a little endian architecture the leftmost byte (low byte) is the LSB. It is not possible to distinguish the least significant byte without taking byte ordering or endianness into consideration.

Example: The 32-bit hex value 0x12345678 is stored in memory as follows:

Endian Order	Byte 00	Byte 01	Byte 02	Byte 03
Big Endian	12	34	56	78(LSB)
Little Endian	78(LSB)	56	34	12

little endian architecture An order in which the "little end" (least significant value in the sequence) is stored first. The most significant byte in is stored in the rightmost position. Intel, Alpha, and VAX architectures use the little endian model, where the least significant byte is at the lowest address in memory.

LSB See **least significant byte**.

MESI Protocol One of several cache coherency protocols for shared memory architectures with local caches. Each cache line exists exclusively in one of four states: Modified (contains only correct content for underlying memory line), Exclusive (only copy of the line in cache), Shared (several caches hold the line, unmodified), and Invalid (cache line contains garbage). Other protocols may use more or fewer states.

MID Mobile Internet device.

most significant byte (MSB) The byte in a multi-byte value that represents the largest quantity or weight. On a big endian architecture, the left most byte (low byte) is the MSB. On a little endian architecture, the rightmost byte (high byte) is the MSB. It is not possible to distinguish the most significant byte without taking byte ordering or endianness into consideration.

Example: The 32-bit hex value 0x12345678 is stored in memory as follows:

Endian Order	Byte 00	Byte 01	Byte 02	Byte 03
Big Endian	12 (MSB)	34	56	78
Little Endian	78	56	34	12 (MSB)

MIPS MIPS Technologies, Inc.

MSB See **most significant byte**.

multi-byte value A value containing more than one byte. This results in having to consider how the set of bytes is to be ordered.

Example: The value 1 is stored in a computer in binary and can be represented in hexadecimal notation as follows:

Endian Order	Single-byte Value (8-bits)	Multi-byte Value (16-bits)
Big Endian	01	0001
Little Endian	01	0100

multi-core processor An architecture that supports multiple cores in a single processor package that replicates the cache coherent, shared address space architecture common to traditional multiprocessor computers. Typically, multi-core processors put multiple cores in a given thermal envelope and emphasize the best-possible single-thread (or single-core) performance.

mutex A mutual exclusion lock. A mutex serializes the execution of multiple **units of execution** (UEs) by limiting access to an object to only one thread/ process at a time.

NEON The advanced SIMD technology marketed by ARM.

NVR Networked video recorder.

OEM Original equipment manufacturer.

OSV Operating system vendor.

PCIe Peripheral Control Interconnect Express.

PLC Programmable logic controller.

POC Proof of concept.

POS Point of service.

POSIX The "Portable Operating System Interface" as defined by the Portable Applications Standards Committee (PASC) of the IEEE Computer Society. While other operating systems follow some of the POSIX standards, the primary use of this term refers to the family of standards that defines the interfaces in UNIX and UNIX-like (such as Linux) operating systems.

PowerPC (performance optimization with enhanced RISC, abbreviated as PPC).

process A complete collection of resources needed to enable the execution of program instructions. These resources can include memory, I/O descriptors, a runtime stack, signal handlers, user and group IDs, and access control tokens. A more high-level view is that a process is a "heavyweight" **unit of execution** with its own address space.

processing element A generic term used to reference a hardware element that executes a stream of instructions. The context defines what unit of hardware is considered a processing element (such as a core, processor, or computer). Consider a cluster of SMP workstations. In some programming environments, each workstation is viewed as executing a single instruction stream; in this case, a processing element is a workstation. A different programming environment running on the same hardware, however, may view each processor or *core* of the individual workstations as executing an individual instruction stream; in this case, the processing element is the processor or core rather than the workstation.

Pthreads An abbreviation for POSIX threads; that is, the definition of threads in the various POSIX standards. See POSIX.

race condition An error condition peculiar to parallel programs in which the outcome of a program changes as the relative scheduling of **units of execution** (UEs) varies. This is often the result of modifications to a shared or global variable by more than one UE without an appropriate synchronization mechanism (such as a barrier, mutex, or semaphore).

reduction An operation that takes a collection of objects (usually one on each *unit of execution* - UE) and combines them into a single object on one UE, or combines them such that each UE has a copy of the combined object. Reductions typically involve combining a set of values pairwise using an associative operator such as addition or max.

reader/writer locks This pair of locks is similar to mutexes except that multiple **units of execution** (UEs) may hold a read lock while a write lock excludes both other writers and all readers. Reader/writer locks are often effective when resources protected by the lock are read far more often than they are written.

RISC Reduced instruction set computer.

RTOS Real-time operating system.

semaphore An abstract data type used to implement certain kinds of synchronization. There are different types of semaphores. The *binary semaphore* uses a shared single binary value to control access to a single resource. A *counting semaphore* uses a shared integer to regulate a collection of some resource (like buffers or I/O channels) and has the following characteristics: its value is constrained to be a nonnegative integer, and supports two *atomic operations*. The allowable operations are V (sometimes called up) and P (sometimes called down). A V operation increases the value of the semaphore by one. A P operation decreases the value of the semaphore by one, provided it can be done without violating the constraint that the value be non-negative. A P operation initiated when the value of the semaphore is 0 suspends. It may continue when the value is positive.

serial fraction Most computations consist of parts that contain exploitable concurrency and parts that execute serially. The serial fraction is that fraction of the program's execution time taken up by the parts that must execute serially. For example, if a program decomposes into setup, compute, and finalization, we could write

$$Ttotal = Tsetup + Tcompute + Tfinalization$$

If the setup and finalization phases must execute serially, then the serial fraction would be

$$? = (Tsetup + Tfinalization)/Ttotal$$

SIMD Single instruction multiple data.

simultaneous multithreading (SMT) Simultaneous multithreading is an architectural feature of some processors that allows multiple threads to issue instructions on each cycle. In other words, SMT allows the functional units that make up the processor to work on behalf of more than one thread at the same time. Examples of systems utilizing SMT are microprocessors from Intel

Corporation that use Intel® Hyper-Threading Technology.

SMBIOS System Management BIOS.

symmetric multiprocessing (SMP) A shared-memory computer, in which each processor is functionally identical and has "equal-time" access to every memory address. In other words, both memory addresses and operating system services are equally available to each processor. This is contrasted with a NUMA computer, which has a shared address space, but the access times to memory vary over physical address ranges and between processing elements.

task This term can have several meanings, depending on context. We use it to mean a sequence of operations that together make up some logical part of an algorithm or program.

task parallelism A class of parallelism where the concurrency is expressed in terms of the tasks that execute concurrently. This is a very broad class of techniques and includes *master-worker algorithms*, systems such as OpenMP that creates both explicit tasks and tasks from loop iterations, *SPMD* programs with explicit message passing, and many more approaches to parallelism. Note that any data parallel algorithm can be cast in terms of tasks, but the converse is not true. Hence task parallelism is the more general model. Compare to **data parallel**.

TDP Thermal design power.

thread A fundamental *unit of execution* (UE) on certain computers. In a UNIX context, threads are associated with a process and share the environment of that process. This makes the threads relatively lightweight compared to processes (that is, a context switch between threads is cheap versus a context switch between processes). A more high-level view is that a thread is a "lightweight" UE that shares an address space with other threads. See **unit of execution** and **process**.

thread-level parallelism Multiple threads running under a symmetric multiprocessing system are executed simultaneously.

UEFI Unified EFI forum.

union In the C programming language, a union is a variable that may hold objects of different types and sizes, with the compiler keeping track of the size and alignment requirements. Objects of different types and sizes can only be held at different times. A union provides a way to manipulate different kinds of data in a single area of storage.

unit of execution A generic term for one of a collection of concurrently executing entities, usually either processes or threads. See **process** and **thread**.

VA Video analytics.

VCA Video content analysis.

VFP Vector floating point.

WSN Wireless sensor network.

XDR See **external data representation**.

References

Adeneo. http://www.adeneo-embedded.com

Akhter, Shameem, and Jason Roberts. *Multi-core Programming*. Hillsboro, OR: Intel Press, 2006.

American Megatrends, Inc. http://www.ami.com

Apple Inc. *Architectural Differences Universal Binary Programming Guidelines* (2007). http://developer.apple.com/documentation/MacOSX/Conceptual/universal_binary/universal_binary_intro/chapter_1_section_1.html

Apple Inc. *Altivec/SSE Migration Guide* (2010). http://developer.apple.com/documentation/Performance/Conceptual/Accelerate_sse_migration/Accelerate_sse_migration.pdf (PDF).

Arium ECM-XDP3 Intel JTAG Debugger. http://www.arium.com/product/55/ECM-XDP3-Intel-JTAG-Debugger.html

ARM Limited. *Exception Handling ABI for the ARM® Architecture* (2002–2005, 2007). http://infocenter.arm.com/help/topic/com.arm.doc.ihi0038a/IHI0038A_ehabi.pdf (PDF)

Breshears, Clay. *The Art of Concurrency*. Sebastopol, CA: O'Reilly Media, 2009.

BSQUARE. http://www.bsquare.com/home.aspx

CriticalBlue. http://www.criticalblue.com

Del Vecchio, Paul. *De-Mystifying Software Performance Optimization*. Santa Clara, CA: Intel Corporation (2008). http://software.intel.com/en-us/articles/de-mystifying-software-performance-optimization/

Domeika, Max. *Software Development for Embedded Multi-core Systems*, Boston: Newnes, 2008.

EFI and Framework Open Source Community. http://www.tianocore.org

Embedded Intel® Architecture Chipsets Web site. Santa Clara, CA: Intel Corporation. http://www.intel.com/products/embedded/chipsets.htm?iid=embed_body+chip

Extensible Firmware Interface (EFI) and Unified EFI (UEFI) Web site. Santa Clara, CA: Intel Corporation. http://www.intel.com/technology/efi

Freeman, Tim and Dave Murray. *Intel® Atom™ Processor Performance for DSP Applications*. Birkenhead, UK: N.A. Software Ltd. (2009). http://www.nasoftware.co.uk/home/attachments/019_Atom_benchmarks.pdf (PDF)

Green Hills Software, Inc. http://www.ghs.com

Insyde Software Corporation. http://www.insydesw.com

Intel® Atom™ Developer Program. http://appdeveloper.intel.com/en-us/

Intel® Boot Loader Technology Web site. Santa Clara, CA: Intel Corporation. http://edc.intel.com/Software/Intel-Boot-Loader-Development-Kit

Intel® Compilers Products Web site. Santa Clara, CA: Intel Corporation. http://software.intel.com/en-us/intel-compilers/

http://software.intel.com/en-us/articles/improved-linux-smp-scaling-user-directed-processor-affinity/

Intel Corporation. *Avoiding and Identifying False Sharing Among Threads* (2010). http://software.intel.com/en-us/articles/avoiding-and-identifying-false-sharing-among-threads/

Intel Corporation. *Improved Linux† SMP Scaling: User-directed Processor Affinity*. Santa Clara, CA: (2008).

Intel Corporation. *Installing the Intel® C++ Compiler and Intel® Integrated Performance Primitives into KVM* for Intel® Atom™ Processor targeted development*. Santa Clara, CA: 2009. http://software.intel.com/en-us/articles/installing-compiler-into-kvm-atom/

Intel Corporation. *Integrating Intel® Software Development Tool Suite Components with Moblin* Image Creator*. Santa Clara, CA: 2009. http://software.intel.com/en-us/articles/moblin-integration-software-development-tool-suite-atom/

Intel Corporation. *Intel® Guide for Developing Multithreaded Applications*. Santa Clara, CA: 2010. http://software.intel.com/en-us/articles/intel-guide-for-developing-multithreaded-applications/

Intel Corporation. *Intel® 64 and IA-32 Architectures Software Developer's Manuals Web site. Santa Clara*, CA: 2010. http://developer.intel.com/products/processor/manuals/index.htm

Intel Corporation. *OpenPeak† Conversion from RISC architecture with External DSP to Intel® Architecture Boosts Performance Up to 10X* (2010). http://www.intelrethinkthepossibilities.com/Applications/Download/Intel_CaseStudy_Open_Peak.pdf (PDF)

Intel Download Center. http://downloadcenter.intel.com/

Intel® Embedded Alliance. http://www.intel.com/design/network/ica/

Intel® Embedded Design Center. http://edc.intel.com/

Intel® Embedded Graphics Device Driver Web site. http://edc.intel.com/Software/Downloads/IEGD/

Intel® Embedded Media and Graphics Drivers. http://edc.intel.com/Software/Downloads/EMGD Intel® Performance Libraries. http://www.intel.com/cd/software/products/asmo-na/eng/perflib/219780.htm

Intel® Platform Innovation Framework for UEFI. http://www.intel.com/technology/framework/

Intel Processor Family. http://ark.intel.com/

Intel Product Information. http://ark.intel.com

Intel Product Technologies. http://www.intel.com/technology/product/

Intel® Software Development Products. http://software.intel.com/en-us/intel-sdp-home/

Intel® Software Network. http://software.intel.com/en-us/

Intel® Thread Building Blocks Open Source Web site. http://www.threadingbuildingblocks.org

Intel® Thread Building Blocks. http://software.intel.com/en-us/intel-tbb/

Intel® Thread Checker. http://software.intel.com/en-us/intel-thread-checker/

Intel® Tools for Intel® Atom™ Processors. http://software.intel.com/en-us/articles/intel-tools-for-intel-atom-processors/

Intel® VTune™ Performance Analyzer and Intel® Thread Profiler. http://software. intel.com/en-us/intel-vtune/

Johnson, Randy, and Stewart Christie. *JTAG 101; IEEE 1149.x and Software Debug.* Santa Clara, CA: Intel Corporation (2009). http://download.intel. com/design/intarch/papers/321095.pdf (PDF)

Kean, Lee Eng. *Microcontroller to Intel® Architecture Conversion: Programmable Logic Controller (PLC) Using Intel® Atom™ Processor.* Santa Clara, CA: Intel Corporation (2010). http://download.intel.com/design/intarch/papers/323213.pdf (PDF)

Kreitzer, David and Max Domeika. *Ensuring Development Success by Understanding and Analyzing Assembly Language.* http://download.intel.com/design/intarch/ papers/321059.pdf (PDF)

Lauterbach. http://www.lauterbach.com

Levinthal, David. *Cycle Accounting Analysis on Intel Core 2 Processors.* http://assets. devx.com/goparallel/18027.pdf (PDF)

LynuxWorks, Inc. http://www.lynuxworks.com/

MacInnis, John. *Implementing Firmware on Embedded Intel Architecture Designs.* Santa Clara, CA: Intel Corporation (2009). http://download.intel.com/design/ intarch/papers/321072.pdf (PDF)

Mattson, Timothy G., Beverly A. Sanders, and Berna L. Massingill. *Patterns for Parallel Programming.* Boston, MA: Pearson Education, Inc., 2005.

Macraigor Systems LLC. http://www.macraigor.com/

MeeGo Web site. http://meego.com/

Microsoft Corporation. *Innovation Comes "Standard" in New Microsoft Auto Platform* (2009). http://download.microsoft.com/download/6/5/0/6505FA0E-1F39-4A34-BDC9-A655A5D3D2DB/AutoPlatformInnovationPR.pdf (PDF)

MSC Vertriebs GmbH and Gleichmann Electronics. http://www.mscsystems.de/ en/home/home/index.html

N.A. Software Ltd. http://www.nasoftware.co.uk

Nagpal, Muneesh, Gururaj Nagendra, and Alexey Omelchenko. *Boosting Cryptography Performance with Intel Libraries.* http://software.intel.com/en-us/ articles/boosting-cryptography-performance-with-intel-libraries/

Nanjing Byosoft Co.,Ltd. http://byosoft.com.cn/en_about.asp

National Instruments LabVIEW. http://www.ni.com/labview/

OpenMP Specification. http://openmp.org/wp/

OpenPeak, Inc. http://www.openpeak.com

Pallipadi, Venkatesh and Alexey Starikovskiy. *The Ondemand Governor*. http://kernel.org/pub/linux/kernel/people/lenb/acpi/doc/OLS2006-ondemand-paper.pdf (PDF)

Phoenix Technologies, Ltd. http://www.phoenix.com

QNX Software Systems. http://www.qnx.com

QNX Software Systems. *QNX Technology and the Intel Atom Processor* (2008). http://www.qnx.com/download/download/18173/qnx_intel_atom_ds_p3.pdf (PDF)

Red Bend Software. http://www.redbend.com

Ruggiero, Joshua. *Measuring Cache and Memory Latency and CPU to Memory Bandwidth*. Santa Clara, CA: Intel Corporation (2008). http://download.intel.com/design/intarch/papers/321074.pdf (PDF)

Sensory Networks, Inc. http://sensorynetworks.com

TenAsys Corporation. http://www.tenasys.com/

Unified EFI Forum. http://www.uefi.org

VirtualLogix, Inc. http://www.virtuallogix.com/

Weinberg, Bill and Jim Ready. *How to move from legacy OS to Linux in easy stages*. http://www.electronicsweekly.com/Articles/2008/10/13/44513/how-to-move-from-legacy-os-to-linux-in-easy-stages.htm

Wind River. http://www.windriver.com

Wipro Technologies. http://www.wipro.com

ZigBee Organization. http://www.zigbee.org

Zimmer, Vincent, Michael Rothman, and Robert Hale. *Beyond BIOS: Implementing the Unified Extensible Firmware Interface with Intel's Framework*. Hillsboro, OR: Intel Press, 2006.

References for the Intel® Atom™ Processor System Boot Flow

Advanced Configuration and Power Interface Specification. http://www.acpi.info/spec.htm

ATA/ATAPI Command Set Specifications. http://www.t13.org/Documents/MinutesDefault.aspx?keyword=atapi

Conventional PCI Local Bus Specification. PCI-SIG. http://www.pcisig.com/specifications/conventional/

Intel Corporation. *MultiProcessor Specification 1.4.* Santa Clara, CA: Intel Corporation (1993–1997). http://www.intel.com/design/pentium/datashts/24201606.pdf (PDF)

Intel Corporation. *Intel® 64 and IA-32 Architectures Software Developer's Manuals.* Santa Clara, CA: Intel Corporation (2010). http://developer.intel.com/products/processor/manuals/index.htm

Intel Corporation. *BIOS/Firmware Writer's Guides.* See your Intel account representative. If you don't have an Intel account representative get help online. http://edc.intel.com/Get-Help

Intel Corporation. *Memory Reference Code.* See your Intel account representative. If you don't have an Intel account representative get help online. http://edc.intel.com/Get-Help/

JEDEC DRAM Specifications. http://www.jedec.org/

PCI Express® Base 2.1 Specification. PCI-SIG. http://www.pcisig.com/specifications/pciexpress/base2/

PCI Firmware Specification. PCI-SIG. http://www.pcisig.com/specifications/conventional/pci_firmware/

PCI IRQ Routing Table Specification. Microsoft Corporation. http://www.microsoft.com/whdc/archive/pciirq.mspx

SD Specifications Part 1 Physical Layer Simplified Specification. SD Association. http://www.sdcard.org/developers/tech/sdcard/pls/

SD Specifications Part 2A SD Host Controller Simplified Specification. SD Association. http://www.sdcard.org/developers/tech/host_controller/simple_spec/

SD Specifications Part E1 SDIO Simplified Specification. SD Association. http://www.sdcard.org/developers/tech/sdio/sdio_spec/

Simple Firmware Interface Specification. http://www.simplefirmware.org

The Serial ATA International Organization. SATA-IO. http://www.sata-io.org/

Universal Serial Bus Specification. http://www.usb.org/developers/docs/

Index

Continuing Education is Essential

It's a challenge we all face – keeping pace with constant change in information technology. Whether our formal training was recent or long ago, we must all find time to keep ourselves educated and up to date in spite of the daily time pressures of our profession.

Intel produces technical books to help the industry learn about the latest technologies. The focus of these publications spans the basic motivation and origin for a technology through its practical application.

Right books, right time, from the experts

These technical books are planned to synchronize with roadmaps for technology and platforms, in order to give the industry a head-start. They provide new insights, in an engineer-to-engineer voice, from named experts. Sharing proven insights and design methods is intended to make it more practical for you to embrace the latest technology with greater design freedom and reduced risks.

I encourage you to take full advantage of Intel Press books as a way to dive deeper into the latest technologies, as you plan and develop your next generation products. They are an essential tool for every practicing engineer or programmer. I hope you will make them a part of your continuing education tool box.

Sincerely,

Senior Fellow and Chief Technology Officer Intel Corporation

Turn the page to learn about titles from Intel Press for system developers

ESSENTIAL BOOKS FOR SYSTEM DEVELOPERS

Multi-Core Programming
Increasing Performance through Software Multi-threading

By Shameem Ashter and Jason Roberts

ISBN 978-0-976483-24-3

Discover programming techniques for Intel multi-core architecture and Hyper-Threading Technology.

Software developers can no longer rely on increasing clock speeds alone to speed up single-threaded applications; instead, to gain a competitive advantage, developers must learn how to properly design their applications to run in a threaded environment. Multi-core architectures have a single processor package that contains two or more processor "execution cores," or computational engines, and deliver—with appropriate software—fully parallel execution of multiple software threads. Hyper-Threading Technology enables additional threads to operate on each core.

This book helps software developers write high-performance multi-threaded code for Intel's multi-core architecture while avoiding the common parallel programming issues associated with multi-threaded programs.

Multi-Core Programming

Increasing Performance through Software Multi-threading

Shameem Akhter and Jason Roberts

Intel PRESS

Books by Engineers, for Engineers

(intel)

This book is a practical, hands-on volume with immediately usable code examples that enable readers to quickly master the necessary programming techniques. The companion Web site contains pointers to threading and optimization tools, code samples from the book, and extensive technical documentation on Intel multi-core architecture.

Programming with Hyper-Threading Technology
How to Write Multithreaded Software for Intel® IA-32 Processors

By Andrew Binstock and Richard Gerber

ISBN 0-976-4832-0-3

Programming with Hyper-Threading Technology helps software developers write high-performance multithreaded code while avoiding the common parallel programming issues that usually plague threaded programs. This book highlights how software developers can use Intel Hyper-Threading Technology to maximize processor throughput, efficiency, and parallelism. It is a practical, hands-on volume with immediately usable code examples that enable readers to quickly master the necessary building blocks.

A programming guide for software application developers targeting the Itanium® processor family

The Software Optimization Cookbook, Second Edition
High-Performance Recipes for IA-32 Platforms

By By Richard Gerber, Aart J.C. Bik, Kevin B. Smith, and Xinmin Tian

ISBN 0-9764832-1-1

The Software Optimization Cookbook, Second Edition, provides updated recipes for high-performance applications on Intel platforms. Through simple explanations and examples, four experts show you how to address performance issues with algorithms, memory access, branch prediction, automatic vectorization, SIMD instructions, multiple threads, and floating-point calculations.

Software developers learn how to take advantage of Intel® Extended Memory 64 Technology (Intel® EM64T), multi-core processing, Hyper-Threading Technology, OpenMP†, and multimedia extensions. This book guides you through the growing collection of software tools, compiler switches, and coding optimizations, showing you efficient ways to improve the performance of software applications for Intel platforms.

"This book simplifies the task for engineers who strive to develop high-performance software..."

Lars Petter Endresen, Doctor of Engineering, Physics, Scandpower Petroleum Technology

Special Deals, Special Prices!

To ensure you have all the latest books
and enjoy aggressively priced discounts,
please go to this Web site:

www.intel.com/intelpress/bookbundles.htm

Bundles of our books are available,
selected especially to address the needs
of the developer. The bundles place
important complementary topics at
your fingertips, and the price for a
bundle is substantially less than
buying all the books individually.

About Intel Press

Intel Press is the authoritative source of timely, technical books to help software and hardware developers speed up their development process. We collaborate only with leading industry experts to deliver reliable, first-to-market information about the latest technologies, processes, and strategies.

Our products are planned with the help of many people in the developer community and we encourage you to consider becoming a customer advisor. If you would like to help us and gain additional advance insight to the latest technologies, we encourage you to consider the Intel Press Customer Advisor Program. You can **register** here:

www.intel.com/intelpress/register.htm

For information about bulk orders or corporate sales, please send email to
bulkbooksales@intel.com

Other Developer Resources from Intel

At these Web sites you can also find valuable technical information and resources for developers:

www.intel.com/technology/rr	Recommended Reading list for books of interest to developers
www.intel.com/technology/itj	Intel Technology Journal
www.developer.intel.com	General information for developers
www.intel.com/software	Content, tools, training, and the Intel Early Access Program for software developers
www.intel.com/software/products	Programming tools to help you develop high-performance applications
www.intel.com/embedded	Solutions and resources for embedded and communications